EDIACARAN–ORDOVICIAN OF EAST LAURENTIA—
S. W. FORD MEMORIAL VOLUME

EDIACARAN–ORDOVICIAN OF EAST LAURENTIA— S. W. FORD MEMORIAL VOLUME

12th International Conference of the Cambrian Chronostratigraphy Working Group

Edited by Ed Landing

New York State Museum
The State Education Department, Albany, New York 12230

New York State Museum Bulletin 510
2007

The University of the State of New York
The State Education Department

Printed in the United States of America

Copies may be ordered from:
        Publication Sales
        3140 CEC
        New York State Museum
        Albany, New York 12230
        Phone: (518) 402-5344
        Fax: (518) 486-2034
        Email: nysmpub@mail.nysed.gov

Library of Congress Catalog Card Number: 2007934602

ISSN: 0278-3355
ISBN: 1-55557-239-1

This book is printed on acid-free paper.

Cover picture—Dunham Formation dolostone boulder (left side of hammer) in debris flow at base of Parker Formation records caving of an E–W submarine fault scarp that developed in the terminal Early Cambrian and formed the long-term dysoxic/anoxic Franklin Basin on the northern Vermont platform (field trip Stop 4.7).

CONTENTS

MEETING ACKNOWLEDGMENTS 1

DEDICATION TO S. W. FORD 2
Ed Landing

EAST LAURENTIA 2007—A PRE-MEETING VIEWPOINT 3
Ed Landing

EDIACARAN–ORDOVICIAN OF EAST LAURENTIA—GEOLOGIC SETTING
AND CONTROLS ON DEPOSITION ALONG THE NEW YORK PROMONTORY REGION 5
Ed Landing

Abstract 5
Introduction 5
Laurentian shield and Rodinia supercontinent 7
Rodinia break-up—origin of Ediacaran–Lower Paleozoic cover sequence 7
Rift–passive margin transition and the oldest carbonate platform 8
Early Cambrian–Late Ordovician platform succession in the Appalachians 10
    Passive margin sequence 10
    Eustatic controls on deposition 10
Franklin Basin Cambrian–Ordovician succession 12
    Location and significance 12
    Shelf–slope break 13
    Epeirogenic interpretation 13
    Upper slope dysoxia/anoxia 13
Cambrian–Ordovician of the craton and southern flank of the Ottawa aulocogen 14
    Overview of succession 14
    Cambrian deposition 14
    Post-Potsdam Cambrian faunas 16
    Cratonic Ordovician 16
Ediacaran(?)–Ordovician of the Taconic allochthon 17
    Location and significance 17
    Structure and metamorphism 17
    Rift–passive margin transition 18
    Passive margin succession: a proxy for global sea-level and climate changes 18
    Biostratigraphy of Cambrian black–green macroscale alternations 20
    Ordovician black–green macroscale alternations 21
    End of passive margin deposition in the Taconic allochthon 22
Afterward—post-passive margin geological history 23
    Taconic orogeny 23
    Acadian orogeny 23
    Alleghanian orogeny 23
    Break-up of Pangaea 24

Acknowledgments 24

References 24

CAMBRIAN OF EAST LAURENTIA: FIELD WORKSHOP IN EASTERN NEW YORK AND VERMONT ... 25
Ed Landing, David A. Franzi, James W. Hagadorn, Stephen R. Westrop, Björn Kröger, and James C. Dawson

Prospectus 25
July 30: Thin platform succession in Saratoga and Washington Counties, eastern New York 25
  Overview 25
  Travel to Stop 1.1 25
  Stop 1.1, Cambrian–Ordovician (intra-Skullrockian Stage) boundary unconformity near Petrified
      Gardens: eustatic and epeirogenic controls 26
  Travel to Stop 1.2 28
  Stop 1.2, Lester Park 29
  Travel to Stop 1.3 29
  Stop 1.3, Galway Formation roadcut 29
  Travel to Stop 1.4 29
  Stop 1.4, Lower Potsdam Formation trilobites near Fort Ann 30
  Travel to Stop 1.5 30
  Stop 1.5, Potsdam–middle Proterozoic nonconformity near Fort Ann 30

July 31: Thin platform succession in Washington and Essex Counties, eastern New York 31
  Overview 31
  Travel to Stop 2.1 31
  Stop 2.1, Potsdam Formation at base of Skene Mountain 31
  Travel to Stop 2.2 31
  Stop 2.2, Cambrian succession at Skene Manor 31
  Travel to Stop 2.3 31
  Stop 2.3, Crossman quarry: Sunwaptan Stage–Ibexian Series boundary in the
      middle Little Falls Formation 33
  Travel to Stop 2.4 34
  Stop 2.4, Uppermost Cambrian cephalopods and Cambrian–Ordovician boundary at Steve's Farm .. 34
  Travel to Stop 2.5 36
  Stop 2.5, Cambrian–Ordovician boundary unconformity near Comstock 36
  Travel to Stop 2.6 36
  Stop 2.6, Trace fossils and medusae from the upper PotsdamFormation, Ausable Chasm 37

**August 1: Oral and poster sessions. Key note address "Review of the timing and constraints on the
Neoproterozoic–Cambrian record of metazoan evolution"by S. A. Bowring** 40

**August 2: Middle–Upper Cambrian siliciclastic cover of the northwestern Adirondack Mountain
massif, Clinton County, New York** 40
  Overview 40
  Travel to Stop 3.1 40
  Stop 3.1, Terminal Proterozoic Rand Hill Dike Swarm 40
  Travel to Stop 3.2 41
  Stop 3.2, Middle Proterozoic–Cambrian nonconformity 41
  Travel to Stop 3.3 41
  Stop 3.3, "Altona Formation" at Atwood Farm 41
  Travel to Stop 3.4 42
  Stop 3.4, Observation well at Altona Flat Rock 42
  Travel to Stop 3.5 43
  Stop 3.5, Altona Flat Rock overlook 44
  Travel to Stop 3.6 44
  Stop 3.6, Upper Potsdam Formation on Rock Road 44
  Travel to Stop 3.7 44
  Stop 3.7, Upper Potsdam Formation and trace fossils, Great Chazy River 44
  Travel to Stop 3.8 45
  Stop 3.8, Upper Potsdam Formation trace fossils, Gadway Pine Barrens 46
  Travel to Stop 3.9 46
  Stop 3.9, Upper Potsdam trace fossils, Clinton Farm Supplies locality 46
  Travel to Stop 3.10 46

Stop 3.10, Theresa Formation (middle Lower Ordovician) 47
Travel to Plattsburgh 47

August 3: Epeirogenic and eustatic controls on Cambrian deposition in the dysoxic Franklin basin, northwestern Vermont **48**
    Overview 48
    Travel to Stop 4.1 48
    Stop 4.1, Marjuman Stage through Cambrian–Ordovician boundary in slope deposits at
        Highgate gorge, and "early" *Cordylodus* elements 49
    Travel to Stop 4.2 54
    Stop 4.2, Lower Ibexian (lower Skullrockian) type *Parakoldiniodia stitti* (i.e., "*Missisquoia typicalis*")
        assemblage at Highgate gorge 54
    Travel to Stop 4.3 55
    Stop 4.3, Dysoxic Tremadocian–lower Arenigian of the Highgate Formation at Highgate gorge 55
    Travel to Stop 4.4 55
    Stop 4.4, Dysoxic/anoxic Parker Formation (Middle Cambrian) on Donaldson Road 55
    Travel to Stop 4.5 56
    Stop 4.5, Pre-Franklin basin deposition: Cheshire Formation at Shawville, Vermont 56
    Travel to Stop 4.6 56
    Stop 4.6, Pre-Franklin basin deposition: Dunham Formation at Swanton Junction 57
    Travel to Stop 4.7 57
    Stop 4.7, Epeirogenic development of the Franklin Basin and Schuchert's "mushrooms" 57
    Travel to hotel 58

**August 4: Lower–Middle Cambrian boundary interval of the eastern platform and
Ediacaran(?)–Cambrian of the western Green Mountain anticlinorium** **58**
    Overview 58
    Travel to Stop 5.1 59
    Stop 5.1, Winooski Dolostone and Hawke Bay eustasy 59
    Travel to Stops 5.2A–C 59
    Stops 5.2A–C, Terminal Proterozoic?–Lower Cambrian near Birch Hill Road–North Birch Hill
        Road intersection 60
    Stop 5.2A, Lower Cheshire Formation, marine retrogradation and onlap 60
    Stop 5.2B, Moosamaloo Phyllite, shelf anoxia 60
    Stop 5.2C, Forestdale Formation, upper arenaceous facies 60
    Travel to Stop 5.3 60
    Stop 5.3, Forestdale Formation—east Laurentia's oldest carbonate platform 60
    Travel to Stop 5.4 60
    Stop 5.4, Pinnacle–Forestdale contact 60
    Travel to Stop 5.5 62
    Stop 5.5, Pinnacle Formation 62
    Travel to Stop 5.6 62
    Stop 5.6, Pinnacle–Cheshire fault contact 62
    Travel to Stop 5.7 62
    Stop 5.7, "Shelburne Marble" at Pittsford Mills 62
    Travel to hotel 62

**August 5: Cambrian of the Taconic allochthon, eastern New York—continental slope
mudstone colors, eustasy, and oceanic oxygenation** **62**
    Overview 62
    Travel to Stop 6.1 63
    Stop 6.1, Lower Cambrian Bomoseen Formation and Taconic masterthrust 63
    Travel to Stop 6.2 63
    Stop 6.2, Late Early Cambrian Browns Pond dysoxic/anoxic interval and lower *Elliptocephala*
        asaphoides assemblage 64
    Travel to Stop 6.3 64
    Stop 6.3, Hatch Hill dysoxic/anoxic interval (terminal Early Cambrian–earliest Ordovician)
        through early Late Ordovician paleo-oceanographic changes 64
    Travel to Stop 6.4 65
    Stop 6.4, Cambrian–Ordovician boundary in upper Hatch Hill dysoxic/anoxic interval 65
    Travel to Stops 6.5 and 6.6 66
    Stop 6.5, Browns Pond dysoxic/anoxic interval—Hawke Bay regression oxygenated slope facies .. 66

Stop 6.6, Oxygenated Middle Granville Slate and the Hawke Bay regression 67
Travel to Stop 6.7 67
Stop 6.7, Early Cambrian Bomoseen Formation–Truthville Slate: oldest units in the
    Giddings Brook slice 67
Travel to Stop 6.8 68
Stop 6.8, Logan cycles: mesoscale cycles in the Milankovitch band 68
Travel to Stop 6.9 68
Stop 6.9, Schaghticoke gorge, upper lower Tremadocian dysoxic/anoxic interval (optional stop) ... 69
Travel to Stop 6.10 69
Stop 6.10, Schodack Landing: upper *Elliptocephala asaphoides* assemblage and onset
    of terminal Early Cambrian–earliest Ordovician Hatch Hill dysoxic/anoxic interval 71
Travel to Albany 71
August 6: Morning plenary session in New York State Museum 71
Acknowledgments 72
References 72

ABSTRACTS OF ORAL AND POSTER PRESENTATIONS 81

MEETING ACKNOWLEDGMENTS

The organizers of the "Cambrian of East Laurentia" extend our deep appreciation for the financial and technical aid from a number of organizations and individuals that supported this international field conference.

FINANCIAL SUPPORTERS INCLUDED:
   The International Cambrian Subcommission, via Drs. Loren Babcock and Shanchi Peng
   The Cambrian Institute, via Drs. Alison R. ("Pete") Palmer and Pete Wagner,
      Department of Geological Sciences, University of Chicago, Chicago, IL 60637
   The Reservoir Characterization Group of the New York State Museum
   The New York State Academy of Mineralogy
   Dr. Ed Landing, New York State Museum, Albany, New York

VEHICLES WERE ARRANGED BY:
   Dr. David Franzi (SUNY-Plattsburgh vehicles were provided for the field day on the Potsdam Formation)
   Dr. John Hart, New York State Museum (bus rental)

THANKS ARE EXTENDED TO:
   Richard Nyahay, New York State Museum, for assisting in field trip coordination before and during the meeting.
   Donna Jornov of the New York State Museum and Clare Sedgwick of the New York State Museum
      for receiving the funds for the meeting.
   John B. Skiba, New York State Museum, for assisting in publication of Bulletin 510.
   Dr. Samuel Bowring, Massachusetts Institute of Technology, for the key note lecture on Cambrian geochronology.
   Vermont Geological Survey, for copies of Vermont Geologic Map for meeting participants, via State Geologist
      Dr. Laurence Becker and Marjorie H. Gale

2

DEDICATION TO S. W. FORD

2

ED LANDING

2

New York State Museum, The State Education Department, Madison Avenue, Albany, NY 12230,
elanding@mail.nysed.gov

Just as the Cambrian of the New York Promontory region is the focus of the 2007 meeting of the International Cambrian Subcommission, the self-taught paleontologist and geologist Silas Watson Ford (1848–1895) focused his energies on the record of Cambrian life in eastern New York. Relatively little is known about Ford's life. Photographic images or any representations of him are unknown, and he died in obscurity after a self-funded career that included publication of numerous professional and popular articles. Hernick's (1999) study, from which much of the following is abstracted, is probably as thorough an examination and reconstruction of Ford's life as can be done on the basis of available records.

S. W. Ford was a contemporary of Charles Doolittle Walcott, only two years and 112 km separated their births in upstate New York. Ford was born west of Albany in Glenville, just outside of Schenectady. Orphaned by age six, he and his siblings were brought up by an older brother. That brother, Stephen, may have helped Ford get training and a job as a telegraph operator at age eighteen for the Rensselaer and Saratoga Railroad in Troy, New York. By his early twenties, Ford developed an intense interest in what are now known to be Cambrian-age rocks and fossils at the western edge of the Taconic allochthon in the Troy area.

Both C. D. Walcott and S. W. Ford were in contact in their early twenties with James Hall, the *doyen* of American paleontology. Both were self-trained, but showed the intense energy, acuity, and interest in paleontology that Hall respected—and had the sort of collections that Hall wanted and regularly acquired almost as a condition of his hiring of young staff members (Yochelson, 1998; Landing, 2003d). However, Walcott was hired by Hall and entered a profession that ultimately led to his being head of the U. S. Geological Survey and Smithsonian Institution, and even director of a part of the U. S. Army Air Force in World War I. Ford never had the opportunity to engage in science as a paid professional, and continued to write and work on his own time and money.

From 1871–1888, Ford published 23 short reports in the *American Journal of Science*, as well as several other papers and abstracts in other journals and a popular account involving ancient life ("Life in the Silurian Age") in the *New York Tribune* newspaper. His publications helped resolve the "Taconic problem" by showing that much of the terrane immediately east of the Hudson River is "Primordial," based on the Lower Cambrian fossils he described and illustrated, and far older than the "Hudson River slates" [Upper Ordovician] that they structurally overlay. Ford (1885) correctly interpreted the "great fault" [i.e., the Taconic master thrust] that separated the Lower Cambrian rocks at Stuyvesant, south of Troy, from the "Hudson River slates" (see Stop 6.10 in Landing *et al.,* this volume). His "Bivalve of uncertain class; gen. nov.?" from Troy (Ford, 1873) was subsequently described as *Fordilla troyensis* by Barrande, and remains Earth's oldest bivalve. Ford's (1877, 1878, 1881) publications also included the first North American studies on trilobite ontogeny, and other reports provided descriptions of new trilobite and brachiopod taxa and hyolith occurrences. His publications remain useful because, unlike the poor quality of locality data provided by such contemporary paleontologists as W. B. Dwight of Vassar College (Kröger and Landing, In press b), Ford's localities are well described, and can be relocated.

Ford's only professional employment was a brief tenure as a salaried field assistant for the U. S. Geological Survey. Walcott hired him for eight months in 1884–1885 for field work in the central Taconic region. During this time he apparently drew sixteen of the figures in Walcott's (1886) bulletin on Cambrian paleontology.

Ford's last contribution to a scientific publication was to the "Report of the Sub-committee on the Lower Paleozoic" at the International Congress of Geologists in 1888. This year seems to have marked a low point in Ford's life that included separation from his wife, a continuing law suit over a bad debt, and with such important mentors as James Dwight Dana distancing themselves from him. Ford's life after 1888 and the reason for his death on June 25, 1895, by "general debility" (perhaps suggesting alcohol or opium addiction) remain unknown. His personal library was acquired by the New York State Library after his death, but was lost in the State Capitol fire of 1911. However, his fossil collection was bought (for $70.70) by the New York State Museum, and remains in the Paleontology Collection, along with Ford's meticulous labels. Very fittingly, specimens from it have been regularly loaned and studied by Lower Cambrian trilobite workers, and have continued to have important research value (e.g., Whittington, 1957).

ACKNOWLEDGMENTS

Linda Van Aller Hernick is thanked for reviewing this summary of S. W. Ford.

REFERENCES

All references in this section are cited at the end of the field trip guide by Landing *et al.* (this volume).

EAST LAURENTIA 2007—A PRE-MEETING STATEMENT

ED LANDING

New York State Museum, The State Education Department, Madison Avenue, Albany, NY 12230,
elanding@mail.nysed.gov

CAMBRIAN WORKSHOPS

I am very pleased to host the 12th meeting of the International Subcommission on Cambrian Stratigraphy, and gratefully acknowledge the co-sponsorship of this meeting by the New York State Museum and State University of New York at Plattsburgh. Previous meetings of the Cambrian Subcommission, as well as those of the now-concluded Precambrian-Cambrian Boundary Working Group, have included field trips and working sessions in Morocco; Siberia; China; South Korea; eastern Newfoundland and New Brunswick; the western states of Utah, Nevada, and California; Spain; southern France; England and Wales; Sweden; and, in 2006, Australia.

This Cambrian Subcommission meeting is the first to take place in the eastern United States, and thus the first to feature the Cambrian of the southern margin (in terms of Early Paleozoic coordinates) of the Laurentian paleocontinent. The Cambrian of eastern New York and adjacent Vermont lies in a geologically diverse area that spans the stable Proterozoic shield and Early Paleozoic craton, and extends into the Appalachian Mountains. There is as much variety in Cambrian geological setting in the short (ca. 40 km) distance from the Proterozoic Adirondack Mountains massif at Lake George village to the front of the Taconic overthrust belt immediately east of Whitehall village line as that seen in a trip from the Black Hills of South Dakota to the Antler overthrust belt of western Nevada. Geological relationships in the field trip region led to the first proposal that mountain belts originated at various times through Earth history (Hall, 1860a), and did not originate all at one time during a Biblical Creation. The rocks of the field trip area provided the fossils that led to important contributions to Cambrian paleontology and geology by such workers as Joachim Barrande and S. W. Ford (see Dedication), James Hall, Benjamin F. Howell, Arthur Keith, Cecil Kindle, Christina Lochman, Franco Rasetti, Percy E. Raymond, Charles Schuchert, Alan B. Shaw, and C. D. Walcott.

The organization of this conference is part of a long-term contribution to the refining of the best standards for international correlation of the Cambrian. I was part of a group that proposed a Global Stratotype Section and Point (GSSP) for the Precambrian–Cambrian boundary (Narbonne et al., 1987), and co-lead a field trip that included the candidate stratotype in eastern Newfoundland (Landing et al., 1988). Subsequent field conferences that focused on the Cambrian that I had a hand in included excursions in Morocco (Geyer and Landing, 1995, 2006) and eastern Newfoundland and New Brunswick (Landing and Westrop, 1998).

The acceptance of the eastern Newfoundland GSSP by the Precambrian–Cambrian Boundary Working Group and then by the International Stratigraphic Commission in 1992 was followed by my prediction that the pre-trilobitic Early Cambrian constituted the longest part of the Cambrian (Landing, 1994). This prediction was subsequently confirmed by high-resolution U-Pb work on volcanic zircons (Landing et al., 1998). In addition, the later proposal that the Cambrian should be divided into four "natural" series, with the sub-trilobitic Cambrian constituting the lowest series (Landing, 1998a, b), was subsequently adopted by the International Subcommission on Cambrian Stratigraphy (e.g., Babcock et al., 2005). At the end of May 2007, a ballot proposal by Landing et al. to name the lowest Cambrian series the "Terreneuvian Series" and its lowest subdivision the "Fortunian Stage" was accepted by a vote of the Cambrian Subcommission. These designations have been submitted for approval and ratification by the International Stratigraphic Commission. The Cambrian Subcommission's approval of the Terreneuvian Series and Fortunian Stage buoyed my efforts in organizing this field trip for late Summer 2007—indeed if the origin of many and diversification of most marine animals actually took place quite late and in the earliest Cambrian (Landing and Westrop, 2004), perhaps the "Cambrian evolutionary radiation" is better termed the "Terreveuvian evolutionary radiation."

TWO CAVEATS AND A CHRONOSTRATIGRAPHIC SUGGESTION

A Cambrian focus

For the field trip participants: yes, this meeting is focused on the Cambrian. The two longest sections of this volume, the regional overview and the field trip, detail the stratigraphy; depositional environments; epeirogenic history; paleontology; and climate, sea-level, and oxygenation history of the Cambrian of the New York Promontory. However, as the Cambrian must be put into a geological perspective, the volume is titled "Ediacaran–Ordovician of east Laurentia." Of course, this title will be of interest to a wider audience, and will help sales of this bulletin. More importantly, this treatment of a broader span of geological time serves to identify the shallow- and deep-water Cambrian of east Laurentia as a largely passive margin succession that succeeds the active margin, rift-facies of the Ediacaran and precedes the active margin, collisional stratigraphic succession that developed later in the Ordovician.

EDIACARAN-ORDOVICIAN OF EAST LAURENTIA—S.W. FORD MEMORIAL VOLUME, Edited by Ed Landing, New York State Museum, The State Education Department, Albany, New York 12230. New York State Museum Bulletin 510. © 2007 by The University of the State New York, The State Education Department. All rights reserved.

Cambrian divisions in this volume

The now-accepted four-fold division of the Cambrian (discussed above) has voided the traditional terms that evoke the traditional tripartite, series-level division of the Cambrian (i.e., Early/Lower, Middle/Middle, and Late/Upper) that proved to have different definitions between different Cambrian paleocontinents. However, only the uppermost series, the Furongian, had been ratified by the ICS (see Peng *et al.*, 2004), by the time of preparation of this volume. Thus, there was no convenient way to refer to refer to series-level subdivisions of earlier/lower parts of the Cambrian during preparation of this volume. As used herein, the Cambrian is divided into three parts (Early/Lower, Middle/Middle, and Late/Upper) largely as they have traditionally defned in Laurentia on the basis of Laurentian faunal province faunas. The exception here is that the "Upper/Late" Cambrian in this volume corresponds to the Furongian Series, and assigns strata traditionally assigned to the Laurentian lowest Upper Cambrian (*Crepicephalus* Zone and older) to the Middle Cambrian. As a result, the lower Potsdam Formation onlap on the southern part of the New York Promontory is referable to the late Middle Cambrian, and no longer to the Late Cambrian.

Cambrian subsystems?

Despite the recognition and acceptance of four series-level divisions of the Cambrian by the Subcommission, difficulties remain in that a tripartite division of the Cambrian is entrenched in the literature of all countries. Similarly, a linguistic problem exists in referring to quadripartite divisions. Two-fold divisions (e.g., upper and lower) and tripartite divisions are easily accommodated and traditional in most languages, particularly Indo-European languages. Perhaps the best accommodation of the great mass of existing literature on the Cambrian, as well as the linguistic problem in conveniently referring to a four-fold division, is the following: that the Cambrian should be divided into three sub-systems. Indeed, the Carboniferous is now formally divided into two subsystems, the Mississippian and Pennsylvanian Subsystems, for work specific to North America.

This chronostratigraphic subdivision of the Cambrian would include a "Subsystem 1" largely identical to the sub-trilobitic Cambrian plus, essentially, the trilobite-bearing Lower Cambrian as it has been recognized on different Cambrian paleocontinents. Subsystem 1 would be termed the "Early/Lower Cambrian." Subsystem 1 would correspond to the Terrenauvian Series and the presently unnamed "Series 2." Cambrian Subsystem 1 would comprise much of the Cambrian, but it would not conflict with the existing literature's casual but traditional use of "Lower Cambrian." The higher subsystems, "Subsystem 2" and "Subsystem 3,"would then each correspond to a single series, presently termed the unnamed Series 3 and the Furongian Series. However, there would be distinct subsystem names. Subsystems 2 and 3 would roughly correspond to the existing concepts of the "Middle" and "Upper" Cambrian as they have been used on separate Cambrian paleocontinents. It should be noted that there are no evident reasons why chronostratigraphic divisions *must* 1) have somewhat comparable duration [e.g., compare the durations of the very short Silurian Period and the long Cretaceous Period] or 2) be composed of two or more smaller chronostratigraphic divsisions.

IN APPRECIATION

I am pleased at the amount of interest shown in this summer's Cambrian Subcommission field workshop, and apologize to those whose request to be included had to be turned down—the trip filled to capacity. The participants are thanked for submitting their abstracts of oral and poster presentations by the date requested.

However, a review of the registrants for the trip shows an obvious trend in the support of science by certain national governments. With seventeen participants from eastern Asia (China and South Korea), eight from Europe and Australia, and seven from North America (all from the U. S. and none from Canada) at the time this volume went to press, it is evident that the pendulum of scientific energy and financial support is swinging away from the West. With the National Science Foundation of the U. S. funding only 6% of grant applications in paleontology and earth science, we are simply seeing only one example of how government financial support of such beneficial cultural activities as science is severely declining, while the financing of militarism and protracted war grows. The support for conferences, scientific research, and travel for educational conferences simply isn't here in the West. All that one can to is compare China, where paleontology has been declared "a career of excellence," with the U. S., where biological evolution is actually debated and contested, its teaching is regularly litigated at the level of state courts or simply avoided by teachers fearful of complaints by parents and some students, and where the acceptance of a literal reading of Genesis is a litmus test for many politicians.

An enthusiastic "thanks" is extended in advance to the efforts of the co-field trip leaders: Dave Franzi (who in "real life" is a Pleistocene geologist and hydrologist), Whitey Hagadorn, and Steve Westrop. Their contributions, as well as those by Björn Kroger and Regent Jim Dawson, are greatly appreciated. Rich Nyahay, an oil and gas geologist with the State Museum, also enthusiastically assisted with the field trip, both in helping organize it and in being the "gopher" during the trip. Sam Bowring of the Massachusetts Institute of Technology took time from his packed schedule of teaching and globe-trotting to give the key note address "Review of the timing and constraints on the Neoproterozoic–Cambrian record of metazoan evolution," and took in part of the field trip because of his own interest in the Cambrian. John Hart, head of research and collections made possible the bus rental for the excursion. Finally, I must acknowledge the patience of Jeanne C. Finley, who acceded to my absence during the workshop—although this coincided with our first wedding anniversary.

REFERENCES

All references in this section are cited at the end of the field trip guide by Landing *et al.* (this volume).

EDIACARAN–ORDOVICIAN OF EAST LAURENTIA—
GEOLOGIC SETTING AND CONTROLS ON DEPOSITION
ALONG THE NEW YORK PROMONTORY REGION

ED LANDING

New York State Museum, The State Education Department, Madison Avenue, Albany, NY 12230, elanding@mail.nysed.gov

ABSTRACT—Deposition of the Ediacaran–Ordovician on the high-grade metamorphics of the Grenville orogen began with the break up of Rodinia and origin of the Iapetus Ocean. Rifting along two active arms of the spreading system defined the Quebec Reentrant and New York Promontory; the failed arm produced the Ottawa aulocogen. The oldest cover unit is in the Appalachians (Ediacaran Tibbit Hill volcanics of northern Vermont and adjacent Quebec). These volcanics are overlain by and replaced by rift-related sedimentary rocks (Pinnacle Formation) that nonconformably overlie the Grenville in southern Vermont and by coeval feldspathic turbidites (Rensselaer Formation and Bomoseen Member) that are the oldest units in the Taconic allochthon. Transition to the passive margin is recorded by the oldest carbonate platform unit (Forestdale Marble and coeval, synonymous units) in east Laurentia. The Forestdale conformably overlies the Pinnacle on the west flank of the Green Mountain axis. Increased subsidence/eustatic rise is recorded by black mudstone (Moosalamoo Phyllite) above the Forestdale. Oddly, the Moosalamoo shoals up into Cheshire Formation tidalites, at the same time that the Cheshire onlaps the Grenville in the southern Green Mountains, Hudson Highlands, and Manhattan (i.e., "Lowerre Quartzite"). *Olenellus* Zone trilobites in the upper Pinnacle and discovery of trilobite sclerites in the uppermost Bomoseen indicate that the rift–passive margin transition took place surprisingly late—in the late Early Cambrian. Post-Cheshire Cambrian platform units in the northern Appalachians include carbonates (largely hydrothermally dolomitized), which record eustatic highs (Dunham, Winooski, and Little Falls) and correlate with dysoxic/anoxic, black mudstones on the continental slope (Browns Pond and Hatch Hill Formations of the Taconic allochthon). Eustatic fall with the terminal Early Cambrian Hawke Bay regression is shown by platform quartz arenite (Monkton) or red shaly dolostone with quartz sand (lower Stissing), and on the continental slope by oxic, green mudstone (Middle Granville Formation) of the Hawke Bay oxic interval (new) in the Taconic allochthon. Quartz sand was swept toward the shelf margin (Danby Formation) as the inner craton was transgressed by the upper Potsdam Formation (terminal Middle–lower Upper Cambrian). The Cheshire and Potsdam/Danby show coeval transgression and progradation onto the outer shelf, and apparently record decreases in sea-level rise rates. Anomalous successions include: 1) the dysoxic/anoxic Franklin Basin of northwest Vermont, formed by late Early Cambrian down-faulting of the shelf and maintained by growth-faults through the Early Ordovician, and 2) the thick Potsdam (500+ m) in northeast New York. Downdrop of the south flank of the Ottawa aulocogen, perhaps at the same time as formation of the Franklin Basin, allowed onlap of red mudstones and sandstones of the "Altona Formation" (new) and accumulation of the overlying, thick, Ausable Member of the Potsdam. The Cambrian–Ordovician boundary is an interformational (Little Falls–Tribes Hill) unconformity on the platform. The overlying Lower–lower Upper Ordovician is a series of unconformity-bounded depositional sequences (Tribes Hill, Rochdale, Fort Cassin, and Providence Island Formations of the upper Sauk sequence and Chazy Group of the lower Tippecanoe sequence) that: 1) record eustatic highs, 2) show a repeated depositional motif (lower transgressive sandstones, upper highstand carbonates), and 3) are coeval with dysoxic/anoxic black mudstone intervals in the green-gray mudstones of the Taconic allochthon (i.e., within the Deep Kill–Mount Merino Formations). These black mudstones record the Schaghticoke, Begin Hill, Levis, Laignet Point, Raceville, and Glenmont dysoxic/anoxic intervals (new) on the east Laurentian continental slope. Late Ordovician convergence and collision of the New York Promontory with the Ammonusuc arc in the Taconic orogeny ended passive margin deposition.

INTRODUCTION

The relatively small area encompassed by eastern New York, adjacent New England, and southern Quebec and Ontario exhibits a geological history and variety of geological features typical of a continent-sized land mass (for general reviews see van Diver, 1985, 1987; Isachsen *et al.*, 1992; Landing, 2005a; Skehan, 2001). In this region, Lower Paleozoic and, locally, Ediacaran rocks overlie middle Proterozoic rocks of the Grenville orogen, and occur in two distinct geologic provinces:

the craton and the Appalachians. The transition from the largely undeformed successions of the craton to the folded and thrust-faulted Ediacaran–Lower Paleozoic of the northern Appalachians is abrupt, and is traditionally designated "Logan's line" (named for the pioneering work done on the

northern Appalachians by the 19th century Canadian geologist Sir William Logan). Logan's line and the western limit of the Appalachians are marked by a sinuous line of master thrusts that enter the region from the St. Lawrence lowlands to the northeast. These thrusts then continue roughly north–south as

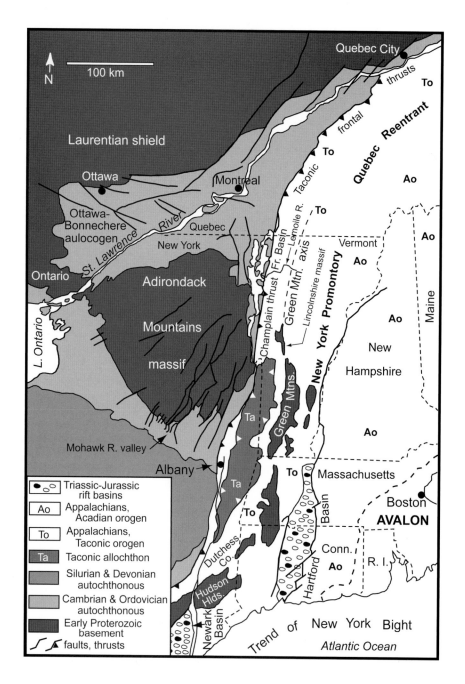

FIGURE 1—Regional geology of eastern New York and adjacent New England, Quebec, and Ontario. Figure emphasizes the features resulting from Ediacaran–earliest Cambrian rifting [i.e., active arms of the Quebec Reentrant and New York Promontory and failed arm of the Ottawa–Bonnechere aulocogen]. Mesozoic rifting led to opening of the Atlantic Ocean ["Trend of New York Bight" defined by SW- and E-trending active arms; north-trending failed arm outlined by Newark and Hartford Basins]. Cretaceous coastal plain deposits of Long Island not illustrated in figure. Modified from Hayman and Kidd (2002, fig. 1).

the Champlain thrust in the eastern Lake Champlain lowlands and as related thrusts along the Hudson River lowlands, and swing southwest in southern New York into New Jersey and Pennsylvania (Figure 1). This summary of the geology of eastern New York and western Vermont provides a background to the 12th meeting of the International Subcommission on Cambrian Stratigraphy (July 29–August 6, 2007) (see Landing *et al.*, this volume).

LAURENTIAN SHIELD AND RODINIA SUPERCONTINENT

Long-stable, middle Proterozoic rocks of the Laurentian (or Canadian) shield crop out from southern Labrador to southern Quebec and Ontario, and comprise the large dome of the Adirondack Mountains massif in northern New York. The northwest-trending Frontenac arch crosses the St. Lawrence River to bridge the main outcrop area of the Laurentian shield in southern Canada with the Adirondack massif. Uplifted, elongate, middle Proterozoic inliers also occur as the oldest rocks in the younger Appalachian Mountains (Figure 1, see Green Mountain anticlinorium, Lincolnshire massif, and Hudson Highlands).

The middle Proterozoic basement of the shield is composed of high-grade metamorphic (granulite-facies) and igneous rocks of the ca. 1.0 Ga Grenville orogen—which culminated in a major continent-continent collision with a compressive thickening of the crust. In the Appalachians, the Grenville massifs underwent subsequent retrograde metamorphism to the biotite zone in Paleozoic orogenies (e.g., Zen, 1967, p. 101).

The modern tectonic analog of the Grenville orogeny is the Himalayas (Dewey and Burke, 1973; Windley, 1986; McLelland *et al.*, 2001). As noted by Gates *et al.* (2004), the Grenville terrane is one of the longest and most deeply exhumed exhumed orogens on Earth. The granulite-facies of the Grenville orogen was produced at a depth of 25 km. However, dramatic uplift has led to the exposure of these lower crustal rocks across the orogen. This uplift was perhaps a result of "simple" post-tectonic relaxation and isostatic rebound or the passage of a syn-orogenic mantle plume under the Grenville margin, The erosive removal of 25 km of rock took place over a protracted period (ca. 300 Ma) that overlapped the Grenville orogeny, but was well prior to the deposition of Ediacaran–Lower Paleozoic cover sequences (Streepey *et al.*, 2004).

The now fragmented Grenville orogen is present in western Scandinavia, northern Scotland and Ireland, western Newfoundland, and Maritime Canada, and also forms the basement of southern Labrador, Quebec, and Ontario and much of the eastern U. S. southwest to the Llano area of Texas. The Grenville orogen records the assembly of the Rodinia supercontinent with the collision of the Amazon craton and its overriding of areas that comprise modern eastern North America (Dalziel *et al.*, 1994). U-Pb zircon ages from the Adirondacks show sedimentary and volcanic protolith ages of 1.3–1.2 Ga. Some zircons from the Hudson Highlands (Figure 1) have a 2.0 Ga age, and suggest that the Hudson Highlands are "exotic" in the Grenville province and represent part of the Amazonian craton (in Gates *et al.*, 2004).

RODINIA BREAK-UP—ORIGIN OF EDIACARAN –LOWER PALEOZOIC COVER SEQUENCE

The break-up of Rodinia included the origin and progressive isolation of Laurentia ("ancestral North America") from other paleocontinents, and the formation of the Iapetus Ocean to the (present) east of the Grenville orogen. Much of the Grenville orogen remained as the basement of much of eastern Laurentia, although a large piece of the Grenville that underlies most of Mexico accompanied Gondwana as it broke away from Rodinia (Keppie, 2004; Landing *et al.*, In press).

A zig-zag series of promontories (or salients) and re-entrants (or recesses) was defined along the Grenville margin by the active arms of the spreading system that formed the Iapetus Ocean (Thomas, 1977; Williams, 1978). In the region of the field excursion (Figure 1), the margin of the Laurentia paleocontinent was defined by active arms that formed the northeast-trending Quebec Reentrant, the N–S-trending New York Promontory, and the Pennsylvania Reentrant to the southwest (Figure 1). The Ottawa aulocogen, the failed arm of the Quebec–New York triple junction, trends WNW into the Grenville orogen. The subsequent epeirogenic histories of the Quebec Reentrant, New York Promontory, and Ottawa aulocogen all had major roles in determining the facies, thicknesses, and continuity of deposition of the cover successions on the Grenville orogen.

Active spreading, initial formation of the Iapetus Ocean, and development of the oldest cover successions on the newly rifted margin of east Laurentia took place during the Ediacaran–earliest Cambrian. Rifting that defined the eastern margin of the New York Promontory is recorded by mafic dikes that cut the Adirondack massif in northeastern New York (Stop 3.1 of field trip) (Isachsen *et al.*, 1988, reported 588–542 Ma ages on the dikes) and the Hudson Highlands in southern New York and New Jersey (Ratcliffe, 1987) (Figure 1).

Interestingly, the southern part of the Adirondacks is a roughly E–W-trending orocline of ductile shear zones, folds, and domes produced as a syntaxis during the collision with Amazonia at the end of the Grenville orogeny (Gates *et al.*, 2004). However, these Grenville structures do not define the modern topography of the Adirondacks. Satellite pictures show that the modern topography of the Adirondacks is defined by a prominent set of conjugate faults that trend NNE and NW (see Rogers *et al.*, 1990; see Figure 1). These brittle fractures of the Grenville basement pre-date the Lower Paleozoic cover sequence, and are best attributed to extension of the New York Promontory with the origin of the Iapetus Ocean.

The oldest post-Grenville cover sequence rocks occur in the Appalachian Mountains, and include the ca. 570 Ma mafic Tibbit Hill volcanics (to 1,700+ m thick) that crop out along the Green Mountain axis from the headwaters of the Lemoile River in northern Vermont (Figure 1) into southern Quebec (Kumarapeli *et al.*, 1981, 1989). Interestingly, the location of the Tibbit Hill Formation volcanics lies at the triple junction where the trends of the Quebec Reentrant, Ottawa aulocogen, and New York Promontory intersect, and may represent the location of a plume. Rift-facies of the Pinnacle Formation (Clark, 1932), interpreted to represent alluvial fan, braided stream, or braid-plain deposits(Cherichetti *et al.*, 1998), overlie the Tibbit Hill volcanics [unconformably in northern Vermont (Dorsey *et al.*, 1983; Doolan *et al.*, 1987) and conformably in southern Quebec

(Dowling, 1988; Colpron, 1990)]. The Pinnacle greatly thickens to the south in central Vermont (to 3,000+ m), where it nonconformably overlies Grenvillian rocks of the Lincolnshire massif (Cherichetti *et al.*, 1998; Figure 1).

RIFT–PASSIVE MARGIN TRANSITION AND THE OLDEST CARBONATE PLATFORM

The transition from a rifted to a passive margin along the eastern margin of the New York Promontory took place within an interval that can be bracketed by the latest Ediacaran and late Early Cambrian. Available evidence suggests that reference of the transition to a surprisingly young interval in the Early Cambrian is most likely.

Along the western flank of the Green Mountain axis, the Pinnacle Formation is conformably overlain by a more-or-less quartzose, relatively thick (to 50 m) dolostone marble [White Brook Dolostone in northern Vermont and Quebec, Forestdale Marble (Keith, 1932) in central Vermont; Figure 2]. Examination of the Forestdale Marble shows that it locally has well-preserved primary sedimentary structures that indicate deposition from high-energy, probably tidally influenced environments (Stops 5.2–5.4 in Landing *et al.*, this volume) to low-energy, subtidal

environments. Thus, the Forestdale and White Brook dolomitic marbles, as well as the Plymouth Marble, their probable equivalent on the east flank of the Green Mountain anticlinorium (see Brace, 1953; Skehan, 1961), represent the oldest carbonate platform unit on the New York Promontory and, apparently, in east Laurentia. As the modern eastern margin of Laurentia faced south and lay at approximately 35° S during the Cambrian (e.g., Scotese and McKerrow, 1990), the development of a tropical carbonate platform facies with the transition into a shallow-water passive margin is not unexpected.

Sea-level rise [whether caused by epeirogenic down-dropping or eustatic rise is presently unresolved] is recorded by the widespread deposition of strongly dysoxic or anoxic black mudstones with abundant pyrite [Moosalamoo Phyllite (Keith, 1932)] above the Forestdale and White Brook carbonates. This anoxic facies is, in turn, transitional upward by shoaling into the tidalite sandstones of the Cheshire Formation (Myrow, 1983)—one of the most prominent marker units for mapping in western and central Vermont (see Stops 4.5 and 5.2A in Landing *et al.*, this volume).

At present, the Cheshire Formation (Emmons, 1892) has yielded the oldest, albeit sparse, fossils from Vermont and eastern New York. These fossils include trilobites, and demonstrate that the Cheshire is not a particularly old unit in the Cambrian,

FIGURE 2— Ediacaran–lower Upper Ordovician of the New York Promontory and southern margin of the Ottawa–Bonnechere aulocogen. Autochthonous cratonic successions in Mohawk River valley and Champlain lowlands. Depositional history of platform on epeirogenically active southern margin of Ottawa–Bonnechere aulocogen in Beekmantown to southern Quebec column. Parautochthonous Appalachian successions in columns for Dutchess County, New York, and western flank of Green Mountains; Trenton Group limestone and overlying shales overlie unconformity surface as low as Grenville orogen on west flank of Green Mountains as result of Taconic orogeny (not shown). Correlation of "Altona Formation" and Ausable Member uncertain, but tentatively related to faulting on southern margin of Ottawa–Bonnechere graben and formation of Franklin Basin in northwest Vermont. Cambrian–Ordovician boundary everywhere a hiatus between the Little Falls and Tribes Hill Formations. *Paraprioniodus costatus-Chosonodina rigbyi-Histiodella holodentata* Interval conodonts (Ethington and Clark, 1981, = conodont Fauna 4 of Sweet *et al.*, 1971) in upper Providence Island Formation (E. Landing, unpub. data) indicate that traditional Beekmantown Group includes the Middle Ordovician. Most of the Chazy Group and all of the Black River and Trenton Groups are Upper Ordovician (see Mitchell *et al.*, 1997), and the "Knox unconformity" is the lower bracket of the Upper Ordovician (Landing, 2003c). Abbreviations: B.R.G., Black River Group; "F. D.," Finch Dolostone; Moosa. Ph., Moosalamoo Phyllite; Rath., Rathbunville School Limestone; "S.F.," "Steves Farm Limestone;" V, Van Wie Member; "W. H.," "Warner Hill Limestone." Column "west flank of Green Mountains" is Middlebury, Vermont, area and east to Green Mountains; asterisks note first uses of unified stratigraphic nomenclature on east New York–Vermont platform. The following synonymies are based on lithologic comparison, comparable upper and lower contacts, and coeval faunas—Cambrian synonymies: 1) "Poughquag Quartzite" in Dutchess County, New York (Merrill, 1902) with Cheshire Formation of Massachusetts and Vermont (Emerson, 1898) (see Wilmarth, 1938; Landing and Bartowski, 1996); 2) "Ticonderoga Formation" of east New York and adjacent Vermont (Rodgers *in* Welby, 1961) with the Galway Formation (Fisher and Hansen, 1951); 3) "Clarendon Springs Formation" of Vermont, "Whitehall Formation" (Rodgers, 1937) and "Briarcliff Formation" of eastern New York with the Little Falls Formation (Clarke, 1903) (see Landing, 2002; Landing et al., 2003a). Ordovician synonymies: 4) "Shelburne Marble" of Vermont (Keith, 1923; Cady, 1945) and "Halcyon Lake Formation" (Knopf, 1927, 1962) of Dutchess County with the Tribes Hill Formation (Ulrich and Cushing, 1910) (see Kröger and Landing, In press a; E. Landing, unpub. data); 5) "lower Benson Formation" [intervals 1 and 2 of Cady (1945, p. 542) in Vermont and "Fort Ann Formation" in New York (Wheeler, 1942) with the Rochdale Formation of Dutchess County (Knopf, 1927, 1962) (see Landing and Westrop, 2006; Kröger and Landing, In press b; E. Landing, unpub. data); 6) "upper Benson Formation" [intervals 3 and 4 of Cady (1945, p. 542) with interval 3 equated with the Ward Member] and "Bascom Formation" (Cady, 1945) of Vermont, "Copake Limestone" of Dutchess County (Knopf, 1927, 1962), lower "Beauharnois Formation" of Quebec (Raymond, 1913), and "Ogdensburg Formation/Member" of New York–Quebec (Chadwick, 1919) with the Fort Cassin Formation (Whitfield, 1890) (Landing, 2002; Landing and Westrop, 2006); 7) "Bridport Dolomite" of Vermont (Cady, 1945, type section description and location and upper and lower contacts never specified) and upper "Beauharnois Formation (Huntingdon Member)" and "Carillon Formation" of Quebec (Globensky, 1982a, b) with the Providence Island Formation (Flower, 1964) (see Landing and Westrop, 2006).

Ediacaran–Ordovician of East Laurentia—Geologic Setting and Controls on Deposition Along the New York Promontory Region

9

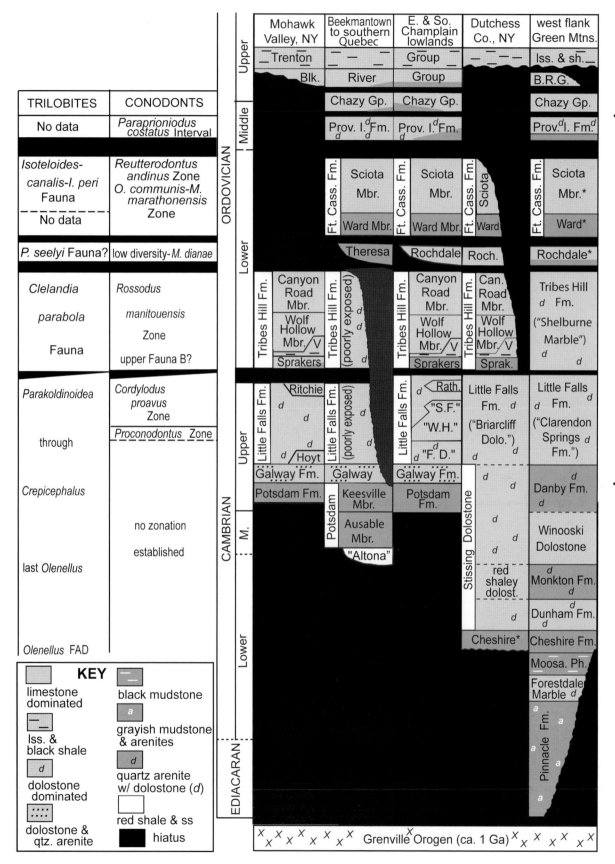

and is late Early Cambrian (e.g., Landing *et al.*, 1998). Fragmentary *Olenellus* specimens were reported by Walcott (1888) from quartzites near Bennington, Vermont, and from the south end of the Green Mountain anticlinorium at Clarksburg Mountain in northernmost Massachusetts. These localities have commonly been assigned to the Cheshire Formation (e.g., Theokritoff, 1968). In addition, fragmentary *Olenellus* specimens occur in the Cheshire Formation [traditionally called "Poughquag Quartzite" (abandoned designation, see Figure 2 caption)], where it rests on the Grenville of the Hudson Highlands in Dutchess County, New York (Dwight, 1887; Gordon, 1911).

White quartzites and black mudstones are interbedded through the Moosalamoo–Cheshire transition along the western limb of the Green Mountain anticlinorium; and this suggests that the Moosalamoo is not significantly older than the Cheshire. Indeed, even the upper part of the rift facies of the Pinnacle Formation may not range far down into the Lower Cambrian. This suggestion is supported by Prindle and Knopf's (1932) mapping of the North Adams, Massachusetts area and J. B. Thompson and J. Skehan's observation (*in* Brace, 1953, p. 33) that Walcott's (1888) *Olenellus* locality lies only 30 m above the middle Proterozoic (Grenville) Mount Holly Complex (Whittle, 1891), and in an interval that resembles the lower Pinnacle Formation. Skehan (1961) also referred Walcott's (1888) localities to the sub-Cheshire "Mendon Formation" [the Pinnacle Formation of this report]. These observations all suggest that the entire Pinnacle–Cheshire interval is Lower, but not lowermost, Cambrian, and that the rift–passive margin transition along the New York Promontory was late Early Cambrian (Figure 2).

EARLY CAMBRIAN–LATE ORDOVICIAN PLATFORM SUCCESSION IN THE APPALACHIANS

Passive margin sequence

Formation-scale sandstone and dolostone alternations.— The Cheshire–lower Upper Ordovician of the New York Promontory platform succession that lies in the Appalachians (Figure 1) is a succession of alternating carbonates and quartz arenites (Figure 2, columns for Dutchess County, New York, and west flank of Green Mountains). These platform sandstones and carbonates of the New York promontory persist as far east as the west flank of the Green Mountain axis and as far south as New York City. In Manhattan, the Grenville (Fordham Gneiss) is nonconformably overlain by the Cheshire Formation [locally and traditionally termed the Lowerre Quartzite], and the overlying dolomite marble-dominated unit with minor calcareous schists (Inwood Marble) is stratigraphically similar to the post-Cheshire–Lower Ordovician succession of the west Vermont and Dutchess County areas (e.g., Hall, 1968).

The metamorphic grade of these rocks increases to the east, with the parautochthonous rocks at and just east of the Champlain thrust referable to the low chlorite grade. Chlorite–biotite grades characterize the west and north flanks of the Grenville massifs of the Green Mountain axis and Hudson Highlands, respectively. East of the Green Mountain axis [in deep-water (slope and rise) equivalents of the platform succession] and south of the Hudson Highlands, almandine–kyanite grade metamorphism is present (e.g., Zen, 1967, p. 101).

*Biostratigraphy and dolomitization.—*Much of the Cambrian in these Appalachian successions has yielded very sparse macrofaunas, even when metamorphic grade is quite low (however, see section on Franklin Basin, below). Thus, biostratigraphic correlation, except for that based on more recent work on Upper Cambrian–Middle Ordovician conodonts, has been limited in resolution. Traditionally, the only locally abundant body fossils in the older part of the succession have been moldic trilobites in Cheshire and Monkton Formation sandstones (e.g., Walcott, 1888; Kindle and Tasch, 1948; Tasch, 1949; Shaw, 1962b).

The relative lack of skeletalized macrofaunas in the carbonate intervals reflects restricted marine environments with low diversity macrofaunas that are frequently dominated by mollusks and with such more offshore/open marine components as trilobites limited in abundance and diversity (Landing *et al.*, 2003a). A more important factor in the absence/low abundance of macrofaunas is the pervasive dolomitization that has affected the carbonates of much of the sequence, and has limited recovery of macrofaunas to a relatively limited number of localities.

These fossiliferous localities are typically in very geographically restricted lenses or "pods" of limestones in Appalachian and nearby cratonic settings that were not dolomitized (e.g., Landing *et al.*, 2003a; Kröger and Landing, In press a, b). A number of syntheses have followed the reflux/evaporitic shelf/meteoritic "paradigms" dominant in the 1960s and 1970s in explaining this dolomitization [e.g., Friedman (1980) who related dolomitization of the Tribes Hill Formation in the Mohawk River valley to evaporitic depositional conditions]. However, regional dolomitization by hydrothermal fluid movement during the Late Ordovician Taconic orogeny or subsequent orogenies (Collin-Wait and Lowenstein, 1994; Benison and Lowenstein, 1997), particularly along reactivated faults that extend into the Grenville, is a more persuasive model for this dolomitization. [Landing *et al.* (1996) related dolomitization of the Lower Ordovician Tribes Hill Formation to hydrothermal activity along re-activated Mohawk River valley faults]. Hydrothermal dolomitization also helps explain the lateral transitions from local "pods" of non-dolomitized, normal-marine limestones with abundant primary sedimentary features and calcareous fossils to dominant, non-fossiliferous, sucrosic dolostone in this region (Landing *et al.*, 2003; see Landing *et al.*, this volume, Stop 2.3 of field trip).

Eustatic controls on deposition

*Slow subsidence and eustatic signatures.—*Palmer (1971, p. 184–189) referred to the Cambrian successions along the southern New York Promontory as "thin sequences." These "thin sequences" extend from the southern end of the Green Mountain axis in western Massachusetts through western Connecticut and Dutchess County, New York, and west into northern New Jersey. The "thin sequences" differ from those of central and western Vermont where sub-Cheshire units are present. However, the entire Cambrian–lower Upper Ordovician platform succession everywhere on the eastern margin of the New York Promontory can be viewed as a "thin sequence" that is far thinner (only ca. 2 km in thickness) than coeval successions, for example, in the Great Basin or the southern Canadian Rockies. This passive margin succession records subsidence rates that were so slow that sedimentary facies and unconformities accurately record global sea-level (eustatic) changes (Landing *et al.*, 2003a). Thus, a simple, though appropriate, summary of the Cambrian–lower Upper Ordovician platform succession is that sandstones record proximal facies (eustatic offlaps or the initial deposits of eustatic onlap), while carbonate-dominated units record eustatic high-stands.

Early Cambrian eustasy.—Within the long range of *Olenellus* Zone faunas (Figure 2), a strong eustatic onlap/deepening interval followed by an offlap/shallowing interval occurs on the east Laurentian platform from western Newfoundland to Georgia. Landing and Bartowski (1996) proposed that the onlap–highstand succession includes two distinctive parts.

The lower part of the onlap–highstand succession in the Appalachians is a sparsely fossiliferous quartz arenite or heterolithic siliciclastic unit that nonconformably overlies Grenville basement locally and yields the lowest faunas with *Olenellus* [i.e., Bradore, Cheshire, Anteitum, and Helenmode Formations]. The higher part is a carbonate platform unit [Forteau, Dunham, Tomstown, Vintage, and Shady Formations].

The succeeding offlap/lowstand unit is a mixed quartz arenite-carbonate unit or inner detrital belt lithosome (red and green shale with minor carbonates) with the highest faunas with *Olenellus* [Hawke Bay, Monkton, red shaley dolostones of the Stissing Dolostone, Hardystown, Waynesboro, and Rome Formations].

In short, the Lower Cambrian of the New York Promontory reflects a cumulative eustatic rise (Cheshire–Dunham Formations) prior to the Hawke Bay regression (reddish quartz arenites with dolostones of the Monkton). The Hawke Bay eustatic regression (Palmer and James, 1979) is terminal Early Cambrian (within the latest *Olenellus* Chron) in terms of traditional Laurentian chronostratigraphy (Figure 2) and earliest Middle Cambrian in terms of west Gondwanan (Moroccan and Iberian) successions (Landing *et al.*, 2006).

Two caveats should be added to Landing and Bartowski's (1996) eustatic history. The first is the seemingly contradictory sea-level record provided by the Cheshire Formation. The Cheshire records eustatic rise because it transgresses the Grenville at in the southern part of the New York Promontory—at the south end of the Green Mountain anticlinorium; in Dutchess County, New York; and (as the "Lowerre Quartzite") in Manhattan. However, the Cheshire also records a shoaling and appearance of proximal facies above the Moosalamoo Phyllite. Transgression with shoaling can only be accommodated by a slowing in rate of eustatic rise—an explanation that also seems appropriate in explaining the lateral transition of the Potsdam and Danby Formations (noted below).

The second caveat involves Palmer's (1971) and Landing and Bartowski's (1996) mis-correlation of the so-called "Poughquag Quartzite" (see Cheshire Formation in Figure 2) in Dutchess County, New York, with Hawke Bay regression sandstones elsewhere in eastern Laurentia. Sparse faunas from the lowest Stissing Formation include the phosphatic problematicum *Discinella micans* Billings, 1872 (Gordon, 1911; E. Landing, unpub. data) and indicate a correlation with the late Early Cambrian eustatic deepening recorded by the Forteau Formation in western Newfoundland and Labrador (Landing and Bartowski, 1996). More distantly in Laurentia, the deepening–shoaling cycle recorded by the upper Bastion–Ella Island

Formation sequence in North Greenland is coeval with the deepening of the Forteau Formation (Skovsted, 2006). In short, available biostratigraphic evidence; lithology (a massive, siliceous, light gray to greenish, coarse-grained quartz arenite), and its deposition as a tidalite (E. Landing, unpub. data) all indicate that the "Poughquag Quartzite" is merely a junior synonym of the Cheshire Formation and is not the record of the Hawke Bay regression (see Figure 2, caption).

Latest Early–latest Cambrian eustasy.—Following the Hawke Bay regression, dramatic eustatic rise is recorded in passive margin successions in eastern and western Laurentia from western Newfoundland to the White-Inyo region of California–Nevada (Landing and Bartowski, 1996; Landing *et al.*, 2003a). The Winooski Formation (dolostones with minor quartz arenites) above the Monkton Formation records this eustatic rise. Its position above the uppermost Lower Cambrian Monkton Formation has meant a traditional assignment to the Middle Cambrian, although it has not yielded biostratigraphically useful macrofossils (Cady, 1945). [Perkins' (1885) report of fossils from the "Winooski Marble" records faunas from the Dunhan Dolostone.] Middle Cambrian, post-Hawke Bay onlap, locally recorded by shaley facies below highstand carbonate platform facies is recorded in Appalachian successions from western Newfoundland to Alabama [March Point, Monkton, upper Stissing (above regressive shaley dolostones with coarse quartz sand; Figure 2), Elbrook, Brierfield Formations].

Relatively high sea-levels were maintained through the end of the Cambrian in the Appalachians (Landing *et al.*, 2002), and carbonate platform deposition was dominant in this region through the end of the period. The one major exception to this in the field trip area is the Danby Formation—an interval of mixed quartz arenites and dolostones that has not yet yielded biostratigraphy useful macrofossils.

As shown in Figure 2, the best correlation of the Danby is with two units of the craton: the sand-rich Potsdam Formation—a unit that transgresses the Grenville of the central New York Promontory in the terminal Middle Cambrian (discussed below)—and with the overlying, mixed carbonates and quartz arenites of the lower Upper Cambrian Galway Formation (senior synonym of the "Ticonderoga Formation). The Galway has Steptoean Stage (*Elvinia* Zone) faunas (see Ludvigsen and Westrop, 1983) (Stops 1.4, 1.5, 2.1 of field trip in Landing *et al.*, this volume). Predominantly shallow-water dolostones of the Little Falls Formation [traditionally referred to by the junior synonym "Clarendon Springs Formation" in Vermont (Landing, 2002; Landing *et al.*, 2003a)] occur above the Danby Formation, and provide an upper age bracket on the Danby. An unillustrated trilobite fauna reported from the Little Falls formation in Vermont (Stone and Dennis, 1964; with *Hungaia magnifica*, *Idiomesus*, *Levisella*, *Onchonotus*, *Pseudosaukia*, *Richardsonella*) includes taxa known from the upper, but not uppermost, Upper Cambrian. The top of the Little Falls in Vermont and cratonic New York has upper *Cordylodus proavus* Zone conodonts (Landing *et al.*, 1996, 2003a). The "Lower Ordovician" trilobites listed by Stone and Dennis (1964) from the Little Falls Formation in Vermont are now referable to the uppermost Cambrian following the "raising" and standardization of the Cambrian–Ordovician boundary at the base of the *Iapetognathus fluctivagus* Zone (Cooper *et al.*, 2001).

Ordovician eustasy.—The Lower–Middle Ordovician part of

the Beekmantown Group on the easternmost craton and in the Appalachian sequences of Dutchess County, New York, consists of four, unconformity-bounded formations (Landing *et al.*, 1996, 2003a; Landing, 2002; Landing and Westrop, 2006; Kröger and Landing, In press a, In press B). Current work by E. Landing (unpub. data, 2007) has extended this synthesis above the Rochdale Formation, and allows the proposal of a unified Lower–Middle Ordovician stratigraphic nomenclature that includes western Vermont (see Figure 2, caption).

The Cambrian–Ordovician boundary, and Little Falls–Tribes Hill formational contact, is a type 1 sequence boundary (van Wagoner et al., 1988) that shows subaerial erosion. This systemic and interformational boundary is a biostratigraphically resolvable unconformity (upper *Cordylodus proavus*–upper conodont Fauna B or *Rossodus manitouensis* Zone) everywhere on the New York Promontory (Landing *et al.*, 1996, 2003a). Early, but not earliest, Tremadocian onlap of the Tribes Hill Formation is marked by initial deposition of a transgressive sandstone or sandy dolostone with a local basal conglomerate of Little Falls dolostone clasts (Sprakers Member), a higher dark subtidal shale-dominated unit (Van Wie Member), and finally a highstand carbonate facies with thrombolites (Wolf Hollow Member) and a peritidal/restricted marine cap (Canyon Road Member) (see Landing *et al.*, 2003a). [The Tribes Hill Formation is the senior synonym of the following lithologically comparable and coeval unconformity-bounded units: "Halcyon Lake" Formation in eastern New York and "Cutting Formation" and "Shelburne Marble" in Vermont (Landing and Westrop, 2006)].

The eustatic rise that led to deposition of the Tribes Hill Formation was a major Early Ordovician (late early Tremadoc) event. This sea-level rise led to a marine inundation of much of Laurentia, and included carbonate deposition as far into the continent interior as the upper Mississippi River valley (Landing, 1988a; Ross and Ross, 1992; Landing *et al.*, 2003a).

This depositional motif of a basal unconformity, initial quartz arenite onlap deposits, and a highstand carbonate interval, commonly with thrombolites, is largely repeated in three successive Lower–Middle Ordovician units (Figure 2):

1) The first is the Rochdale Formation [upper Tremadoc and Laurentian Stairsian Stage]. Junior synonyms of the Rochdale include the following lithologically comparable and coeval unconformity-bounded units: "Fort Ann Formation" (Landing and Westrop, 2006) and "lower Benson Formation" [intervals 1 and 2 of Cady (1945, p. 542) in Vermont], which have a basal conglomerate with Tribes Hill clasts locally up to 2 m in diameter (Mazzulo, 1974; Landing *et al.*, 2003a; Kröger and Landing, In press b).

The Rochdale Formation represents a relatively modest eustatic rise (Landing and Westrop, 2006). The formation does not seem to appear in western successions of the Champlain slice (Welby, 1964), although it appears in more southerly sequences on the eastern limit of the craton in Washington County, New York (Landing *et al.*, 2003a) (i.e., just east of Stop 2.5 in Landing *et al.*, this volume). The Rochdale did not onlap further east in the Lake Champlain lowlands, and does not appear in cratonic successions at Beekmantown near Plattsburgh (Figure 2, Beekmantown to southern Quebec column). In the latter area, the younger Fort Cassin Formation unconformably overlies the Tribes Hill Formation (Landing and Westrop, 2006).

2) the Fort Cassin Formation [lower–middle Arenig or Laurentian Tulean–lower Blackhillsian Stages; also known by the junior synonyms "Ogdensburg Member/Formation" and "lower Beauharnois Formation" in northwest New York–southern Ontario and Quebec; "Copake Formation" in Dutchess County, New York; and "upper Benson Formation" (intervals 3 and 4 of Cady, 1945) and "Bascom Formation" of Vermont (see Landing and Westrop, 2006)]. A lower transgressive sandstone (Ward Member), which may have a basal conglomerate of Rochdale clasts deposited on an eroded type 1 sequence boundary (E. Landing, unpublished data), and an upper highstand carbonate (Sciota Member) [see Fisher (1984) for definition of members of the Fort Cassin] are represented in the Fort Cassin Formation (Landing and Westrop, 2006).

3) The Beekmantown Group ends with the unconformity-bounded Providence Island Formation [lithologically comparable and coeval units that are junior synonyms include: "Bridport Formation" in Vermont and "Carillon Formation" in southern Quebec (Landing, 2002; Landing and Westrop, 2006)]. *Paraprioniodus costatus* Interval conodonts indicate that the Providence Island Formation is lower Middle Ordovician (Landing 2002, 2003a, c). A conglomerate of dolostone clasts locally occurs at the base of the Providence Island Formation (on Providence Island, Vermont), and the unit can be divided into a lower sandy facies and an upper carbonate dominated in eastern sections near Middlebury, Vermont (E. Landing, unpub. data). The top of the Providence Island Formation corresponds to the Laurentian-wide, eustatic Knox unconformity at the base of the Chazy Group (Sloss, 1963; Ross and Ross, 1995).

End of the passive margin.—Early Late Ordovician epeirogenic activity on the easternmost part of the New York Promontory marked the end of passive margin platform deposition, and the transition to an active margin. This epeirogenic activity included block faulting and subsidence of the eastern Laurentian platform by loading of the Taconic accretionary prism at the onset of the Taconic orogeny. This loading of the east Laurentian platform margin is seen by the transition of the open-shelf facies of the lower Upper Ordovician Chazy Group in the Lake Champlain lowlands into the turbiditic limestones of the Middlebury Limestone on the western flank of the Green Mountain axis (Washington and Chisick (1994).

FRANKLIN BASIN CAMBRIAN–ORDOVICIAN SUCCESSION

Location and significance

The Franklin Basin (Shaw, 1958) lies north of the Lemoile River valley, in the northwestern corner of Vermont and adjacent Quebec (Figure 1). This area lies within the Appalachians, but is distinguished herein from other Appalachian successions because it features an anomalous sequence of dark gray to black mudstones with carbonate-clast debris flows and turbiditic sandstones (Figure 3). The Franklin Basin lies within the narrow, N–S-striking St. Albans synclinorium (Stops 4.1–4.4, 4.7 of field trip; Landing *et al.*, this volume).

These strata contain the most diverse upper Lower Cambrian–Lower Ordovician macrofaunas (particularly trilobites) along the New York Promontory (see reviews in Shaw, 1959, Theokritoff, 1968, p. 14, 15). The lower Parker Formation

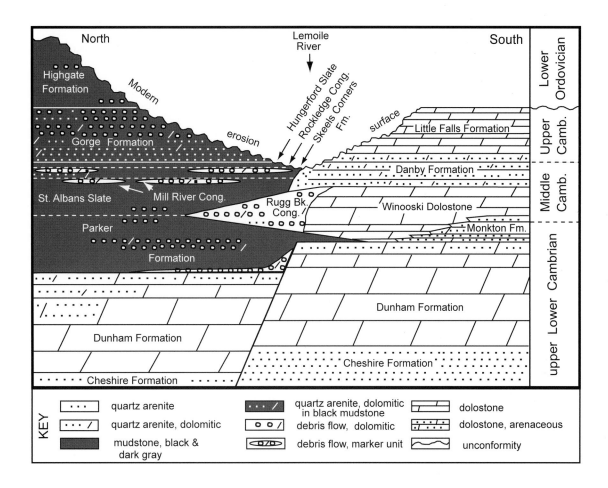

FIGURE 3—Epeirogenic development and lithostratigraphy of the dysoxic/anoxic Franklin Basin in northeast Vermont. Monkton Formation marks the Hawke Bay regression; Danby Formation is lateral equivalent of the Potsdam (Keesville Member) and Galway Formations of the inner platform. Figure re-interprets Rodgers (1968, fig. 10-1).

in the Town of Georgia, Vermont, provided the "typical" *Olenellus* Zone fauna of Laurentia. Elements of this fauna were first described by Hall (1859, 1860b) of the New York State Museum, and later became the "characteristic" Lower Cambrian fauna in Walcott's (1886, 1891a) reports. In addition, the upper *Olenellus* Zone at the Parker quarry (now lost) yielded superbly preserved specimens of what was the first-discovered Cambrian Lagerstätte (see illustrations in Walcott, 1886; Resser and Howell, 1938).

Shelf–slope break

The upper Lower Cambrian–Lower Ordovician of the St. Albans synclinorium is abruptly transitional along strike into the coeval platform succession of the Middlebury synclinorium. This transition takes place in the roughly E–W-trending Lemoile River valley (Shaw, 1958; Stone and Dennis. 1964). Rodgers (1968) compared this abrupt facies transition in northwest Vermont to the lateral facies transition of the Cambrian in the Lancaster, Pennsylvania, area. He concluded that these were the only two areas in eastern Laurentia that preserve the lateral transition from the Early Paleozoic carbonate platform to the upper slope.

A vertical transition from the underlying, Lower Cambrian platform succession [Cheshire and Dunham Formations; Stops 4.6 4.7 of field trip; Landing *et al.*, this volume] is seen in the Middlebury synclinorium with an abrupt change from the shallow-marine carbonates of the Dunham Formation (e.g., Merhtens and Gregory, 1988) into the dark-gray to black mudstones of the Parker Formation (Figure 3). Schuchert (1937, p. 1025, 1034, fig. 8) and Shaw (1954, locality SA C 5) correlated the sharp lithologic break from the carbonates of the Dunham Formation into the mudstone-dominated Parker Formation with a "distinct erosion interval," and reported 3 m-deep channels and erosive pedestals on the Dunham. Re-examination of Schuchert's (1937) locality VII (Stop 4.7 of field trip; Landing *et al.*, this volume) and numerous other Dunham–Parker contacts in the area shows that these "pedestals" that resulted from subaerial erosion are actually blocks in debris flows of Dunham Dolostone at the base of the Parker Formation.

Epeirogenic interpretation

The abrupt lateral and vertical transitions from the Dunham into the Parker, the presence of a debrite at the contact of these formations, and the persistence of dark gray–black mudstone and turbidite/grain flow deposition from the late Early Cambrian through the Early Ordovician in the Franklin Basin are considered herein to be the result of faulting along the trend of the present Lemoile River valley. Caving along the front of a submarine scarp in the Dunham Formation apparently produced the clasts at the Dunham–Parker contact. Continued subsidence of the Franklin Basin from the late Early Cambrian through Early Ordovician apparently precluded both 1) northerly progradation of the carbonate platform succession of the Middlebury synclinorium and 2) a filling of the Franklin Basin to peritidal depths. In short, the Lemoile River valley fault(s) were growth fault(s).

The growth fault(s) that defined the southern margin of the Franklin Basin and, thus, the shelf–slope break in northwestern Vermont, lay on a WNW-trending line that links other important Ediacaran–Early Paleozoic depositional features on the New York Promontory. This trend parallels the southern flank of the Ottawa aulocogen, which controlled deposition of the Cambrian–Upper Ordovician (discussed below; Figure 1), and lines up with a syndepositional fault that sharply separated the Tibbitt Hill Formation volcanics of northern Vermont from the thickest deposits of the Pinnacle Formation in central Vermont (Cherichetti *et al.*, 1998). This southern Ottawa aulocogen –Lemoile River valley–southernmost Tibbitt Hill volcanic "line" may represent a line of fracture along the cooling, rifted margin at the north end of the New York Promontory.

Upper slope dysoxia/anoxia

All evidence indicates that the Franklin Basin remained relatively deep through the Early Ordovician, despite a continual influx of quartz sand and carbonate clast debrites after its formation (Figure 3). The presence of large, shelf-derived carbonate blocks in some of the debris flows (Landing, 1983; Stop 4.2 in section C of Landing *et al.*, this volume) suggests an upper slope depositional setting, comparable to that of the Levis Formation—a unit that lies at the leading edge of the Taconic thrust and just across the St. Lawrence River from Quebec City (e.g., Landing and Benus, 1985). By comparison, lower slope debris flows in the Taconic allochthon, eastern New York, contain slope-derived, typically flat limestone clasts derived from slope-deposited "ribbon limestones" (Landing and Bartowski, 1996).

The bottom water of the Franklin Basin lay below the depths to which wind-driven waves could oxygenate the sediment–water interface. The characteristic bottom facies of the Franklin Basin remained persistently dysoxic or anoxic from the late Early Cambrian through the Early Ordovician. This persistent dysoxia or anoxia is indicated by a number of features: 1) the characteristic organic-rich, dark gray–black mudstones of the succession; 2) absence of or limited borrowing; 3) locally abundant diagenetic pyrite; and 4) diagenetic replacement of allochthonous limestone clasts and sand by dolomite (compare Garrison *et al.*, 1984; Sageman *et al.*, 1991). Despite persistent dysoxia/anoxia from the late Early Cambrian through the Early Ordovician, the Franklin Basin succession has yielded abundant macro- and microfossils from shales, bedded limestones, and debris flow blocks. However, these collections are all of allochthonous specimens derived from the uppermost slope or shelf (Landing, 1983).

CAMBRIAN–ORDOVICIAN OF THE CRATON AND SOUTHERN FLANK OF THE OTTAWA AULOCOGEN

Overview of succession

The Grenville orogen is non-conformably overlain by an essentially undeformed, cratonic succession of Lower Paleozoic rocks in the St. Lawrence, Lake Ontario, Lake Champlain, and Mohawk River lowlands. An abrupt thickening of Cambrian and Ordovician rocks takes place in the belt between Plattsburgh, northern New York, and Montreal, Quebec, in the Ottawa aulocogen (Figure 1). The cratonic succession is particularly incomplete in the Mohawk River valley, where much of the Lower Ordovician has been lost below the Upper Ordovician Black River Group, presumably as a result of uplift and erosion with passage of the peripheral bulge with Taconic orogeny (Landing, 1988b). [The Grenville–Cambrian nonconformity and cratonic Cambrian and Lower Ordovician rocks at the eastern margin of the craton are featured during days 1–3 of the field trip (Landing *et al.*, this volume).] Overlying Silurian and Devonian rocks crop out south of the Mohawk River valley and west of the Hudson River. The Silurian–Devonian rocks of the latter region are primarily flat-lying, and show obvious tectonic deformation only along a narrow belt immediately west of the Hudson River (e.g., Marshak, 1990). The broad Silurian–Devonian belt west of the Hudson comprises the northeastern limit of the Allegheny Plateau that extends from the mid-continent region of the U. S.

Cambrian deposition

Initial Cambrian onlap and deposition.—The sandstone-dominated Potsdam Formation records the earliest marine onlap of the Grenville in cratonic successions of the New York Promontory (Figure 2). The timing of this onlap has long been problematical—the Potsdam typically has limited macrofossils, and those that have been found largely occur in the upper Potsdam [i.e., the quartz arenite-dominated Keesville Member of Fisher (1968), an interval deposited under the influence of wave activity (Wolf and Dalrymple, 1984)]. Although generally devoid of skeletal macrofossils, many surfaces of the Keesville Member have abundant traces formed in peritidal environments, as well as local casts of stranded medusae (Hagadorn and Belt, In press; Landing *et al.*, this volume, Stops 2.6, 3.7–3.9).

Terminal Middle Cambrian trilobites (*Crepicephalus* Zone) have been reported, but not illustrated, from the lowest Potsdam (Keesville Member) in Washington County, east-central New York (Flower, 1964, p. 156) (Landing *et al.*, this volume, Stop 1.4 of field trip). An approximately coeval fauna with *Komaspidella seelyi* and *Lonchocephalus minutus* was early reported from about the middle of the Potsdam, perhaps in the upper part of the lower member (or Ausable Member) further north at Ausable Chasm (Walcott, 1891b; Fisher, 1955; Flower, 1964).

Cambrian onlap and epeirogeny of the Ottawa aulocogen.—The impressive thickening of the Potsdam from a few tens of meters at more southerly localities on the New York Promontory to over 650 m north of Plattsburgh and the lack of macrofossil control from its lowest beds in the north has led to a number of speculations: 1) that the oldest Potsdam deposits on the northern New York Promontory are Early–Middle Cambrian (Walcott, 1891b; Fisher, 1968), 2) or could even range down into the Ediacaran (Kirchgasser and Theokritoff, 1971; Fisher, 1977;

McRae *et al.*, 1986), and 3) that the formation youngs from south to north (Lewis, 1963; Flower, 1964; Fisher, 1977). However, new evidence from the Plattsburgh, New York, area and a re-interpretation of the role of the Ottawa aulocogen during marine onlap allow some weeding out of these earlier interpretations.

As demonstrated for the first time during this conference's field trip (Landing *et al.*, this volume, Stops 3.2–3.4), the sandstone-dominated Potsdam Formation at the north end of its outcrop on the New York Promontory is conformably underlain by a lithologically distinctive interval represented by ca. 80 m of red silt-shales and fine-grained sandstones with dolostone beds. Although fossils remain limited, the presence of the trace fossils *Cruziana* and *Rusophycus* in the siliciclastics and ghosts of brachiopod shells in the dolostones allow two conclusions: 1) the new unit under the Potsdam, provisionally termed the "Altona Formation," is no older than upper Lower Cambrian, and 2) the Potsdam cannot be considered to range below the upper Lower Cambrian.

Both the "Altona Formation" and the overlying feldspathic, trough cross-bedded Ausable Member are limited to the south limb of the Ottawa aulocogen. This geographic restriction of these two units, the mineralogically immature (i.e., feldspathic) composition of the Ausable, and the great thickening of the Potsdam in northeasternmost New York all suggest that epeirogenic activity (i.e., possible growth fault activity) along the south limb of the Ottawa aulocogen was responsible for the earliest record of marine onlap in this area. The available evidence obviously does not support a general younging of the Potsdam to the north, as the oldest interval of the Potsdam, the Ausable Member, and the underlying "Altona Formation" are restricted to the south flank of the Ottawa aulocogen.

The precise timing of this marine onlap remains uncertain, but the interpretation favored during the field trip is that it was roughly coincident with the formation of the Franklin Basin. The Franklin Basin lies along strike of the Ottawa graben, and formed on the outer platform in the latest Early Cambrian as a result of growth fault activity that down-dropped the northern Vermont platform (discussed above).

Comparison with Cheshire Formation.—As discussed above, the deposition and onlap of the Potsdam Formation can be divided into two member-specific histories. Onlap and deposition of the "Altona Formation" and overlying, current cross-bedded feldspathic Ausable Member of the Potsdam seem to have been defined by epeirogenic activity on the southern flank of the Ottawa aulocogen. Further south on the New York Promontory, the quartz arenites of the wave-dominated Keesville Member nonconformably overlie the Grenville orogen as a result of onlap with sea-level rise beginning in the terminal Middle Cambrian and continuing into the Late Cambrian.

This onlap and depositional history of the upper Potsdam on the craton has similarities with that of the late Early Cambrian Cheshire Formation in the Appalachian successions (discussed above). Both the upper Potsdam and Cheshire onlap Grenvillian basement. However, coincident with the aggradation of both units and presumed continuing transgression of shorelines is the offlap/progradation of peritidal quartz arenites onto the open shelf—with the Cheshire appearing over the deeper-water, black mudstones of the Moosalamoo Phyllite, and sand-rich facies of the Danby Formation appearing above the carbonate-dominated Winooski Formation (Figure 2). One possible interpretation of these seemingly contradictory facies relationships is that the spreading of quartz sands seaward and across the carbonate platform indicates a decrease in rate of sea-level rise during deposition of the Potsdam and Cheshire Formations.

Post-Potsdam hiatus in the Ottawa aulocogen.—The subsequent history of Late Cambrian–earliest Ordovician epeirogeny and deposition in northeastern New York and adjacent Canada and its comparison with the history of the Franklin Basin is problematical. Indeed, there is no terminal Cambrian through lowest Ordovician succession in northernmost and northeasternmost New York and adjacent Ontario and Quebec. Physical evidence for unconformity exists at the top of the Postdam across the Ottawa aulocogen (Salad Hersi *et al.*, 2002), and the next overlying deposits are those of the middle Lower Ordovician Theresa Formation (Salad Hersi *et al.*, 2003). A significant hiatus is present between the Potsdam and the Theresa (Figure 2; Landing *et al.*, this volume, Stop 3.10).

Salad Hersi *et alii*'s (2003) recovery of Stairsian (*Macerodus dianae* Zone) conodonts from the Theresa resolved a long-standing problem in correlation. The conodonts allow the Theresa to be placed into a sequence stratigraphic framework of the Lower Ordovician of the New York Promontory (Figure 2).

The Theresa Formation lithologically resembles the mixed dolostone-quartz arenite facies of the older Galway Formation in the Mohawk River valley. This lithologic similarity led to repeated interpretations of the Theresa on the north side of the Adirondack massif in New York as a transitional facies of the lowest Beekmantown Group that conformably succeeds the Potsdam, and may range down into the Upper Cambrian (Fisher, 1977). However, limited macrofossil evidence based on molluscan faunas early suggested an assignment of at least part of the Theresa to the Lower Ordovician. These early conclusions were used: 1) to support a Waltherian model by which the Potsdam and Theresa Formation "climbed" in age from the Late Cambrian in the Mohawk River to the Early Ordovician in the St. Lawrence lowlands, and 2) to justify the use of the designation "Theresa Formation" in the Mohawk River valley for a mixed dolostone-quartz arenite interval above the Potsdam (e.g., Fisher, 1965; Lochman-Balk, 1971, p. 107, 140, 141). Indeed, the oil industry still uses the term "Theresa Formation," not Galway Formation, in central New York south of the Adirondacks for the mixed dolostone and quartz arenite unit above the Potsdam Formation.

However, the unconformity on the Potsdam Formation and the middle Early Ordovician age of the Theresa Formation in its type area in the Ottawa aulocogen area of northernmost New York and adjacent southern Ontario and Quebec are evidence against regional diachronous onlap of the Potsdam and Theresa. The new data further suggest that changes in epeirogenic activity on the south flank of the Ottawa aulocogen terminated Potsdam deposition (by uplift), while much later subsidence allowed deposition of a siliciclastic-rich Theresa Formation in the aulocogen that differs from the relatively "pure" carbonates of the coeval Rochdale Formation further south on the New York Promontory (Figure 2).

Cambrian stratigraphy south of the Ottawa aulocogen.—A more continuous Cambrian–Ordovician cratonic succession is present south of the Ottawa aulocogen. These more continuous successions extend from the Beekmantown area near Plattsburgh to Washington County in east-central New York

(Landing and Westrop, 2006). In this N–S belt and its extension west along the Mohawk River valley (Figures 1, 2), the quartz arenites of the Potsdam are conformably overlain by the mixed dolostone-quartz arenite facies of the peritidal Galway Formation (Fisher and Hansen, 1951) [= "Ticonderoga Formation" of Rodgers *in* Welby (1961)]. The Galway is then transitional upward into the highest Cambrian unit, the carbonate-dominated Little Falls Formation (Clarke, 1903; see Zenger, 1980) [= "Whitehall Formation" of Rodgers (1937); see synonymies in Landing (2002) and Landing *et al.* (2003a)].

Post-Potsdam Cambrian faunas

Macrofossils are locally abundant in the Galway and Little Falls Formations. Middle Upper Cambrian (Steptoean Stage) *Elvinia* Zone trilobites occur in the lower Galway Formation. Younger (middle Sunwaptan Stage) trilobites are well known from the Hoyt Limestone member of the lowest Little Falls Formation in the Saratoga area (Figure 2; see Ludvigsen and Westrop, 1983; Landing *et al.*, this volume, Stops 1.2, 1.3). Fisher and Hansen (1951) reported a small assemblage with somewhat younger taxa, including *Ptychaspis*, in talus blocks of dolostone from the lower Little Falls Formation in the Mohawk River valley.

Taylor and Halley (1974) illustrated uppermost Cambrian trilobites [upper Sunwaptan Stage (*Saukia* Zone) and lower Skullrockian Stage (*Parakoldinioidia stitti* Subzone)] from Washington County, easternmost New York. These trilobites came from several localities that expose non-dolomitized intervals in the middle Little Falls Formation (Figure 2, "Warner Hill Limestone;" see Stops 2.2, 2.3 and Figure 17 for biostratigraphy in Landing *et al.*, this volume). Restudy of Taylor and Halley's (1974) sections shows that the biomere boundary corresponding to a major replacement of conodonts and trilobites at the Sunwaptan–Skullrockian boundary is marked by a lithofacies change. This lithofacies change features a change from muddy, restricted shelf carbonates to an overlying thrombolite-dominated interval (Stop 2.3 in Landing *et al.*, this volume). It might be noted that this biomere boundary in the southern Canadian Rockies features a comparable lithofacies change from open shelf carbonates to thrombolites (e.g., Landing *et al.*, 1980).

The highest strata of the Little Falls Formation in Washington County lie in the middle and upper, but not uppermost, *Cordylodus proavus* Zone. The characteristic yield of conodont elements from the Little Falls in this area is depressingly low—frequently less than one element per kilogram of acid-disaggregated limestone or dolostone (Landing *et al.*, 2003a). The associated macrofaunas from non-dolomitized, massive limestone intervals of the upper Little Falls Formation in Washington County (Figure 2, "Steves Farm" and "Rathbunville School" Limestones). These limestone intervals are dominated by sparse mollusks (common gastropods and rare polyplacophorans), with trilobites generally even lower in abundance, as might be expected in these shallow, restricted marine carbonates [peritidal mudstones, ooid and fossil hash wackestones, and thrombolites]. This near absence of trilobites accords with the shallow (peritidal) depositional environments of the Little Falls (see Westrop *et al.*, 1995).

The oldest ellesmeroceroid cephalopods in eastern Laurentia occur in non-dolomitized lenses ("Rathbunville School Limestone" member) near the top of the Little Falls Formation

in Washington County (Stop 2.4 of field trip in Landing *et al.*, this volume). Flower (1964, p. 157, 158) had regarded these presently unillustrated cephalopods as Lower Ordovician, but conodonts indicate an assignment to the uppermost Cambrian (*Clavohamulus hintzei* Subzone of the *Cordylodus proavus* Zone). Although these cephalopods are only one conodont subzone younger than the oldest known forms from Texas and south China, they show a range of morphologies that indicate a rapid early diversification in Cambrian cephalopods (B. Kröger and E. Landing, unpublished data). Further west on the craton in Saratoga County, the uppermost Little Falls Formation also includes a coeval, nondolomitized, massive limestone under the unconformity with the Tribes Hill Formation (Figure 2, Ritchie Limestone; see Landing *et al.*, this volume, Stop 1.1).

Cratonic Ordovician

The passive margin Ordovician of the craton is comparable formation-by-formation with the platform succession in the Appalachians west of the Green Mountain axis, and does not require a lengthy discussion (see *Ordovician eustasy*, above). In both tectonic regions, the Cambrian–Ordovician boundary corresponds to a biostratigraphically resolvable unconformity between the Little Falls and Tribes Hill Formations (Figure 2). The Ordovician succession is relatively complete only along the eastern margin of the craton because uplift and erosion during the Late Ordovician Taconic orogeny completely removed all of the Ordovician above the Tribes Hill Formation and below the Black River Group on more western parts of the craton (Figure 2, Mohawk valley column) (Landing, 1988a, b). The only significant lateral facies change is the replacement of the carbonate-dominated, middle Lower Ordovician Rochdale Formation of the eastern craton and Appalachian regions by the coeval, but lithologically distinct (mixed dolostones and quartz arenites) of the Theresa Formation in the Ottawa aulocogen (discussed above; Stop 3.10 in Landing *et al.*, this volume).

The Ordovician part of the Beekmantown Group on the eastern craton in the Lake Champlain lowlands shows a repeated depositional motif from the Lower Ordovician Tribes Hill Formation through the Middle Ordovician Providence Island Formation. This repeated pattern includes unconformity-bound formations with a lower transgressive sandstone and an upper highstand carbonate facies that may include a thrombolitic interval under a restricted marine cap that records evaporitic conditions (Landing *et al.*, 1996, 2003a; Kröger and Landing, In press b). This motif persists even higher to include the highest unit deposited on the passive margin—the terminal Middle–lower Upper Ordovician Chazy Group, which has a transgressive sandstone [The Head Member, see Fisher (1968)] that overlies the Knox unconformity (Sloss, 1963).

The Chazy Group is particularly significant in the Ordovician radiation of metazoans and in the evolution of marine communities. Patch reefs of the Chazy Group represent the second appearance of metazoan-constructed reefs in the Phanerozoic, and the reappearance of the reef habitat after a long hiatus following the extinction of the Early Cambrian archaeocyathans. The Chazy Group features Earth's oldest (early Caradocian) bryozoan-coral reefs. Chazy bioherms are generally dominated by one or two species of bryozoans, corals, or sponges. Coeval buildups occur along the eastern margin of Laurentia from Tennessee, to the Ottawa aulocogen (in the

Champlain lowlands of northeastern New York and adjacent Vermont and Quebec), and western Newfoundland (e.g., Raymond, 1924a; Pitcher, 1964; Batten Hender and Dix, 2006). The other significant paleontological component of the Chazy Group is its silicified trilobites. [It might be noted that Shaw's (1968) report should be regarded as only a preliminary study of the very diverse silicified trilobites of the Chazy.] Replacement of trilobite sclerites and mollusk shells by coarsely crystalline silica is relatively common in Cambrian–Ordovician limestones on the New York Promontory, but only the Chazy Group and a locality in the Trenton Group (Evitt, 1953) have yielded finely replaced, silicified trilobites in the Lake Champlain lowlands.

EDIACARAN(?)–ORDOVICIAN SUCCESSION OF THE TACONIC ALLOCHTHON

Location and significance

The Taconic allochthon of eastern New York and adjacent Vermont and Massachusetts is an important structural unit within the Appalachian thrust and fold belt (Figure 1). Discussion of the partly coeval succession of the craton and the largely coeval succession of the parautochthonous Appalachians has preceded that of the Taconics in this report. This was done because the Taconic Ediacaran(?)–Ordovician shows how epeirogenic and eustatic events can be integrated into a geological synthesis of the New York Promontory.

The Taconic allochthon is one of a number continental slope and rise successions originally deposited on the margin of Laurentia that were thrust across the platform during the Taconic orogeny. Taconian allochthons lie at the western or northwestern margin of the Taconic orogen in western Newfoundland, along the Quebec Reentrant, the east margin of the New York Promontory (i.e., the Taconic allochthon), and along the Pennsylvania Reentrant and Virginia Promontory (e.g., Williams, 1978). The folding and thrusting of the Taconic orogeny was diachronous along the East Laurentian margin [e.g., Middle Ordovician on the Newfoundland Promontory in western Newfoundland and Late Ordovician along the New York Promontory], and reflected a non-orthogonal collision of the Ammonusuc volcanic arc with the promontories and reentrants of eastern Laurentia (e.g., Zen, 1972). The "root zone" of the Taconic allochthon of eastern New York and adjacent areas lay east of the Green Mountain axis (Figure 1), and generalized lithostratigraphic correlations of the rocks of the Taconic allochthon with the more highly metamorphosed rocks of the east Vermont succession are possible (Zen, 1967).

The Taconic overthrust belt in east-central New York and adjacent Vermont and Massachusetts (Figure 1) is perhaps the most thoroughly studied Taconian allochthon in the northern Appalachians (e.g., see Zen, 1967). The realization that the Lower Cambrian rocks that frequently form the western margin of the Taconic "slate belt" were thrust over Late Ordovician "Hudson River slates" (e.g., synorogenic sedimentary rocks) was one of the most important developments in the history of geology as a science. James Hall used this evidence to demonstrate that mountains were not formed during a Biblical "Creation," but were successively uplifted and eroded through geologic time. Hall's (1860a) proposal and techniques for interpretation were applied by European geologists to explain the

rise of the Alps. [Cambrian and Ordovician rocks of the Taconic allochthon are featured on day 6 of the field trip of this conference.]

It should be remembered during the field trip that the modern Taconic allochthon is a thin, erosional remnant of the accretionary prism that was pushed across the margin of Laurentia. Some stream and river valleys that cross the allochthon have eroded completely through it. The result is that windows of structurally underlying synorogenic flysch or even of Laurentian Cambrian–Ordovician platform successions occur below gentle hills capped by rocks of the allochthon. The western limit of the Taconic allochthon is generally marked by a mélange of underlying and younger synorogenic flysch that is exposed along the upper Hudson River valley and elsewhere along the eroded margins of the allochthon. The eastern border of the allochthon is the Vermont Valley, which is dominated by structurally underlying but coeval platform carbonates of the Vermont "marble belt."

Structure and metamorphism

Taconic accretionary prism.—The Taconic allochthon consists of seven imbricated slices that comprise an accretionary prism dominated by siliciclastic rocks (Figure 4). The western slices were the last formed in the accretionary prism as the eastern margin of Laurentia approached the subduction zone under the Ammonusuc volcanics. Thus, the leading (western) slices have rock successions that include the youngest (Caradocian) rocks of the Taconic allochthon, and more eastern slices do not have units younger than Ediacaran(?) or Early Cambrian (see Zen, 1967). The structural grain of the Taconic allochthon (fold axes, minor thrusts within the slices, cleavage) is approximately N–S. The intensity of metamorphism increases from chlorite-grade in the Giddings Brook slice to biotite-grade in the eastern slices (Zen, 1967, p. 101).

The Taconic master thrust under the entire allochthon and the thrusts between the successive slices of the Taconic accretionary prism are marked by mélanges, large slices of Laurentian carbonate platform rock that can reach 8 km in length [Bald Mountain Limestone; see Landing *et al.*, this volume, discussion of *Bald Mountain block* on day six of field trip), or Wildflysch conglomerates. The Wildflysch conglomerates are a mixture of synorogenic sediment derived from erosion of the accretionary prism, allochthonous blocks of the Taconic allochthon, and parautochthonous blocks of Early Paleozoic carbonates (none of them younger than the Trenton Group) and Grenville basement. The carbonate and Grenville blocks were broken off the eastern margin of Laurentia and overrun by the allochthon as it was pushed onto the margin of Laurentia (see Zen, 1967, 1972). Caradocian graptolites (*Cornoides americanus* Zone) from the Wildflysch just south of Rensselaer, New York, provided the first biostratigraphic control on the arrival of the Taconic allochthon in the interior of the New York Promontory (Berry, 1962; see Landing *et al.*, this volume, *Synorogenic Wildflysch south of Rensselaer*).

Giddings Brook slice.—The last day of the field trip (Landing *et al.*, this volume) illustrates the latest rift–drift (passive margin)–active (collisional) margin succession that comprise the uppermost Ediacaran(?)–Upper Ordovician of the Taconic allochthon in eastern New York. The Cambrian of this sequence illustrates the latest rift–early passive margin history of the most

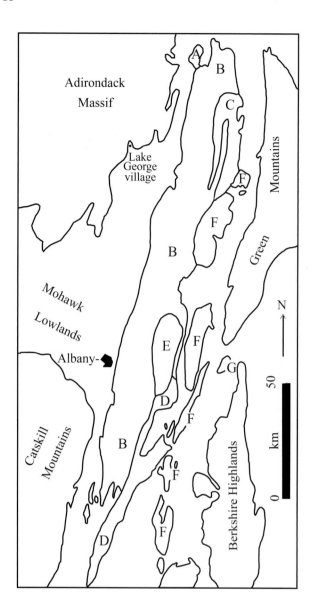

FIGURE 4—Generalized geologic map showing succession of slices in the Taconic allochthon: A, Sunset Lake; B, Giddings Brook; C, Bird Mountain; D, Chatham; E, Rensselaer Plateau; F, Dorset Mountain–Everett; G, Greylock. Modified from Zen (1967).

seaward part of the New York Promontory (Figure 5).

The condensed succession of the Giddings Brook slice, in which only 600 m of section includes the entire uppermost Eadicaran(?)–Upper Ordovician, was deposited off the eastern margin of the Laurentian platform east of the Green Mountain axis (e.g., Zen, 1967), and represents the deepest-water succession on the trip. The most coherent (i.e., weakly tectonically deformed) stratigraphy preserved in the Taconic allochthon is exhibited by the structurally lowest Giddings Brook slice (Stop 6.1 in Landing *et al.*, this volume)). Almost all known fossil localities have come from and all slate production occurred in the Giddings Brook slice. Natural exposures, quarries, and road

cuts allow examination of the complete Cambrian–Ordovician succession in a series of closely spaced localities in northern Washington County.

Rift–passive margin transition

The oldest unit of the Taconic allochchthon [the Rensselaer Formation (Dale, 1893)—dark gray, medium- to coarse-grained, turbiditic feldspathic lithic arenites with interbeds of green-gray and maroon slate] is largely confined to the Rensselaer slice (Potter, 1973; Figures 4, 5). The oldest strata of the Giddings Brook slice include two successive units that comprise the Nassau Formation (Ruedemann, 1914): 1) the fine- to medium-grained, olive-green, feldspathic, turbiditic sandstones, silty slates, and local quartz arenites of the Bomoseen Member (Ruedemann, 1914) and 2) the micaceous olive-green to purple slates of the Truthville Member (W. S. F. Kidd *in* Fisher, 1984) (Figure 5). The mineralogically immature Rensselaer and Bomoseen record the end of rifting and rapid subsidence of the east Laurentian margin and origin of the Iapetus Ocean. Local pillow basalts in the lower Rensselaer (Potter, 1973, 1979) are reminiscent of the Tibbitt Hill Formation volcanics of northern Vermont–Quebec, and probably indicate submarine flows during late stages of extension. Lithologic similarities exist between the Bomoseen–Truthville Slate succession (Landing *et al.*, this volume, Stops 6.1, 6.7) and the Pinnacle Formation on the west flank of the Green Mountain anticlinorium. Correlation of the Rensselaer and Nassau Formations has long been problematical due to the absence of macrofossils. However, the presence of the trace fossil *Oldhamia* Forbes, 1849, in the Bomoseen Member (Dale, 1904; Ruedemann, 1929), and its occurrence with large horizontal hypichnial burrows excavated at the sediment–water interface in the section at Poestenkill gorge in Troy, New York (E. Landing, unpub. data), indicate that the Bomoseen is Cambrian. Even more significant is the recovery of rare, allochthonous trilobite sclerites from quartz arenites (Zion Hill) at the very top of the Bomoseen Member (Landing *et al.*, this volume, Stop 6.7), because this indicates a correlation into the trilobite-bearing (upper Lower) Cambrian (e.g., Landing *et al.*, 1998). This discovery indicates that deposition of rift-related sediments persisted on the east Laurentian margin well into the Cambrian— a conclusion suggested above with the reported presence of *Olenellus* in rocks referred to the upper Pinnacle Formation in southern Vermont.

Passive margin succession: a proxy for global sea-level and climate changes

Cambrian through lower Middle Ordovician units feature black–green mudstone macroscale alternations (Figure 5) that are persistent along the western margin of the Taconian allochthons from eastern Pennsylvania to western Newfoundland (e.g., Landing *et al.*, 1992). Black shale alternations are more-or-less pyritic, and have traditionally yielded the majority of macrofossils and acid-resistant microfaunas from the Cambrian and Ordovician of the Taconian allochthons (Landing *et al.*, 1992).

These fossils include graptolites from Ordovician black slates with bedding-parallel cleavage. Allochthonous trilobites, unrestricted marine conodonts [i.e., North Atlantic Realm and non-Laurentian-aspect], and small shelly faunas come from the thin-bedded "ribbon" and nodular limestones and slope-derived

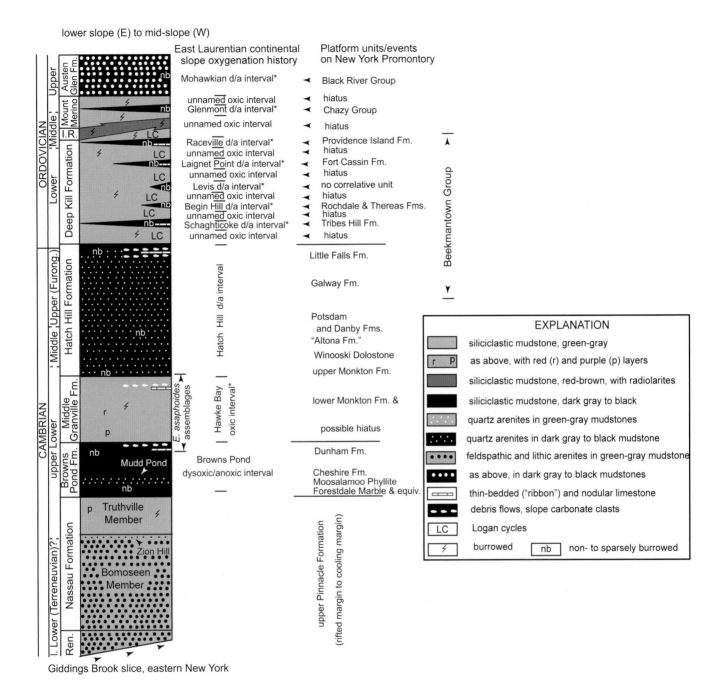

FIGURE 5—Allochthonous Ediacaran(?)–lower Upper Ordovician of the Giddings Brook and Rensselaer slices of the Taconic allochthon, eastern New York and southwest Vermont. Correlations with platform succession shown to right of column. Newly proposed and named dysoxic/anoxic intervals indicated by asterisk (*). Abbreviations" "d/a," dysoxic/anoxic; "Ren." is Rensselaer Formation.

limestone debris-flows that are largely restricted to the black mudstones (e.g., Ruedemann, 1901, 1902; Lochman, 1956; Berry, 1959, 1961, 1962; Landing, 1976, 1984; Landing and Bartowski, 1996; Landing *et al.*, 2002a). Green mudstone intervals, by comparison, are non-pyritic, and generally lack skeletalized macrofossils because of the typical lack of limestone interbeds (but see Landing *et al.*, this volume, Stop 6.10).

The green mudstones have abundant ichnofossils—often large sediment-probing traces and *Spreiten*-burrows, that are largely absent from the black mudstones. Thus, with exception of the behaviorly complex, lobate, "flower-like" trace *Dactyloidites* Hall, 1886, currently known only from the upper Lower Cambrian of the Middle Granville Formation in the Taconic allochthon, eastern New York (Figure 5) and lower

Parker Formation of the Franklin Basin, northwest Vermont (e.g., Shaw, 1958, tab. 2), the green mudstones typically lack biostratigraphically useful fossils. As a result, the age of green mudstone intervals generally must be bracketed by fossils from the under- and overlying black mudstones. In addition, U-Pb geochronology cannot be used for dating as no volcanic ashes occur in the Taconic allochthon below the Indian River Formation (discussed below).

The black and green mudstones, respectively, mark dysoxic/anoxic and oxygenated intervals on the east Laurentian continental slope in the Cambrian (Landing and Bartowski, 1996; Landing *et al.*, 2002) and Ordovician (Landing *et al.*, 1992) (Figure 5). As detailed in these latter reports and in Landing (2002), the black–green alternations are a proxy for major eustatic changes. Low eustatic levels correspond to: 1) intervals of maximum radiation of sunlight back to space from largely subaerial continents, 2) "ice house" intervals with high latitudinal gradients in temperature, and 3) a consequent maximum aeration of the deep ocean with increased storminess and sinking of cold, dense polar waters. Thus, eustatic lows equate to oxic, green and associated purple and red mudstones in the Taconian allochthon.

By comparison, eustatic maxima correspond to: 1) intervals of maximum storage of heat in extensive shallow seas, 2) enhanced "greenhouse" intervals (global "hyperwarming") with reduced latitudinal gradients in temperature, and 3) limited aeration of the deep ocean as a result of reduced storminess and reduced sinking of warmed, less dense polar waters. As a result, the oxygen-minimum zone characteristic of the upper slope would intensity and thicken during eustatic highs. By its thickening down-slope, green, purple, and red mud deposition would be replaced by black mud (sapropel) deposition. Upward expansion of the slope dysoxic/anoxic water mass would even allow it to expand onto the shelf. Thus, organic-rich mud deposition and the preservation of Burgess-type Lagerstätten would take place in outer shelf settings (Landing, 2002).

In addition, carbonate production would increase with the inundation of tropical shelves with eustatic highs. As a result, carbonate would be shed onto the slope to appear as the thin-bedded limestones characteristic of black mudstone intervals. Nodular carbonates also appear in black slope mudstones of the Taconic allochthon as a result of diagenetic unmixing of originally calcareous black muds or by bacterially-mediated, methanogenic precipitation of carbonates.

In some slope facies of the Taconic allochthon, allochthonous carbonate shell debris derived from the shelf is replaced by phosphate. This replacement allows the recovery of phosphatized small shelly fossils, and is ultimately the result of the action of denitrifying bacteria in anoxic mud (Sageman *et al.*, 1991; see Landing and Bartowski, 1996; Landing *et al.*, 2002).

The transition from black to green mudstones in mesoscale alternations is locally so abrupt that it literally lies at a line between facies dominated by black and green mudstones. At Stop 6.5 of the field trip (Landing *et al.*, this volume), the top of a black mudstone interval includes several meters of thin-bedded, slope deposited limestone capped by a thin carbonate-clast debris flow comprised of the same type of limestone. At this locality, instability of the upper slope, perhaps as a result of the rapid deposition of shelf-derived carbonate debris with eustatic fall at the onset of the Hawke Bay regression was coeval with the black–green transition between the Browns Pond and overlying Middle Granville Formation.

Biostratigraphy of Cambrian black–green macroscale alternations

Browns Pond dysoxic/anoxic interval.—The lowest black, dysoxic/anoxic interval in the Giddings Brook slice is the Browns Pond Formation (Kidd *et al.* in Fisher, 1984). The Browns Pond has one or two thick, coarse-grained quartzites in its lower part (Figure 5, see Mudd Pond quartzites) that texturally resemble beds in the Lower Cambrian Cheshire Formation on the east Laurentian platform. These Mudd Pond quartzites are correlated with the Cheshire (Landing *et al.*, 2002). The lowest body fossil assemblage in the Taconic allochthon, the "lower *Elliptocephala asaphoides* assemblage," occurs at the top of the Browns Pond (Landing and Bartowski, 1996). This fauna occurs as allochthonous specimens of trilobites, hyoliths, small mollusks, calcareous and phosphatic problematica, and archaeocyathans transported from the shelf margin. These fossils occur in the bedded limestones and a debris flow that cap the Browns Pond Formation (Landing *et al.*, this volume, Stops 6.2, 6.5).

The lower *Elliptocephala asaphoides* small shelly fossil assemblage is comparable to that known from carbonate units on the Laurentian platform that record a eustatic high that led to the deposition of carbonates above a transgressive sandstone. Thus, Landing and Bartowski (1996) equated the upper Browns Pond fauna with that of the Forteau Formation, which overlies the Bradore Sandstone in western Newfoundland and southern Labrador. In North-East Greenland, small shelly and other fossils indicate a correlation of the lower *Elliptocephala asaphoides* assemblage with a deepening-shoaling cycle marked by the distal shale of the upper Bastion Formation and highstand carbonates of the overlying Ella Island Formation (Skovsted, 2006). In short, the available biostratigraphic and lithostratigraphic data support correlation of the Cheshire–Dunham eustatic high with dysoxic/anoxic deposition of the Browns Pond Formation on the east Laurentian slope.

This correlation contravenes Theokritoff's (1968) and Landing and Bartowski's (1996) earlier correlation of the lower *Elliptocephala asaphoides* assemblage into sub-*Olenellus* Zone strata. Theokritoff (1968) had originally used supposed, phosphatized *Wanneria* sclerites (with raised polygonal microsculpture) to correlate the *Elliptocephala asaphoides* assemblage(s) with sub-*Olenellus* Zone strata. These so-called "*Wanneria*" fragments now prove to have no biostratigraphic utility, as they are also found with faunas with that contain *Olenellus* and typical *Elliptocephala asaphoides* small shelly fossils (Skovsted, 2006). It should also be noted that one consequence of trilobite studies in the Giddings Brook slice has been the demonstration that the trilobites and many microfossils of the outer shelf/uppermost slope *Elliptocephala asaphoides* assemblage have a very long stratigraphic range (Landing and Bartowski, 1996), as they persist through three formations and three dysoxic/anoxic alternations (Figure 5).

Hawke Bay oxic interval (new).—The Browns Pond dysoxic/anoxic interval (Landing and Bartowski, 1996) is abruptly succeeded by the green mudstone-dominated, oxic (heavily burrowed) Middle Granville Formation (Kidd *et al. in* Fisher, 1984). As noted above, the thin shell hash limestones and carbonate clast debris flow at the top of the Browns Pond are the likely result of sea-level fall shortly prior to the re-establishment of oxic bottom waters on the slope (Landing *et al.*, this volume, Stop 6.6).

The Middle Granville Formation (Landing *et al.*, this volume, Stops 6.2, 6.5, 6.6, 6.10) yields trilobites and small shelly fossils of the upper *Elliptocephala asaphoides* assemblage (Landing and Bartowski, 1996) from an interval of bedded limestones and an overlying debris flow in the upper third of the formation (Landing *et al.*, this volume, Stop 6.10), but the rest of the formation lacks body fossils. The Middle Granville and equivalent units in the Taconian allochthons elsewhere along the Quebec Reentrant have been equated with the global Hawke Bay regression in the latest Early Cambrian of Laurentia (Palmer and James, 1979; equated to the early Middle Cambrian of Gondwana, see Landing *et al.*, 2006). This conclusion was based on the presence of Laurentian terminal Lower Cambrian faunas from the lower part of the overlying dysoxic/anoxic black mudstone interval (Landing *et al.*, 2002). For this reason, the Middle Granville Formation is regarded herein as representative of the "Hawke Bay oxic interval" (new) on the east Laurentian slope (Figure 5).

Hatch Hill dysoxic/anoxic interval.—Geyer and Landing (2002) concluded that a protracted interval of dysoxia/anoxia and high sea levels (terminal Early Cambrian through earliest Ordovician, ca. 20 m. y.) is recorded in slope sequences of the Taconian allochthons. This Hatch Hill dysoxic/anoxic interval is represented by the Hatch Hill Formation [termed the "West Castleton Formation" or "Germantown Formation" in some earlier reports; Landing (1993, 2002)].

The Hatch Hill Formation [average thickness 150 m; Rowley *et al.* (1979)] includes black mudstones with abundant dolomite-cemented, turbiditic quartz arenites and local ribbon limestones and carbonate clast debris flows in the Giddings Brook slice (Figure 5). Hatch Hill deposition has been compared with that of a submarine canyon and fan complex (Keith and Friedman, 1978, 1979; Friedman, 1979; Rowley *et al.*, 1979). However, the absence of amalgamated channel deposits in the Giddings Brook slice and the indication of slow accumulation rates (ca. 150 m in ca. 20 m.y.) suggests that the sands and debris flows of the Hatch Hill Formation are sheet-like sandstones and debris/grain flows that originated at many points along an upper continental slope, and were not related to a persistent point source (a submarine canyon) that was fixed on the shelf margin and upper slope (Landing, 1993).

The Hatch Hill Formation has the highest *Elliptocephala asaphoides* assemblage near its base (Bird and Rasetti, 1968, collections cs-24 and unnumbered collection at 38 feet). Terminal Lower Cambrian *Acimetopus* and *Pagetides* faunas occur somewhat higher in the formation (Rasetti, 1966, 1967). Quite thorough search of Hatch Hill outcrops in the central part of the Giddings Brook slice has also led to the discovery of allochthonous, disarticulated trilobite assemblages referable to the upper Middle Cambrian (Laurentian *Bathyuriscus-Elrathina* and *Bolaspidella* Zones) and Upper Cambrian (*Aphelaspis*? and middle *Saukia*-equivalent Zones). The upper part of the Hatch Hill ranges into the lower Tremadocian, as indicated by the presence of early forms of the dendroid graptolite *Rhabdinopora* with earliest Ordovician conodonts and rare trilobites (*Clelandia*) (Landing, 1993; Landing *et al.*, this volume, Stop 6.4). Although the Cambrian–Ordovician boundary is an interformational

unconformity on the platform of the New York Promontory, no evidence for this unconformity exists on the east Laurentian continental slope. Indeed, strata corresponding to the latest Cambrian–earliest Ordovician hiatus on the platform exist in continental slope facies of the Taconic allochthon.

Ordovician black–green macroscale alternations

Previous work.—As discussed above, the terminal Lower Cambrian–lowest Ordovician Hatch Hill Formation reflects a long interval of generally high eustatic levels reflected by persistent deposition of dysoxic/anoxic black mud on the east Laurentian slope (Landing *et al.*, this volume, Stops 6.3, 6.4, 6.10). By contrast, the Ordovician of the Taconic allochthon shows a number of shorter-term black (dysoxic/anoxic)–green (oxic) mudstone alternations that appear through the Early and lower Upper Ordovician within the green-mudstone-dominated slope facies (Figure 5; Landing *et al.*, this volume, Stops 6.3, 6.9). Though relatively thin (generally < 10 m), the black dysoxic/anoxic intervals are persistent geographically, and are individually distinguishable on the basis of associated graptolite and conodont faunas for over 1,000 km in the continental slope facies of the Taconic allochthons from eastern Pennsylvania to western Newfoundland (Landing *et al.*, 1992). Thus, they are given names in this report, just as the older Browns Pond and Hatch Hill dysoxic/anoxic intervals.

Schaghticoke dysoxic/anoxic interval (new).—An upper lower Tremadoc black mudstone and thin-bedded limestone interval is well developed in the Taconic allochthon, and appears at numerous localities at the leading edge of the Taconic allochthons along the Quebec Reentrant. This black mudstone interval correlates on the basis of conodonts with the depositional sequence of the Tribes Hill Formation (Landing *et al.*, 1986, 2003a). Thus, it is regarded as an interval of intensified slope water dysoxia that correlates with an interval of strong eustatic rise that brought shorelines into the middle of the Laurentian craton (Landing *et al.*, 2003, In press). This upper lower Tremadoc black shale interval had been earlier termed the "Schaghticoke Shale" (Ruedemann, 1903). The "Schaghticoke Shale" is now regarded as part of the lower Deep Kill Formation (Ruedemann, 1902) (see Landing, 2002). However, the excellent exposure of this dysoxic/black shale interval in the Hoosic River gorge at Schaghticoke, New York (Stop 6.9 in Landing *et al.*, this volume) is the basis for naming this the "Schaghticoke dysoxic/anoxic interval" (new) (Figure 5).

Begin Hill dysoxic/anoxic interval (new).—A few upper slope localities in the Taconic allochthons of Quebec and New York yield upper Tremadoc dendroids (*Clonograptus flexilus* Hall) without graptoloids in a dark gray shale alternation. This interval with *C. flexilus* occurs at a few localities in the Deep Kill Formation in the Taconic allochthon (Ruedemann, 1947) and at the base of the classic Begin Hill section in Levis, Quebec (Landing and Benus, 1985), below Clark's (1924) Zone B. For this reason it is termed the "Begin Hill dysoxic/anoxic interval" (new) (Figure 5). This dysoxic/anoxic interval correlates with the weak, upper Tremadoc eustatic rise recorded by the depositional sequence of the Rochdale Formation on the margin of the New York Promontory (discussed above) and, possibly, with the brief Hagastrand Drowning Event in Baltica (Nielsen, 2005). This relatively small sea-level rise and its suggested brevity may have led to a limited intensification and expansion of the low-oxygen water mass on the slope, and explain why the "Begin Hill dysoxic/anoxic locality is only known from a limited number of localities.

Levis dysoxic/anoxic interval (new).—The earliest Arenig "Levis dysoxic/anoxic interval" (Figure 5) is proposed with some hesitation for two black shale localities with *Tetragraptus approximatus* Zone faunas in black shale with thin-bedded limestones. An interval at Logan's (1865) "G" (for graptolite) locality at Levis, Quebec [subsequently Clark's (1924) Zone C1] (Landing and Benus, 1985) supplies the name for this black mudstone interval. The only other known locality with earliest Arenig black mudstone is in the Deep Kill Formation in the central part of the Taconic allochthon of eastern New York (Potter, 1972). The Levis dysoxic/anoxic interval does not correlate with a platform unit on the New York Promontory, and the early Arenig is an interval of eustatic low (Ross and Ross, 1995; Nielsen, 2004). Thus, the Levis dysoxic/anoxic does not seem to represent an intensification/expansion of the slope water mass with eustatic rise. Its absence from most areas of the Taconian allochthons and occurrence at only two localities may be explained by these two localities being an artifact of local preservation of the dysoxic/anoxic facies that is persistent on the upper slope near the leading edge of the Taconian allochthons.

Laignet Point dysoxic/dysoxic interval (new).—A lower middle Arenig black mudstone interval, commonly with thin-bedded "ribbon" limestones, is regularly present in the Taconian allochthons from eastern Pennsylvania to western Newfoundland (Landing *et al.*, 1992). Landing and Westrop (2006) equated this slope black mudstone interval with a strong eustatic rise recognizable across Laurentia [Tulean–Blackhillsian interval of Ross and Ross (1995)] and in Baltica [Billingen Transgressive Event and Evae Drowning Event of Nielsen (2004)]. The depositional sequence of the Fort Cassin Formation is the local record of this eustatic rise on the New York Promontory. The Laignet Point eustatic maximum, earlier proposed for the middle of the Fort Cassin Formation (Landing and Westrop, 2006), provides the name "Laignet Point dysoxic /anoxic interval" for the coeval black mudstone interval in the middle Deep Kill Formation (Landing, 1976) and coeval intervals in the Taconian allochthons.

Raceville dysoxic/anoxic interval (new).—Graptolites traditionally referable to the lower Llanvirnian occur in a relatively thick, black mudstone interval with thin-bedded limestones known from a number of localities in the Taconian allochthons of New York and Quebec (Landing *et al.*, 1992). Conodonts from this black mudstone and limestone interval of the upper Deep Kill Formation (Landing, 1976) allow correlation with the surprisingly abundant conodonts that occur in the restricted marine facies that comprise the depositional sequence of the Providence Island Formation (Landing, 2002, and unpublished data). These new conodont data now show that the New York Promontory region actually has a stratigraphic unit, the Providence Island, deposited during an interval of sea-level rise that featured strong transgression of Laurentia. This eustatic rise led to the deposition of stratigraphic units (e.g., Everton Sandstone) as far in the interior of Laurentia as the Illinois Basin (see Ross and Ross, 1995, fig. 1). This sea-level rise seems to correlate with the Gårdlösa Drowning Event in Baltica (Nielsen, 2004). The black mudstones and thin-bedded limestones of this Middle Ordovician dysoxic/anoxic interval occur in the upper

Deep Kill Formation, and are termed the "Raceville dysoxic/anoxic interval." This interval is well exposed at a readily accessible roadcut on the west side of Rte. 22, just 2.8 miles north of Middle Granville, New York, and near the hamlet of Raceville (Landing, 2002, stop 11).

Glenmont dysoxic/anoxic interval (new).—The highest black shale macroscale alternation in the Taconic allochthon is in the green mudstone-dominated Mount Merino Formation (Ruedemann, 1942; Figure 5). Early Late Ordovician graptolites (lower *Nemagraptus gracilis* Zone) are abundant and diverse in this black mudstone interval that is well exposed just south of Albany in the classic railroad cut at Glenmont, New York (Ruedemann, 1908; Ruedemann and Cook, 1914). This locality provides the name "Glenmont dysoxic/anoxic interval" to this lowest Upper Ordovician black mudstone interval on the Taconic continental slope. The lower *Nemagraptus gracilus* Zone corresponds to a strong eustatic rise recorded by the latter part of the Furudal Highstand in Baltica (Nielsen, 2004) and the "late Whiterockian" highstands coincident with deposition of the Chazy Group on the New York Promontory and the St. Peter Sandstone of the Laurentian Midcontinent (Ross and Ross, 1995). This strong eustatic rise after a continent-wide offlap in Laurentia defined the base of the Tippecanoe Sequence of Sloss (1963).

End of passive margin deposition in the Taconic allochthon

An important change in deposition of the Taconic succession is marked by a red mudstone known as the Indian River Formation (Keith, 1932). Key lithologic features of the thin (ca. 50 m) Indian River indicate that it is a condensed unit: 1) very thorough bioturbation and 2) radiolarites [which suggest very low depositional rates and a lack of dilution by siliciclastic input] and 3) red color [which probably reflects long residence time at the sediment–water interface, rather than the quick burial of organic-rich hemipelagic mud which would produce greenish or gray mudstone] (Landing, 1988b, 2002). The Indian River also marks a change in sediment provenance in the Taconic slope succession—it records the oldest volcanic ashes derived from the Ammonusuc arc (Rowley and Kidd, 1981) and features the loss of the quartz sand eroded from Laurentia that appears in older units in the Taconic succession (Landing, 1988b).

The Indian River and similar red mudstone units in other Taconian allochthons record the initial effects of the Taconic orogeny in the continental slope sequences deposited on the margin of Laurentia. These red mudstone units occur in the Taconian accretionary prisms from the Southern Uplands of Scotland (Leggett, 1978) to western Newfoundland and eastern Pennsylvania. Landing (1988b) concluded that uplift of continental slope and rise successions took place as they passed over the standing lithospheric wave known as the peripheral bulge (Jacobi, 1981). Peripheral bulges appear as the first indication of relative proximity of a subduction zone in collisional regimes. As arc-derived and continent-derived sediment cannot be transported up onto the peripheral bulge, condensed red mudstones, locally with radiolarites, result from the deposition of hemipelagic muds and radiolarian tests on the peripheral bulge. The age of the Indian River can only be bracketed by the graptolites from the black mudstone intervals of the underlying Deep Kill and overlying Mount Merino Formations.

Unfortunately, the only body fossils from the Indian River are radiolarians (Ruedemann and Wilson, 1936) that have not received modern study.

The overlying Mount Merino Formation (Ruedemann, 1942; Figure 5) records a return to green mudstone deposition. Associated chromite grains show the first input of sediment provenance from the Ammonusuc arc. These chromite grains were eroded from obducted mantle rock in the arc (Rowley and Kidd, 1981). The green color of the Mount Merino reflects an increase in sediment-accumulation and -burial rates with descent of the Taconic succession from the peripheral bulge toward the trench (Landing *et al.* 1992). Arc-derived lithic arenites appear in the upper Mount Merino, and it is rapidly transitional upward to the turbidite-dominated Austin Glen Formation (Ruedemann, 1942) [= "Pawlett Formation" in the northern Taconic allochthon; Landing (2002)], which was deposited on the outer and inner trench slopes (Rowley and Kidd, 1981; Landing, 1988b).

AFTERWARD—POST-PASSIVE MARGIN GEOLOGICAL HISTORY

Taconic orogeny

Three successive orogenic episodes can be distinguished in the Appalachian Mountains. The earlier Taconic orogeny featured the collision of the Ammonusuc volcanic island arc during the Late Ordovician and Early Silurian, and its overriding of the eastern margin of Laurentia. Deformation and thrusting of Ediacaran–Ordovician successions deposited on Grenville basement near the eastern margin of Laurentia took place during the Taconian orogeny. The resultant Taconic orogen is a relatively narrow terrane in the northern Appalachians that is bounded by the Taconic master thrusts in the west and a belt of obducted lower crustal and mantle rocks that run approximately north–south through eastern Vermont and swing northeast as the Quebec asbestos belt (Figure 1). The Taconic orogeny was the first stage in the closing of the Iapetus Ocean off the Laurentian margin.

The Taconic orogeny is recorded by a gradual westward unfolding of its effects—with the Taconic succession approaching the trench and a change in its sedimentary provenance (see above, *End of passive margin deposition in the Taconic allochthon*), the first appearance of arc-derived volcanic ashes on the craton in the Late Ordovician Black River Group limestones (Kay, 1942, 1952; Cameron, 1969; Kolata *et al.*, 1996), and the pushing of the Taconic accretionary prism onto the shallow platform successions of eastern Laurentia. Significant uplift, involving both passage of the peripheral bulge as well as the reactivation of Ediacaran faults that transverse the Grenville, led to significant local erosion of the Cambrian–Ordovician succession on the New York Promontory during the orogeny (Figure 2). The load of the Taconic orogen subsequently depressed eastern Laurentia, with the first evidence of this depression recorded by the turbitites of the lower Upper Ordovician Middlebury Limestone on the west flank of the Green Mountain axis (discussed above). Further thrusting of the accretionary prism onto east Laurentia and loading led to development of a foreland basin that filled with synorogenic sediment and terminated the shallow-water carbonate deposition that characterized eastern

Laurentia in the Early–early Late Ordovician. The Ordovician of eastern Laurentia ended with filling of the foreland arc basin and deposition of uppermost Ordovician subaerial sandstones and shales with the major sea-level fall with latest Ordovician glaciation in the north African and South American regions of Gondwana (e.g., Caputo, 1998).

Acadian orogeny

Tectonic quiescence after the Taconic orogeny was followed by the development of terminal Ordovician and Silurian–early Middle Devonian marine successions along the eastern margin of the Taconian orogen. Subduction and closing of the Iapetus Ocean under Laurentia occurred during the Devonian, with resultant Andean-type volcanism on the eastern margin of Laurentia in central and northern New England. Subduction of the Iapetus Ocean included the movement of the non-Gondwanan microcontinent of Avalon (e.g., Landing, 2005a) toward Laurentia, and its collision with Laurentia in the Acadian orogeny during the Devonian. At present, Avalon comprises a terrane within the Acadian–Caledonide orogen of eastern North America (Figure 1), southern Britain, and western Europe (Belgium). It was during the Acadian orogeny that the middle Proterozoic inliers of the Grenville orogen were strongly uplifted within the Appalachians, and their Ediacaran(?)–Ordovician cover sequences further deformed and metamorphosed. These Proterozoic uplifts include the Hudson Highlands (the local name given to the northeast end of the Reading Prong), Lincolnshire massif, and the Green Mountain–Sutton Mountain axis (Figure 1).

A number of general similarities exist between the effects of the Taconian and Acadian orogenies. For example, regional tropical carbonate platform deposition ended during both orogenies, with an influx of sediments derived from both orogen filling a basin developed in eastern North America and spreading west across New York into the mid-continent. These siliciclastic sediments replaced regional Early–early Middle Devonian carbonate-dominated deposition in New York, and aggraded above sea level in the eastern part of the Allegheny Plateau, where they form the Catskill Mountains just west of the Hudson River (Figure 1).

Alleghanian orogeny

The final assembly of the Pangaea supercontinent featured the closure of the Rheic Ocean with the collision of the northern South American and west African margins of Gondwana with eastern and southern Laurentia. This collision marked the third, last, and largest mountain-building interval of the Appalachians. The Alleghanian orogeny is well attested to in the northern Appalachians of coastal New England and Maritime Canada. Its effects included Late Carboniferous–Permian intrusions and the formation, folding, thrusting, and metamorphism of coal basins formed by the sinistral movement between eastern North America and the west African margin of Gondwana.

The imprint of the Alleghanian orogeny in the field trip region is ambiguous. Further south, it is possible that folding, faulting, and development of slaty cleavage in Lower–Middle Devonian rocks on the west side of the lower Hudson River (e.g., Marshak, 1990) took place during the Alleghanian orogeny. Work over the last forty years has shown the pervasive structural effects of the Alleghanian orogeny in the generally flat-lying Paleozoic sequences of the Allegheny Plateau of central and western New York and adjacent Pennsylvania. These structural effects include major bedding plane-parallel decollements; broad (~ 15 km), low-amplitude (< 100 m) folds; cross-fold joints and cleavage; and distorted fossils formed by layer-parallel shortening in Middle Paleozoic rocks (e.g., Nickelsen and Hough, 1967; Engelder and Geiser, 1979, 1980; Engelder *et al.*, 1987). The relatively high thermal metamorphism of Middle Devonian plant remains in the Catskill Mountains of eastern New York (to graphite) reflects a ca. 6 km depth of burial that probably took place during the Alleghanian orogeny (Sarwar and Friedman, 1995).

Break up of Pangaea

The last important events that affected the bed rock of the New York Promontory involved the fragmentation of the Pangaea supercontinent and the opening and widening of the Atlantic Ocean along a spreading system that separated the modern west African margin from coastal eastern North America. Two active arms of the spreading system trended ENE and WSW, and defined the recess of the modern continental shelf known as the New York Bight. The failed arm trended roughly north, and Triassic faulting on the west and east margins of the failed arm defined the half-grabens known as the Newark and Hartford Basins (Figure 1). These basins are filled with thick sequences of Middle Triassic–Early Jurassic rocks that range from fanglomerates to red beds and lake deposits and include Early Jurassic basalt flows. Major Early Jurassic basic intrusions crop out as the Palisades cliff opposite New York City (see summaries in Van Houten, 1969; Hubert *et al.*, 1978).

With the onset of active spreading and widening of the Atlantic Ocean, deposition on the Atlantic coastal plain began along the shoreline of the Atlantic Bight. The oldest deposits are Early Cretaceous fluvial sedimentary rocks that represent upper delta plain environments. These deposits are exposed on Staten Island (southernmost New York City) and south of mainland New York and southern New England on Long Island, New York (Figure 1). A combination of cooling and subsidence of the rifted margin and strong eustatic rise in the Late Cretaceous led to marine incursion of the coastal plain along the New York Bight (e.g., Olsson *et al.*, 1986).

Igneous activity that overlapped the early rift and extensional activity that led to opening of the Atlantic Ocean included development of a hot spot that seems to record a U-shaped track through eastern New York and New England. The oldest record of this hot spot may be small kimberlites (no diamonds have been found) in the Ithaca and Syracuse area of central New York. Much more impressive mafic instructions that track the movement of North America include the Monteregian Hills—a roughly ENE trending series of alkaline igneous plutons, dikes, and sills that were emplaced between 240 and 90 Ma, and coincident with the early opening of the north Atlantic Ocean (Eby, 1987). Over a half dozen mafic necks underlie the island that Montreal lies on (from which "Monteregian" is derived) and trend ENE along a line just south of the St. Lawrence River. At Montreal and along the St. Lawrence, the intrusives are much more erosionally resistant than the surrounding synorogenic (Taconic orogeny) siliciclastics, and form sharp hills, some of which are quarried for fill or are increasingly used as ski slopes. Fossiliferous inclusions of Lower Devonian limestone (Helderberg Group) and sandstone (Oriskany Sandstone) have been found in the mafic intrusives at Montreal, and show that characteristic facies of the Alleghany Plateau once covered the region (e.g., Adams and Barlow, 1913, p. 37). These intrusives then trend south and roughly parallel to the Connecticut River, swing east across northernmost coastal Massachusetts, and end as the modern Bermuda Islands (e.g., Skehan, 2001).

ACKNOWLEDGMENTS

Early research on the Cambrian of eastern New York and Vermont was completed by EL under National Science Foundation (NSF) grant EAR76-10601. More recent study was supported by the New York State Museum. Scanning microscopy of microfaunas that assisted in reports that led to this synthesis has been done under NSF grant 0116551 at the Electron Microscopy Unit, Center for Laboratories and Research, New York State Health Department (via W. Samsonoff). G. Geyer and C. E. Brett are thanked for reviewing the manuscript.

REFERENCES

All references in this section are cited at the end of the field trip guide by Landing *et al.* (this volume)

CAMBRIAN OF EAST LAURENTIA:
FIELD WORKSHOP IN EASTERN NEW YORK AND WESTERN VERMONT

ED LANDING[1], DAVID A. FRANZI[2], JAMES W. HAGADORN[3], STEPHEN R. WESTROP[4],
BJÖRN KROGER[5], AND JAMES C. DAWSON[2]

[1] New York State Museum, Madison Avenue, Albany, New York 12230,
[2] Center for Earth and Environmental Sciences, State University of New York at Plattsburgh,
Plattsburgh, New York 12901
[3] Department of Geology, Amherst College, Amherst, Massachusetts 01002
[4] Oklahoma Museum of Natural History and School of Geology and Geophysics
University of Oklahoma, Norman, Oklahoma 73072, and
[5] Museum für Naturkunde, Humboldt Universität zu Berlin, Invalidenstrasse 43, D–10115 Berlin, Germany

---

PROSPECTUS

This excursion along the eastern margin of the New York Promontory was prepared for the 12th meeting of the International Cambrian Subcommission. The trip includes overviews of the peritidal Cambrian on the craton (field trip days 1–3); the origin and persistence of the deep-water, dysoxic/anoxic Franklin Basin that first developed in the terminal Early Cambrian on the platform in northern Vermont (day 4); the rift–passive margin transition during the late Early Cambrian on the west flank of the Green Mountain axis (day 5); and the relationship of major eustatic changes to slope dysoxia/anoxia macroscale alternations on the east Laurentian continental slope as exhibited in the Taconic allochthon (day 6). A regional overview of Ediacaran–Early Ordovician geological and depositional history that places the stratigraphy and paleontology of the Cambrian of the excursion area into perspective is provided in the preceding summary (Landing, this volume).

JULY 30: THIN PLATFORM SUCCESSION IN SARATOGA AND WASHINGTON COUNTIES, EASTERN NEW YORK

Overview

Day 1 of the field trip reviews the thin Cambrian succession that non-conformably overlies the middle Proterozoic, high-grade metamorphic rock basement of the eastern margin of Laurentia. The stops are in Saratoga and Washington Counties, eastern New York. The upward succession is a terminal Middle Cambrian–latest Cambrian sequence from the Potsdam Sandstone (Stop 1.4) that nonconformably overlies middle Proterozoic gneiss (Stop 1.5), through mixed quartz arenites and dolostones of the Galway Formation (Stop 1.3), and ending with the carbonate-dominated Little Falls Formation (Stop 1.2) (Figure 1). The Cambrian–Ordovician boundary is a type 1 depositional sequence boundary between the Little Falls Formation and overlying Tribes Hill Formation everywhere on the platform in eastern New York and adjacent Vermont (Stop 1.1). The trip today emphasizes stratigraphy and shallow-marine depositional environments. It includes sites that

illustrate the trilobite and conodont biostratigraphy of the Potsdam and Little Falls Formations. The Hoyt Limestone member (lower Little Falls Formation) at Lester Park was the source for C. D. Walcott's trilobites and James Hall's "*Cryptozoon*" stromatolites (Stop 1.2).

Travel to Stop 1.1

Albany–southern Saratoga County.—After departing conference hotel, enter on-ramp to the Northway (Interstate 87) and continue north towards the Canadian border. Local bedrock, Late Ordovician (Caradocian) flysch deposited during the Taconian orogeny is covered by late Pleistocene deposits for the first few miles. This low, gently rolling topography has remnants of the northernmost "Pine Bush" plant community (a fire-dominated community with black oak and jack pine) in the vicinity of Albany International Airport. This flora colonizes sand dunes that accumulated ca. 12 Ka on the west side of Glacial Lake Albany. These dunes provide part of Albany's water (although the Rapp Road garbage dump, the highest point just west of Albany, lies in the Pine Bush). These dunes were greatly modified by early excavations for glass sand and later suburban development. Outwash deposits further north replace the dunes. At mileage marker 7.7 (note the small green signs along the Northway), Late Ordovician flysch [Schenectady Formation, best regarded as a junior synonym of the lower Martinsburg Group farther south in eastern Pennsylvania] is exposed on the right in a roadcut just south of the Thaddeus Kosziascko Bridge, which crosses the Mohawk River (the border between Albany and Saratoga Counties). The strongly metamorphosed, Lower Cambrian rocks of the "High Taconics" on the New York–Massachusetts line form the skyline to the east (right). This part of New York comprised the northern part of New Netherlands, and the exits to Halfmoon (Henry Hudson's ship) and Vischers Ferry reflect the Dutch colonial history of this region in the 17th century (before it passed to the Danes for ten years, and then to the British).

At milepost 13.3 and further north, the low foothills of the middle Proterozoic Adirondack Mountains massif become visible. The region we are traveling through was the frontier

---

EDIACARAN-ORDOVICIAN OF EAST LAURENTIA—S.W. FORD MEMORIAL VOLUME, Edited by Ed Landing, New York State Museum, The State Education Department, Albany, New York 12230. New York State Museum Bulletin 510.

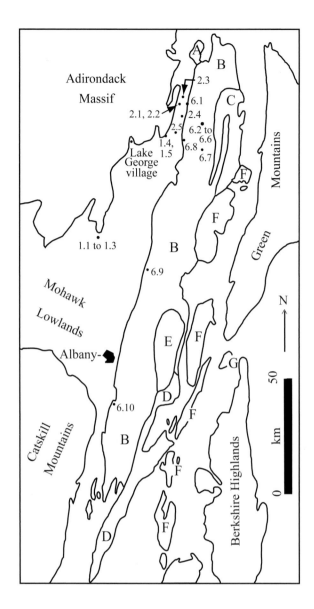

FIGURE 1— Generalized map showing stops on days 1, 2, and 6 of the field trip (1.1–1.5, 2.1–2.5, 6.1–6.10). Map shows Proterozoic Adirondack massif, Berkshire Highlands, and Green Mountains axis; Cambrian–Ordovician of Mohawk Lowlands, southern Lake Champlain Lowlands east of Adirondack massif, and in Hudson River valley east of Catskill Mountains; and Silurian–Devonian of northeast corner of Allegheny Plateau (with Catskill Mountains). Succession of slices in the Ediacaran(?)–Ordovician Taconic allochthon labeled with letters: A, Sunset Lake; B, Giddings Brook; C, Bird Mountain; D, Chatham; E, Rensselaer Plateau; F, Dorset Mountain–Everett; G, Greylock. Modified from Zen (1967).

between French and British interests in the mid-18th century. Round Lake, noted at milepost 17.4, was first known as "Bloody Pond" because the French and their Iroquois allies kidnapped all of the residents of colonial Schenectady, and massacred them on the lake shore. This 1690 massacre took place early in the first

"French and Indian War" [King William's War, 1689–1697].

Snake Hill.—Saratoga Lake, noted at milepost 19.4, has a giant mélange block of near-shore siliciclastics (Snake Hill Formation) with shallow-water, Late Ordovician (Caradocian) macrofaunas. This block is isolated within distal, slightly older (also Caradocian), synorogenic mudstones (Utica Shale). The Snake Hill mélange block on the east side of Saratoga Lake (ca. 4.5 km east of the Northway) marks the preserved western limit of the Taconic masterthrust (English *et al.*, 2006). The long road-cut at milepost 22.2 to the right of the bus is in laminated, black, dysoxic/anoxic Utica Shale.

Saratoga–Petrified Gardens Road.—At milepost 24.6, take Exit 13N from Interstate 87 toward Saratoga. Follow Rte. 9 northwest past the Harness Track and Museum of Dance. After about 2.5 miles, turn left at light onto West Fenlon Street; continue roughly west through light to T-intersection; turn north and travel to light at Rte. 29. Turn left on Rte. 29, and travel about three miles west to stop light at Petrified Gardens Road. Turn right (north) at light, travel 0.4 mi. past quarry properties on both sides of road, and stop in vicinity of the privately owned property called "Petrified Gardens." Petrified Gardens, which features extensive outcrops of the stromatolite layer near the base of the Hoyt Member of the Little Falls Formation (Stop 1.2), was long run as a tourist facility by the Ritchie family. It is now owned by the Pallete Stone Company just to the south, and has seen "better days." Depart bus and walk ca. 125 m east to outcrops in wooded ravine.

Stop 1.1, Cambrian–Ordovician (intra-Skullrockian Stage) boundary unconformity near Petrified Gardens: Eustatic and epeirogenic controls (30 minutes)

Ritchie Limestone.—Despite extensive collecting in this area, Walcott (1879, 1912) did not report a massive, sparsely fossiliferous, gently west-dipping limestone in the wooded ravine just south of Petrified Gardens (Figure 2). This limestone occurs somewhat topographically below the lower Hoyt Limestone at Petrified Gardens. Fisher and Hansen's (1951, p. 804, 805, fig. 2b) interpretation of their newly recognized unit, the Ritchie Limestone, was that its exposure is limited to this outcrop which isolated along a spur of the McGregor fault. They suggested that limited fossil evidence (reported specimens of the gastropod *Rachopea*) suggested a Late Cambrian or earliest Ordovician age of the Ritchie.

A re-investigation of the Ritchie Limestone (E. Landing and S. R. Westrop, unpublished data) shows that it comprises 9.5 m of stylolitic, primarily structureless (burrow-churned), sparse intraclast granule-ooid wackestone and lime mudstone with SH-V stromatolites and thrombolites near its top. The limestones abruptly overlie 8.4 m of buff-gray, sucrosic dolostone (probably of hydrothermal origin) with abundant dark brownish chert that replaced dolostone (Figure 3). These dolostones and limestones are referable to the upper part of the regionally extensive Little Falls Formation, with the Hoyt Limestone member forming the base of the Little Falls (Figure 2). The upper 2.15 m of the dolostone under the limestone has abundant dark brownish chert that replaced dolostone.

Ritchie Limestone trilobites and conodonts.—A single ooid packstone dune with east-dipping foresets (12.3–12.8 m) yields rare gastropods and trilobites. A single, low diversity conodont fauna extends through the lower dolostones and the entire,

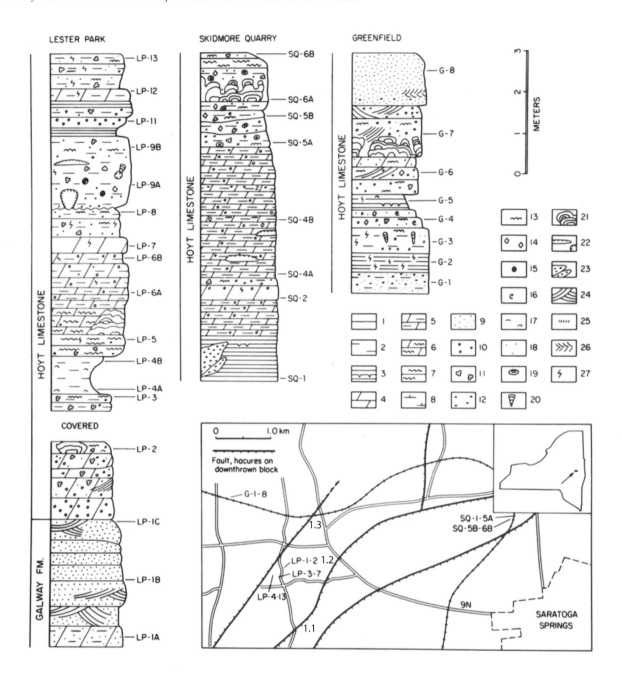

FIGURE 2—Stops 1.1–1.3 Sections in the upper Galway Formation through lower Tribes Hill Formation northwest of Saratoga Springs, New York. Stop 1.1 about 150 m west of Petrified Gardens Road; Stop 1.2 corresponds to LP- sections on east and west side of Lester Park Road; Stop 1.3 is across Rte 9N from numeral "1.3." Figure also shows upper Galway Formation through Hoyt Limestone member of the Little Fals Formation at Stop 1.2. Numbers to right of columns are conodont sample horizons. Small boxes: 1, dolomitic mudstone, dark gray, laminated; 2, dark gray siltstones and lenticular, thin-bedded, dolomitic quartz arenites; 3, lithology 1 with synaeresis cracks; 4, coarse-grained (sucrosic) dolostone; 5, fine-grained dolostone; 6, dolomitized cryptalgalaminate; 7, calcareous cryptalgalaminate; 8, dolomitic silt-shale; 9, dolomitic quartz arenite; 10, coated grains (ooids, spherulites); 11, composite grains (grapestones and botryoidal grains); 12, intraclasts; 13, trilobite fragments; 14, echinoderm debris; 15, dasycladacean algae; 16, gastropods; 17, linguloid brachiopods; 18, quartz sand; 19, algal pisolites; 20, small, club-like (SH-V) stromatolites; 21, domal (SH-V and LLH-C) stromatolites; 22, thrombolites; 23, intraclast- and mud-filled channels; 24, cross-bedding; 25, lenticular beds (1–3 mm thickness); 26, herringbone cross-beds; 27, burrows and/or bioturbation. Figure modified from Landing (1979a, fig. 1).

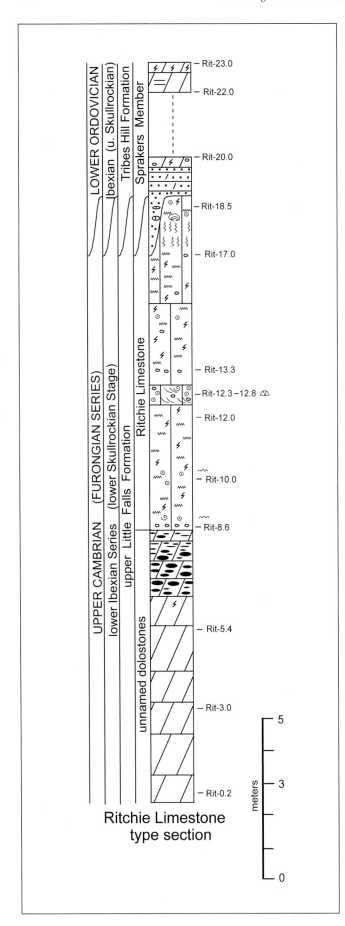

Ritchie Limestone type section

FIGURE 3—Cambrian–Ordovician boundary interval succession at Stop 1.1 just south of Petrified Gardens. Conodont sample horizons (meters above base of section) indicated by numbers to right of column (e.g., Rit-12.0). Symbols: limestones shown by vertical brick-work pattern; dolostones by inclined brick-work pattern; thrombolitic intervals (e.g., 17–18 m interval) shown by vertical "squiggly" lines; SH-V stromatolites by pillow-like forms; reworked limestone clasts by ellipses with vertical line; stylolitic packstones by horizontal "lightning bolt;" burrows by vertical "lightning bolt;" dark gray chert by black ellipses; gastropods by helix; trilobite collection with trilobite head.

overlying limestone sequence to the unconformity with the Tribes Hill. The conodonts *Cordylodus proavus* Müller, 1959, and *Clavohamulus elongatus* Miller, 1969, dominate the fauna. These taxa are referable to the middle *Cordylodus proavus* Zone, and indicate a Late, but not latest, Cambrian age. *Scalpellodus utahensis* (Miller, 1969) emend. Landing (1993), among other conodonts, occurs in the uppermost Ritchie Limestone, and indicates the Ritchie Limestone extends into the uppermost *Cordylodus proavus* Zone *sensu strictu* (e.g., Miller, 1980).

The sparse trilobite fauna of the Richie Formation is problematic. Sclerites recovered from a horizon 12.3–12.8 m above the base of the section include *Acheilops*? (undescribed species with an occipital spine), *Calvinella*, and *Saukia*. None of these genera is known elsewhere in Laurentia above the *Eurekia apopsis* Zone and, if the conodont-based age determination is taken at face value, each trilobite represents a significant range extension. Alternatively, this section could record early occurrences of some conodont species in strata that are no younger than basal Ibexian.

Tribes Hill Formation.—The Ritchie Limestone is abruptly overlain by a thin (10 cm) dolomitic quartz arenite that is laterally replaced by up to 2.1 m of conglomeratic quartz arenite with clasts of Ritchie Limestone. Higher strata (5 m) include lower sucrosic and higher fine-grained dolostone with sparse *Rossodus manitouensis* Zone (upper lower Tremadocian-equivalent) conodonts. Fisher and Hansen (1951) referred these post-Ritchie strata to the "Mosherville Sandstone" and "Gailor Dolomite." However, this interval is best referred to the regionally extensive Tribes Hill Formation (Figures 2, 3).

Fisher and Hansen (1951) correctly interpreted an unconformity at the top of the Ritchie Limestone. The new biostratigraphic data now show that the unconformity corresponds to the Cambrian–Ordovician boundary depositional sequence boundary and eustatic fall–rise couplet recognizeable across eastern New York and western Vermont (Landing *et al.* 1996, 2003a), as well as across the Laurentian platform (Landing, 1988a) and other Early Paleozoic continents (e.g., Landing *et al.*, in press). The lateral pinch-out of the conglomerate indicates the filling of erosive depressions (channels?) of a type one sequence boundary (Van Wagoner *et al.*, 1988).

Travel to Stop 1.2

At end of Stop 1.1, drive ca. one mile north to Lester Park. Petrified Gardens Road changes to Lester Park Road at the Greenfield Center Line. Lester Park is marked by a large blue and yellow New York State Education Department sign on the right (east) side of Lester Park Road.

Lester Park and Stark's Knob—the latter property exhibits a giant mélange block of Late Ordovician pillow basalt (N-MORB composition) in mudstone-dominated, synorogenic (Taconic orogeny) flysch (Landing *et al.*, 2003b)—are outdoor geological exhibits of the New York State Museum. Stark's Knob is located several miles north of the east end of Rte. 29 and just north of Schuylerville. Collecting is not allowed at these protected localities. These are the last of the six "Scientific Reservations" that State Museum Director John M. Clarke acquired in the early 1900s in order to preserve unique geological sites and promote research on them (Landing, 2004). The remaining four were larger than Lester Park, and were transferred to the New York State parks department in the early 1950s. Both Lester Park and Stark's Knob were essentially abandoned by the State Museum for 50 years, until they were renovated by E. Landing at the end of the 1990s.

Stop 1.2, Lester Park (20 minutes)

Galway Formation–Hoyt Limestone of Little Falls Formation.—The classic Upper Cambrian section at Lester Park begins with low outcrops of the uppermost Galway Formation on the low slope above the boggy creek east of Lester Park Road. The contact between the Galway Formation and overlying Hoyt Limestone of the lowest Little Falls Formation is drawn at a horizon marked by the loss of abundant quartz sand and appearance of abundant ooids and coated grains (Figure 2, left column).

Pre-burial beveling of Hoyt stromatolites.—The broad stromatolite-covered surface immediately east of the road in the lower Hoyt Limestone is the type locality of the coalescing SH-V and LLH-C stromatolite forms that Hall (1863) termed *Cryptozoon proliferum*. The stromatolite build-ups are predominantly non-dolomitized, and weather light gray, by comparison with the buff-weathering, dolomitized, interbuild-up facies [originally a sand- to granule-intraclast, ooid and grapestone, and fossil (dasycladacean algae, echinoderm hash, mollusk debris, and rare trilobite hash packstone to grainstone)]. Goldring (1938) attributed the beveling of the stromatolites at Lester Park and Petrified Gardens that reveals the internal growth laminae to erosion by Pleistocene glacial ice movement. However, Landing (1979a, b) determined that the erosion was Late Cambrian, and indicates syndepositional erosion, because the truncated stromatolites are locally mantled by ooid-granule intraclast-grapestone grainstones at Petrified Gardens.

Hoyt Limestone in road cut.—Higher strata in the Hoyt Limestone at Lester Part include the low cut on the west side of Lester Park Road. The lower part of the road cut includes silt shales and lenticular quartz arenites with linguloids and synaeresis cracks above ooid-granule intraclast- grapestone grainstones. Higher strata in the road cut include ooid and intraclast sand–sand pack- to grainstones with low LLH-C and –V stromatolites [the latter are Goldring's (1938) form taxa named *Cryptozoon ruedemanni* and *C. undulatum.*

Hoyt quarry.—The highest strata, with a 1.5 m interval with large thrombolites, occur in the Hoyt quarry in the woods east of the road. The Hoyt quarry workers burned rock from the Hoyt quarry for agricultural lime in the old kiln on the west side of Lester Park Road.

Hoyt trilobites.—Ludvigsen and Westrop (1983) restudied the disarticulated (but unabraded) trilobites of the Hoyt

Limestone and underlying Galway Formation in Saratoga County. Their taxonomic revision indicated the Hoyt fauna is composed of nine species: *Dellea*? *landingi* Ludvigsen and Westrop 1983 (only in basal beds);); *Hoytaspis speciosa* (Walcott, 1879); *Keithiella* cf. *K depressa* Rasetti, 1944 (only in uppermost beds; see Adrain and Westrop, 2005, p. 382 for a recent discussion of this species); *Plethopeltis granulosa* Resser, 1942; *P. saratogensis* (Walcott, 1890); *Prosaukia hartii* (Walcott, 1879); *P. tribulis* (Walcott, 1912); *P.* sp.; *Saratogia (Saratogia) calcifera* (Walcott, 1879).

Ludvigsen and Westrop (1983) made two important re-evaluations of the Hoyt Limestone trilobites: 1) The Hoyt fauna is highly provincial at the species level, and has closest similarities with a low diversity fauna from the Little Falls Dolostone (traditionally referred to the "Briarcliff Dolostone") ca. 150 km SSE in Dutchess County New York. 2) The supposed upper Upper Cambrian correlation of the Hoyt Limestone [i.e., *Saukia* Zone of the Laurentian "Trempealeauan Stage," now upper Sunwaptan Stage, see Palmer (1998)] traditionally favored in many reports (see Kobayashi, 1935; Lochman-Balk, 1970; Taylor and Halley, 1974; Stitt, 1977) is questionable, and a correlation into the middle Sunwaptan Stage ("Franconian Stage") is preferable.

Travel to Stop 1.3

At the end of the stop, travel short distance to end of Lester Park Road. Turn right at stop sign onto Middle Grove Road, and drive for ca. 0.6 mile to stop sign on Rte. 9N. Turn north (left) to roadcut visible several hundred meters to north and located just south of railroad overpass at intersection of Daniels Road and Rte. 9N.

Stop 1.3, Galway Formation roadcut (20 minutes)

Lithofacies.—This long roadcut in the lower Galway Formation exposes 4.5 m of medium- to thick-bedded, weakly to strongly dolomitic, buff-weathering, gray, coarse-grained quartz arenites and minor thin-bedded quartz arenites. Wave ripples occur at ca. 1.5 m, but the upper part of the road cut shows large troughs that indicate a tidal influence in deposition of the massive beds. Scattered dolomite-filled cavities indicate the passage of hydrothermal fluids through the succession, and the possible replacement of early anhydrite nodules.

Fossils and age.—Trilobites in an ooid-intraclast dune at 1.75–2.0m in the roadcut are the same as those in higher strata in the railroad cut just west of the overpass above Rte 9N to the north. The railroad cut has a lower Sunwaptan Stage (*Elvinia* Zone, lower "Franconian") trilobite assemblage in a thin dolostone with abundant quartz sand (Cushing and Ruedemann, 1914; Resser, 1942; Fisher and Hansen, 1951). Ludvigsen and Westrop (1981) re-illustrated this fauna: *Calocephalites* sp. cf. *C. minimus* Kurtz, 1975; *Camaraspis convexa* (Whitfield, 1878); *Dellea saratogensis* (Resser, 1942); *Drabia* sp. cf. *D. curtoccipita* Wilson, 1951; *D.* sp. cf. *D. menusa* Wilson, 1951; and *Elvinia granulata* Resser, 1942.

Travel to Stop 1.4

Greenfield Center–Exit 20 of Northway.—At end of stop, turn south (left) on Rte. 9N, and follow Rte. 9N toward Saratoga Springs to intersection with Rte. 29. Turn left (east) onto Rte. 29, follow through Saratoga Springs to intersection with Interstate 87 (the Northway). Follow Northway North toward Lake George. Shortly after entering Northway, note prominent NNE-trending ridge to right of bus; this uplifted ridge of middle Proterozoic, high-grade metamorphic rocks is bounded in its east by the Glen Falls fault—one of the late Proterozoic faults that originated with the break-up of Rodinia that was re-activated during the Paleozoic, and possibly during the Taconic and Acadian orogenies (Landing, preceding report, this volume). At mileage post 45, note the broad, bowl-shaped depression ahead of the bus that contains Lake George (with a NNE orientation defined by late Proterozoic faults, and which was scoured into a fjord by mountain glaciation in the latest Pleistocene). Exit Northway at Exit 20 and follow road signs at end of exit ramp through commercial strip to Rte. 149 east.

Exit 20–Fort Ann village.—Follow Rte. 149 for 12.6 miles east to village of Fort Ann; this route approximates the middle Proterozoic–Cambrian nonconformity, with the highlands to the immediate north developed on high-grade metamorphic rocks of the southernmost Adirondack massif. After 1.6 miles, the high ridges of the Taconic allochthon first become visible directly in front (east) of the bus. At 4.2 miles, the Queensbury Country Club and its golf course (on left) are developed on the less resistant Cambrian–Lower Ordovician sedimentary rocks. At 5.7 and 6.7 miles, the low road cuts on the north (left) side of Rte. 149 occur in the south end of the Sugar Loaf Proterozoic inlier and at the Hadlock Pond fault, respectively.

At hill crest (9.3 miles), a spectacular view of ridges in the Taconic allochthon is visible due east across pastures developed on glacial outwash; the far skyline is middle Proterozoic rock of the Green Mountains in central Vermont. At 10.7 miles, the view to the left (NE) is the southeasternmost ridge of the Adirondacks east of the Welch Hollow fault. Note the the gently east-dipping slope on the Proterozoic, this is the Proterozoic–Cambrian nonconformity with the Potsdam eroded away.

At the bridge over a small creek (11 miles), note medium–massively bedded dolomitic limestone and replacement dolostone [mapped by Fisher (1984) as Lower Ordovician Tribes Hill Formation (his "Fort Edward Dolostone," designation abandoned, see Landing *et al.* (2003). However, the locally oolitic, thrombolitic, intraclast facies exposed here are more suggestive of the Upper Cambrian Little Falls Formation.

Fort Ann village–Flat Rock Road.—Drive into village of Fort Ann; turn north at light onto Rte. 4 north, and cross bridge over Halfway Creek at north end of village. After ca. 0.5 mi. of driving through lowland occupied by poorly exposed, NNE-striking Beekmantown and Trenton Group carbonates, cross Welch Hollow fault and pass through ca. 1 mile of road cuts in middle Proterozoic Hague gneiss (Fisher, 1984, map). Turn right (east) onto poorly marked dirt road (south end of Flat Rock Road) and stop within 0.5 mile in sight of railroad tracks. Walk 50 m east through woods to tracks and continue north. LISTEN AND WATCH FOR FAST TRAINS ALONG THESE TRACKS!

Stop 1.4, Lower Potsdam Formation trilobites near Fort Ann (30 minutes)

Proterozoic Hague gneiss–lower Potsdam Sandstone.—Cuts through massive, garnet-bearing Hague gneiss occur for a short distance along the tracks. After a covered interval, a long cut in gently dipping (10° SSE) Potsdam Formation sandstones is exposed along the railroad tracks. The 6 m of feldspar-poor, dominantly wave-deposited quartz arenites in this cut are the upper unit (Keesville Member) of the Potsdam Formation. The

feldspathic, current cross-bedded, lower Potsdam (Ausable Member) is seen only further north on the south flank of the Ottawa aulocogen on the New York Promontory (Stop 3.3). The Potsdam likely occupies most of the covered interval above the Hague gneiss, and only about 5 m of lowest Keesville Member is not exposed.

Trilobites.—Flower (1964, p. 156) reported a trilobite fauna (presently unillustrated; in preparation by SRW and EL) from this railroad cut. He claimed that this fauna includes a possible *Crepicephalus* with *Komaspidella* and *Lonchocephalus*, but re-examination of his collection in the New York State Museum Paleontology Collection shows that it contains only *Coosella*?, *Marjumia* s.l., and *Pemphegaspis*. In addition, we have not yet discovered any of the taxa described by Walcott (1912) from the Potsdam. We re-located Flower's sampling horizon 1.6 m above the base of the exposed Potsdam in the cut in cross- and thin-bedded, dolomitic sandstone. Following the recent decision (January 2002) of the Cambrian Subcommission to define the base of the Upper Cambrian at the lowest occurrence of the agnostoid *Glyptagnostus reticulatus*, this traditional Laurentian "Upper Cambrian" *Crepicephalus* Zone assemblage must now be regarded as uppermost Middle Cambrian. This lower Potsdam Formation fauna indicates that the earliest marine onlap in this part of the Lake Champlain–Hudson River lowlands was terminal Middle Cambrian.

Travel to Stop 1.5

At end of stop, drive short distance north to T-intersection, turn hard left (west) and drive ca. 150 m and stop at intersection of Flat Rock Road and Rte. 4. Stop 1.5 is a low, overgrown road cut just to the northeast of the road intersection.

Stop 1.5, Potsdam–middle Proterozoic nonconformity near Fort Ann (10 minutes)

Several meters of medium–coarse grained, slightly dolomitic, brownish-weathering quartz arenite of the Potsdam Formation with a basal quartz pebble conglomerate nonconformably overlie middle Proterozoic Hague gneiss with east-dipping exfoliation surfaces at this stop. We are only about 7 m below the trilobite-bearing horizon at Stop 1.4. A basal quartz pebble conglomerate lies on the nonconformity surface. This photogenic locality records the absence of ca. 600 million years of earth history at this planar nonconformity.

Stop 1.5 emphasizes that the Lower Paleozoic of the eastern New York shelf is generally a very thin succession by comparison with Great Basin and southern Canadian Rockies sequences (i.e., 100s of meters vs. several thousand meters). The ridge crest to the east is underlain by the upper Little Falls Formation and indicates that only ca. 200 m of Upper Cambrian is present above the Grenvillian. Thin Lower Paleozoic successions occur in this region of New York and Vermont due to its location on the slowly subsiding New York Promontory rift-margin of Laurentia (Thomas, 1977; Williams, 1978). For this reason, this passive margin can be expected to record Early Paleozoic eustatic changes as type 1 erosive sequence boundaries (e.g., Landing *et al.*, 2003a). For example, the Cambrian–Ordovician boundary is a type 1 sequence boundaries in eastern New York and western Vermont (Landing, 1988b; Landing *et al.*, 1996, 2003a; Stops 1.1, 2.4).

At end of the stop, drive south on Rte. 4, and continue on to hotel in the village of Lake George.

JULY 31: THIN PLATFORM SUCCESSION IN WASHINGTON AND CLINTON COUNTIES, EASTERN NEW YORK

Overview

Day 2 of the field trip continues an overview of the the relatively thin Cambrian platform succession on the east Laurentian platform in Washington County, eastern New York (Stop 2.2), with a stop further north in Clinton County. The terminal Middle Cambrian–latest Cambrian sequence from the Potsdam Sandstone (Stop 2.1) through Little Falls Formation and overlying Tribes Hill Formation will again be examined. The trip today includes sites with body soft-bodied ("medusoid") remains and trace fossils from the Potsdam Formation (Stop 2.6), and emphasizes the trilobite and conodont biostratigraphy of the Sunwaptan Stage–Ibexian Series boundary in the Little Falls Formation (Stop 2.3). Cambrian cephalopods are known in Laurentia only from the upper Little Falls Formation in eastern New York (Stop 2.4) and from the San Saba Formation in central Texas.

Travel to Stop 2.1

Lake George–Whitehall.—Depart hotel and re-trace yesterday's route to Fort Ann; drive past middle Proterozoic–Potsdam nonconformity (Stop 1.5) and follow combined Rte 4 and 149 north to village of Whitehall New York; note that the road roughly follows a topographic break that corresponds to the the Proterozoic–Cambrian nonconformity. Roadcuts 1.4–3.3 miles north of Stop 1.5 are in Grenville gneisses.

Intersection with Rte 22 on right (East); road to Whitehall is now Rte 4 and 22 (combined). Stop 2.4 later today lies several miles east on Rte 22. At 3.7 miles north of Stop 1.5, large dip slope at 10–12 O'Clock is nonconformity surface on Proterozoic.

At 6.2 miles, hill directly in front (north) of vehicle is Skene Mountain in Whitehall (Stops 2.1, 2.2). The succession comprising this hill (Potsdam–middle Little Falls Formations) corresponds to almost the complete terminal Middle–upper Upper Cambrian of the Lake Champlain Lowlands. Enter Whitehall village (8.4 miles), and turn right (east) at light in Whitehall onto Rte 4.

Rte 4–base of Skene Mountain.—Drive across Champlain Canal and Wood Creek. Turn left (north) at stop light opposite convenience store onto William Street. Continue north through Whitehall along the foot of Skene Mountain. At the stop sign, bear gently right (north) as William Street becomes North William Street; park next to bridge over Champlain Canal. Stop 2.1 is the high road cut on the east side of North William Street.

Stop 2.1, Potsdam Formation at base of Skene Mountain (15 minutes)

Approximately 50 m of Potsdam Formation siliceous quartz arenites and minor dolomitic quartz arenite are exposed in the Whitehall area. The village of Whitehall immediately west of the Champlain Canal lies on the Proterozoic–Cambrian nonconformity, and the canal is excavated in Potsdam Formation sandstones (Figure 4). Herring-bone cross sets, dolomitic quartz arenite pebbles at the base of small channels/dunes, and U-shaped *Diplocraterion* burrows all point to tidally influenced, higher energy deposition of the Potsdam. This quart-

zose, non-feldspathic facies is the upper (Keesville) member of the Potsdam, and the feldspathic, abundantly trough cross-bedded lower (Ausable) member is not present in the southern Lake Champlain lowlands. The Potsdam is overlain by lower Upper Cambrian dolomitic quartz arenites and quartzose dolostones of the Galway Formation (="Ticonderoga Formation," designation abandoned; Landing *et al.*, 2003a, see Appendix) higher on Skene Mountain.

Travel to Stop 2.2

At end of stop, retrace route south through Whitehall, and turn left (east) on one of the steep streets east of William Street. Take street to T-intersection with Mountain Road; turn north on Mountain Road and drive into Skene Manor estate, park in gravel parking lot.

Stop 2.2, Cambrian succession overview at Skene Manor (15 minutes)

Ghost of Skene Manor.—Weather permitting, this is a highly photogenic stop. The parking lot is on the north side of Skene Manor—a tourist site currently undergoing restoration. Skene Manor is a favorite site for those interested in the paranormal. It was build by a British veteran of the War of 1812 and his American wife. When his wife died, it is said that she did not want to be buried, and Major Skene accommodated her wishes by interning her in the counter of the public bar. Obviously, this has led to claims that Skene Manor is haunted.

Proterozoic–lowest Ibexian (uppermost Cambrian).—The view to the west is over middle Proterozoic hills at the southeastern margin of the Adirondack massif, and Whitehall is built on the east-dipping Proterozoic–Cambrian nonconformity surface. The Potsdam Sandstone (Keesville Member) extends upward from the Champlain Canal through the Stop 2.1 section. Contacts are difficult to establish on the wooded west slope of Skene Mountain, and the manor seems to lie on the upper Potsdam (Figure 4). Interbedded quartz arenites, dolomitic quartz arenites, and arenaceous dolostones referable to the Galway Formation (see Stop 1.3) are exposed along the lower part of the power line that extends to the microwave station on the crest of Skene Mountain.

Massive dolostones of the Little Falls Formation appear at least 25 m below the microwave station. The microwave station itself is built on a ledge of gently east-dipping, thin-bedded, fossiliferous limestones that yielded Taylor and Halley's (1974) collections 7098-CO and 7099-CO. EL and SRW have recollected these uppermost Upper Cambrian and lowest Ibexian Series limestones with *Parakoldinioidia* cf. *P. stitti* Fortey, 1983 (=*Missisquoia typicalis* Shaw, 1953; see Fortey, 1983), in large blocks bulldozed away from the microwave station foundation.

Travel to Stop 2.3

At end of stop, descend Skene Mountain and retrace route to Stop 2.1. Continue north on North Williams Street past cuts in Potsdam Formation (Stop 2.1) and drive 0.6 miles to intersection with Doig Street (Washington Co. Rte 10) on left. Turn left, and drive north for 1.2 miles; take sharp turn to right (east), and bear right on Washington Co. Rte 10 for 0.4 miles. Stop along road opposite entrance to old Crossman quarry (Figure 4).

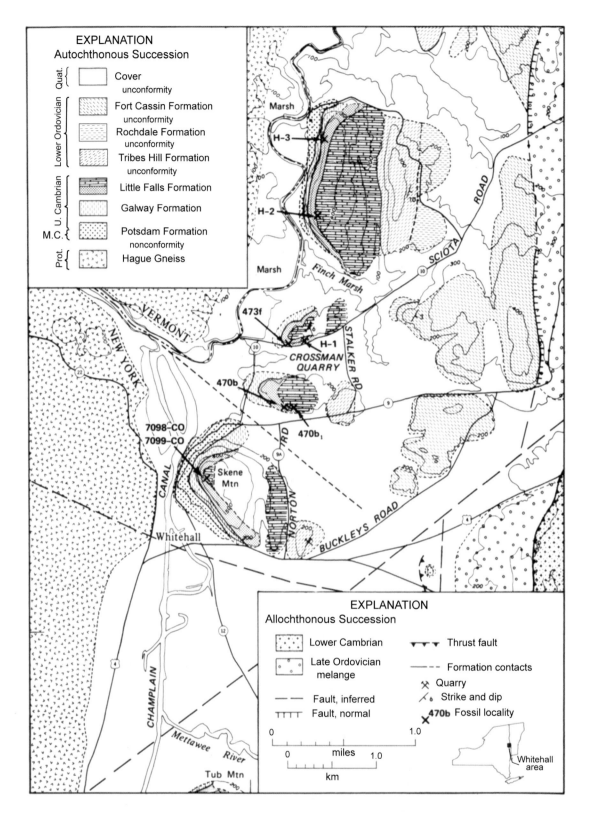

FIGURE 4—Generalized geologic map of Skene Mountain area. Stop 2.1 is road cut at west base of Skene Mountain; Stop 2.2 at Skene Manor below crest of Skene Mountain; Stop 2.3 at Crossman quarry NNE of Skene Mountain. Contour interval 100 feet (ca. 30 m). Figure, stratigraphic nomenclature, and correlations modified from Taylor and Halley (1974, fig. 1).

Stop 2.3, Crossman quarry: Sunwaptan Stage–Ibexian Series boundary in the middle Little Falls Formation (20 minutes)

Geologic setting.—This locality on the north side of Washington County Rte. 10 is one of the few well-exposed, fossiliferous, non-hydrothermally dolomitized successions through the middle part of the Little Falls Formation in eastern New York (Figure 5). EL and SRW have re-investigated the gently east-dipping (ca. 12°) succession for macrofaunas and conodonts. The western end of the quarry is pervasively dolomitized, and has been mapped as the "Skene Dolostone" member (Wheeler, 1941) of the "Whitehall Formation" by Fisher (1977, 1984). The dolomitized limestones at the west end of Crossman Quarry, as at Steves Farm and Comstock (Stops 2.4, 2.5), were likely produced by the movement of hydrothermal fluids during burial with the Taconic orogeny (e.g., Collins-Wait and Lowenstein, 1994). CLIMBING OF THE STEEP QUARRY WALLS IS STRONGLY DISCOURAGED.

Lithostratigraphy.—The dolostones are replaced by 25.5 m of laterally equivalent, limestone-dominated strata in the middle and eastern end of the quarry (Figure 5). The lower limestones are light gray weathering, medium- to massively bedded ooid-granule and sand intraclast-fossil hash wacke- to packstones. Lenticular grainstones and pebble intraclast beds, stromatolitic and thrombolitic intervals, and minor nodular and bedded gray and green chert also are present. Quartz sand is limited in the succession, but forms a thin (30 cm-thick) bed immediately under a prominent SH-V to LLH-V stromatolite bed (11.75–12.0 m). An important facies change occurs in the upper half of the quarry (12.0–23.8 m), where the beds are massive and dominantly thrombolitic (Figure 5).

This shallow carbonate platform facies seen through the quarry is Fisher's (1977) undefined "Warner Hill Limestone" member of the middle "Whitehall Formation" (abandoned designations). Snails and other mollusks are the dominant macrofaunal elements in this sequence, and indicate a restricted, relatively near-shore biofacies that has trilobites as a limited component of the macrofauna (e.g., Westrop *et al.*, 1995).

Late Cambrian trilobite and conodont biostratigraphy.— The Late Cambrian trilobite assemblage reported by Taylor and Halley (1974, their collection H-1, *Saukiella serotina* Subzone, upper *Saukia* Zone) occurs ca. 3.5 m above the base of the eastern quarry wall (our sample 10-10.4; Figure 7). This collection comes from a lenticular, arenaceous, intraclast pebble grainstone that is laterally transitional into an ooid packstone. Associated sparse conodonts through sample 10-10.4 are referable to the

FIGURE 5—Cambrian stratigraphy at Stop 2.3 (Crossman quarry) just north of Washington County Rte. 10. Conodont sample horizons (meters above base of section) indicated by numbers to right of column (e.g., 10-10.4). Symbols: limestones shown by vertical brick-work pattern; dolostones by inclined brick-work; thrombolitic intervals (e.g., 20.5–23.5 m interval) shown by vertical to inclined "squiggly" lines; SH-V stromatolites by pillow-like forms; limestone intraclasts by small ellipses; ooid grainstones by small circles with dot in center; stylolitic packstones by horizontal "lightning bolt;" burrows by vertical "lightning bolt;" dark gray chert by black ellipses; green chert by light gray ellipses; gastropods by helix; trilobite collection with trilobite head.

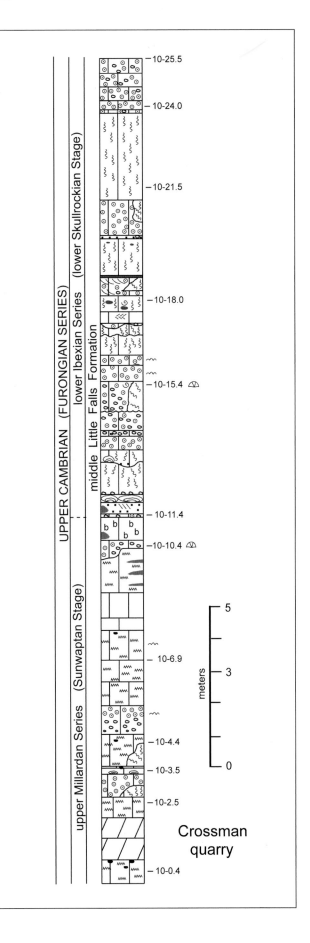

upper *Eoconodontus* Zone.

The Sunwaptan Stage–Ibexian Series contact is now recognized in Crossman quarry at a lithofacies and faunal break only a meter above Taylor and Halley's (1974) collection H-1. This combined lithofacies-faunal break is marked by an interval of distinctive beds [an intraclast pebble-ooid packstone (11.25–11.45), an overlying quartz arenite (11.45–11.75 m), and a prominent SH-V to LLH-V stromatolite interval] that underlie the massive, thrombolite-dominated upper part of the quarry succession. Conodonts of the lowest Ibexian *Cordylodus proavus* Zone first appear in the intraclast pebble-ooid packstone bed. These data demonstrate that the Sunwaptan–Ibexian biomere boundary locally corresponds to a significant lithofacies change.

A trilobite assemblage from the lowest Ibexian was collected at horizon 10-15.4 (Figure 7) from an intraclast packstone lens with abundant snails and other mollusks at the top of a massive thrombolite bed. Sclerites of *Parakoldinioidia* cf. *P. stitti* Fortey, 1983, are common at this horizon. They are probably conspecific with the material illustrated by Taylor and Halley (1976) under the name *Missisquoia typicalis* Shaw, and likely indicate a correlation with the *P. stitti* Zone (= *Missisquoia typicalis* Zone of earlier reports).

Travel to Stop 2.4

At the end of Stop 2.3, continue east a short distance on Washington Co. Rte 10 to the intersection with Stalker Road; turn right (South) (Figure 4). The first ridge to the east of Stalker Road is underlain by units that compose the upper part of the Early Paleozoic carbonate platform in the southern Lake Champlain valley [=middle Lower Ordovician Rochdale (="Fort Ann") Formation–lower Middle Ordovician Providence Island Dolostone]. The second ridge to the east is the front of the Taconic allochthon, which overrides synorogenic lower Upper Ordovician flysch (Fisher, 1984). At stop sign at T-intersection with Washington Co. Rte. 9, turn right and travel a short distance west to intersection with Norton Road. Turn left on Norton Road and drive to stop sign at T-intersection with Rte. 4.

Turn right (west) on Rte 4, and drive to Whitehall. The first road cut on the right (north) is in fine-grained, dolomitic quartz arenites of the lower part (Sprakers Member) of the Tribes Hill Formation [lower Ibexian, Skullrockian, *Rossodus manitouensis* Zone; see Landing *et al.*, 2003a, for section in Tristates quarry immediately on the backside (north) of this road cut. The next road cut immediately to the west is in massive dolostones of the upper Little Falls Formation. This isolated outcrop is Fisher's (1984) type section of the "Skene Member" (i.e., undifferentiated dolostones of the "Whitehall Formation").

Enter Whitehall village. At the first light in Whitehall, turn left (south) onto South William Street (Washington County Rte 12). This street becomes the Truthville–Whitehall Road on the south side of Whitehall. Cross the railroad tracks. At 1.4 miles beyond the tracks, continue straight on Upper Turnpike at the left bend in the road. Cross the bridge over the Mettawee River, and intersect Morse Lane 0.7 miles after the bridge. Bear left (east) and continue on Upper Turnpike. An intersection with Hyatt Lane (dirt) lies 0.6 miles further on; bear left and continue on Upper Turnpike. The farm buildings on both sides of the Upper Turnpike mark Steves Farm. Stop and park 0.2 miles south of the Steves Farm buildings at the gentle left bend on Upper Turnpike. Park on dirt road near trailer on right side of

Upper Turnpike. Ascend hill through woods just to the east of the trailer.

Stop 2.4, Uppermost Cambrian cephalopods and Cambrian–Ordovician boundary at Steve's Farm (30 minutes)

History of study.—Landing *et al.* (2003a) detailed the stratigraphy and conodont biostratigraphy of the Steve's Farm succession (Figure 6). Flower (1964) first drew attention to the section by noting the occurrence of apparent ellesmeroceroid cephalopods and mollusks in what he termed the Rathbunville School Limestone member near the top of the carbonate succession. Flower regarded these cephalopods as Lower Ordovician.

Purpose.—This stop demonstrates: 1) that the Rathbunville School Limestone in the upper Little Falls Formation is one of the three presently known localities for Late Cambrian cephalopods, and 2) that the Cambrian–Ordovician (Little Falls–Tribes Hill) boundary interval hiatus is somewhat shorter in the Lake Champlain lowlands than in the Mohawk valley. The stop will focus on the prominent ledge of thin Rathbunville School Limestone (0.6 m) near the top of the succession.

Stratigraphic succession.—Landing *et alii*'s (2003a) section at Steves Farm is a carbonate-dominated, 85 m-thick succession (Figure 6). The section was measured from the pasture 0.5 km west of Upper Turnpike through gently east-dipping strata on the wooded north side of the 108 m (360 foot) hill at Stop 2.3. The rock immediately south of the trailer is a massive white lime mudstone with lenses of high energy ooid grainstone and intraclast pebble-ooid grainstone and silicified gastropod conchs and black chert. This is the 40–59 m interval of the measured section. This limestone apparently corresponds to Flower's (1964) "Steves Farm Limestone" member of the Little Falls Formation (="Whitehall Formation," latter designation abandoned).

Rathbunville School Limestone.—The Rathbunville School Limestone forms a second 0.6 m-thick, massive white limestone with rare cephalopods, snails, orthoid brachiopods, and unidentifiable trilobite fragments, and is the highest limestone bed on the northern slope of the hill. This second limestone is Flower's (1964) Rathbunville School Limestone.

Cephalopods and conodont biostratigraphy.—Fossils are rare in the Rathbunville School Limestone, but we (BK and EL) have been able to find a few closely septate conch fragments. These specimens are Upper Cambrian specimens of the Plectronocerida or Ellesmerocerida. What is interesting about these specimens is that the only previously described Upper Cambrian cephalopods from Laurentia are quite different in conch form. These earlier described cephalopods come from a slightly older interval (*Clavohamulus elongatus* Subzone of the *Cordylodus proavus* Zone) of the upper San Saba Limestone at Threadgill Creek, central Texas (Flower, 1964, p. 53, 54; Miller *et al.*, 1982, fig. 5), and are of the same age as the Upper Cambrian cephalopods from the Wanjiawan Formation on the South China Platform.

Following a 13 m-thick covered interval, fine-grained, buff-weathering, dolomitic sandstone of the lowest Tribes Hill Formation (Sprakers Member) appears as float near the hill crest.

The restricted marine, mollusk-rich, trilobite-poor Little Falls Formation at this section yields low diversity conodont faunas. The interval from the "Steves Farm" through Rathbunville School Limestones is referable to the uppermost Cambrian

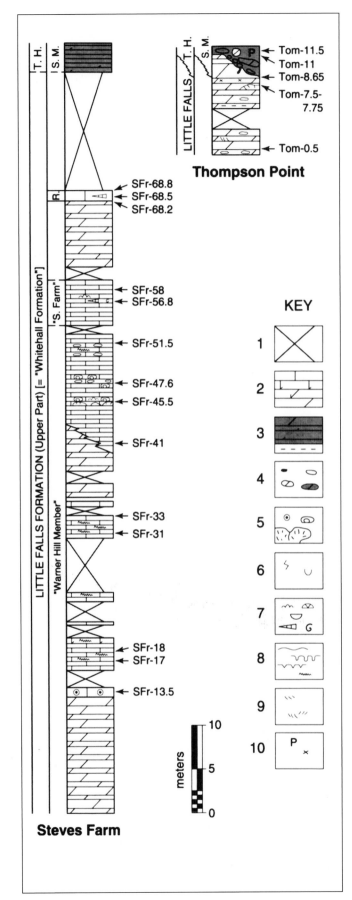

FIGURE 6—Cambrian–Ordovician boundary interval at Stop 2.4 (Steves Farm); coeval, short section at Thompson Point, Vermont, ca. 80 km to the north on the east side of Lake Champlain, demonstrates that the systemic boundary is a type-1 sequence boundary in the New York Promontory region. Sample horizons to right of stratigraphic column in meters above base of section (e.g., SFr-68.8 and Tom-11). KEY: 1, cover; 2, light gray limestone, light gray dolomitic limestone, medium gray calcareous dolostone, medium gray dolostone (from top to bottom of figure, respectively); 3, medium gray sandy dolostone, medium gray dolomitic sandstone, medium gray silt-shale (from top to bottom of figure); 4, light gray chert clast, calcareous intraclast, medium gray dolomitic sandstone clast, and medium gray dolostone clast (clockwise from upper left); 5, ooids, SH-V stromatolite, thrombolite (clockwide from upper left); 6, burrow mottling (left) and *Arenicolites* (right); 7, trilobites (top row), brachiopods (middle), ellesmeroceratoids (lower left), and gastropods (lower right); 8, wave ripples, erosion surface, synaeresis cracks, stylolites (from top to bottom, respectively); 9, small-scale cross bedding (top) and trough cross beds (bottom); 10, reworked phosphate nodules (P) and calcite-filled vugs after anhydrite (x). From Landing *et al.* (2003a, fig. 3).

Clavohamulus elongatus through *C. hintzei* Subzones of the *Cordylodus proavus* Zone s.s. (Landing *et al.*, 2003b).

Regional and interregional correlations.—Use of the lowest occurrence of the conodont *Iapetognathus fluctivagus* Nicoll to define the base of the Ordovician globally (Webby, 1998; Cooper *et al.*, 2001) means that the top of the Little Falls Formation at Steves Farm and elsewhere in the Lake Champlain lowlands does not extend into the lowest Ordovician. Earlier reports that assigned trilobite faunas with *Missisquoia* from the lower Little Falls Formation to the Ordovician (Taylor and Halley, 1974) or used the "Ordovician aspect" of molluscan faunas from the "Steves Farm" and Rathbunville School Limestones (Flower, 1964; Fisher, 1984) are now superceded by this new global standard for the definition of the base of the Ordovician. The conodonts illustrate that the cephalopods from the "Steves Farm" and Rathbunville School Members are Upper Cambrian and among the oldest cephalopods known in North America.

Clavohamulus hintzei Subzone (top *Cordylodus proavus* Zone s.s.) conodonts from the Rathbunville Limestone and top of the Little Falls in the Lake Champlain lowlands (Landing *et al.*, 2003a) are younger than the *C. elongatus* Subzone (middle *C. proavus* Zone s.s.) at the top of the Little Falls in the Mohawk Valley (Landing et al., 1996). In the Mohawk Valley, Fisher and Mazzulo (1976) proposed a major hiatus between the Little Falls and Tribes Hill Formations. However, they equated the lower Tribes Hill with the "Steves Farm"–Rathbunville Members of the "Whitehall," and assigned this interval to the lowest Ordovician. However, these two latter correlations are now known to be incorrect. The new conodont-based data show that the top of the Little Falls is uppermost Cambrian across the New York Promontory and the sub-Tribes Hill hiatus shortens by only two conodont subchrons in the Champlain Lowlands (Landing et al., 2003a).

The eustatic rise equated with deposition of the Tribes Hill Formation is equated with the Schaghtocoke dysoxic/anoxic interval—the middle–upper lower Tremadocian macroscale black mudstone-limestone alternation in the Taconian allochthons of New York and Québec (Stop 6.9).

Travel to Stop 2.5

At end of Stop 2.4, continue south (bear right) on Upper Turnpike for 1.7 miles; turn right (southwest) and follow Thomas Road (dirt and narrow) for 1.3 miles. At T-intersection with Rte 22, turn right (west) onto Rte 22; pass road cuts in Rochdale Formation [="Fort Ann Formation," designation abandoned, of many earlier reports; see Landing and Westrop, 2006] 1.7 miles after intersection. Slow vehicle at Mags Greenhouse on left (south) (a further 0.2 miles). After another 0.1 mile, park on left side of Rte 22 at dirt pull-off to observe top of road cut on north side of road.

Stop 2.5, Cambrian–Ordovician boundary near Comstock (10 minutes)

This is probably the most photogenic and easily accessible locality that shows the Cambrian–Ordovician boundary interval unconformity in the Lake Champlain lowlands.

Comstock section.—Landing *et al.* (2003a, fig. 4) began their Comstock section in the gently east-dipping, uppermost dolostones of the Little Falls Formation in this road cut. They measured a section through the Tribes Hill Formation that begins in the deeply weathered dolomitic, fine-grained sandstones that overlie the Little Falls, continues along the shallow stream at the east end of the cut, crosses a long covered interval to the east in the pastures on the Scalaro farm, and then climbs the west slope of the 132 m (440 foot) hill to the ridge crest. Their section ends at the Tribes Hill–"Fort Ann" (now Rochdale Formation) interformational unconformity (a type 1 sequence boundary that marks the upper lower–upper Tremadocian boundary and records a strong eustatic fall–rise couplet) immediately east of the 132 m ridge crest.

Cambrian–Ordovician sequence boundary and lowest Ordovician.—This roadcut on Rte 22 begins at the east border of Comstock village and exposes ca. 20 m of medium- to massively-bedded, gently-dipping (10° E), upper Little Falls Formation (="Whitehall") dolostone. In 1998, these sucrosic, locally evaporitic (note gypsum molds) dolostones were sharply overlain by a 30 cm bed of fine- to medium-bedded, brown-weathering, current cross-bedded, dolomitic sandstone of the basal Tribes Hill Formation (="Cutting/Great Meadows Formation," latter designations abandoned) at the east end of the cut. Almost all of this dolomitic sandstone bed was collected as a conodont sample.

This dolomitic sandstone-facies (Sprakers Member, ="Winchell Creek Siltstone," latter abandoned designation) is present as float immediately above the exposed Little Falls, crops out in the shallow creek above the road cut, and apparently continues east under the covered interval in the pasture behind the Scalero family farmhouse. This Sprakers Member facies re-appears at the foot of the ridge on the west side of the pasture at the base of the 132 m ridge, where it is overlain by ca. 1.5 m of gray siltstone with a middle storm-deposited sandtsone (Van Wie Member). Thicker-bedded, increasingly dolomitic sandstones continue upward to a cliff with several horizons of

spectacular thrombolites with echinoderm grain- and packstone inter-head matrix (Wolf Hollow Member; = "Kingsbury Limestone" of Fisher, 1984). Higher locally oolitic and overlying structureless (i.e., burrow-homogenized) white limestone (Canyon Road Member; = "Fort Edward" + "Smith Basin" Members of Fisher [1977] and Flower [1968b]) extend to the top of the Tribes Hill. The top of the Tribes Hill Formation forms the crest of the 132 m (440 foot) hill, and has a paleokarst surface with 30 cm of relief overlain infilled by arenaceous dolostone of the "Fort Ann Formation."

Biostratigraphy.—Conodonts from the Tribes Hill Formation comprise a low diversity, restricted marine assemblage that persists unchanged through the formation. This *Rossodus manitouensis* Zone assemblage is referable to the lowest Ordovician (upper lower Tremadocian-equivalent), and shares no taxa either with the underlying Little Falls Formation or the overlying Rochdale Formation ("Fort Ann Formation"). The total replacement of the Upper Cambrian, upper *Cordylodus proavus* Zone fauna of the top Little Falls Dolostone at the base of the Tribes Hill reflects the duration of the trans-Laurentian Cambrian–Ordovician boundary hiatus on the east Laurentian shelf. Similarly, the total replacement of the Tribes Hill Formation conodonts by Fauna D conodonts at the base of the Rochdale ("Fort Ann Formation") reflects the duration of the trans-Laurentian, intra-Lower Ordovician hiatus that occurs in the upper lower–upper Tremadocian boundary interval.

Travel to Stop 2.6

Comstock–Ticonderoga village.—At end of stop, drive west on Rte 22 through Comstock village and past forbidding grounds of Great Meadows Correctional Facility, a maximum security state prison. At T-intersection with Rte. 4, turn right (north) on Rte. 4 and 22 (combined), and re-trace route to Whitehall village. At traffic light in Whitehall, continue straight (north) on Rte. 22 to Ticonderoga village (26 miles). Most outcrops along this section of road are in middle Proterozoic gneisses.

At 6.4 miles, the Lake Champlain lowland to the east (right) is developed on Cambrian–Ordovician sedimentary rocks, and the far skyline to the east is uplifted middle Proterozoic gneisses of the Green Mountains in central Vermont. Lake George and Lake Champlain lie north of the low divide that separates the Hudson River drainage into the New York bight (to the south) from the St. Lawrence drainage (to the north).

At 22.6 miles, descend hill to Ticonderoga village; re-enter Cambrian–Ordovician lowland immediately east of Adirondack massif, and travel along west shore of Lake Champlain; note white cliffs of Cambrian (Little Falls Formation) on east side of lake; pass roadcuts in whitish, middle Proterozoic marble on west side of road. Cross river (25.1 miles), note outcrops of whitish Potsdam Sandstone. At blinking light on east side of Ticonderoga, continue north on combined Rte. 22 and 74.

Ticonderoga–Northway.—At light (26.8 miles) continue straight (north) on Rte. 74 west, and follow Rte. 74 west through the Adirondacks to the intersection with the Northway (Interstate 87). Pass Eagle Lake, an elongate lake which is defined by the less-prominent (roughly E–W) faults formed during the Ediacaran rifting in the middle Proterozoic rocks of the Adirondack massif.

The most spectacular mountain scenery in the Adirondacks

is at about mileage post 112, where the High Peaks (Presidential Range) of the Adirondack Mountains are visible to the left (west) of the Northway. If time and weather permit, a very brief photographic stop will be made. At about milepost 121, the Northway begins a long, gentle descent out of the Adirondacks.

Northway–Ausable Chasm.—At milepost 138.5, take Exit 34 to village of Keesville. Follow road signs for Rte. 9 north, and follow road through Keesville; outcrops along Ausable river to right (east) of road are in gently dipping Keesville Member of upper Potsdam Formation. About a mile north of Keesville, cross high bridge over Ausable Chasm. At 0.5 miles north of bridge turn right (east) onto Rte. 373. Follow Rte. 373 a short distance to sign marking entrance to Ausable Chasm. Follow descending road through picnic and camping area; park close to foot bridge over Ausable River and concrete hydroelectric dam. Visits to the sandstones below the dam must be coordinated with the local utility company (NYSEG).

Stop 2.6, Trace fossils and medusae from the upper Potsdam Formation, Ausable Chasm (20 minutes)

Prospectus.—Three items are of interest at this section (Figure 7): 1) scyphomedusae impressions, 2) siliciclastic microbial structures, and 3) a low-diversity suite of trace fossils. All of these features have low relief, and many are submerged or partially submerged with high spillway discharge. Thus, although most of these features have likely been exposed at this locality for over a century (Walcott, 1891b; Van Ingen, 1902), they probably were not recognized until recently because they are difficult to see except on dry surfaces illuminated with low-angle direct sunlight.

Geologic setting.—Strata exposed in the upper 50 m of the section at Ausable Chasm represent either the Keeseville or Ausable Member of the Potsdam Formation. Beds above the falls and below the spillway are dominated by planar laminated to rippled, thin-bedded, medium-grained orthoquartzites with rare mudstone, and likely represent a suite of shallow subtidal to emergent sand flat facies (Figure 7). It is only in these very shallow to emergent facies that the scyphomedusae and microbial structures are found. The large horizontal trackways *Climactichnites* and *Protichnites* also appear restricted to such facies (MacNaughton *et al.*, 2003; Hoxie and Hagadorn, 2005; Getty and Hagadorn, 2006). Locally, hummocky cross-stratification, and polygonally-cracked mudstones are present.

Taphonomy of medusae.—Fossil medusae, such as those at Ausable, are extremely rare, and soft-bodied preservation in

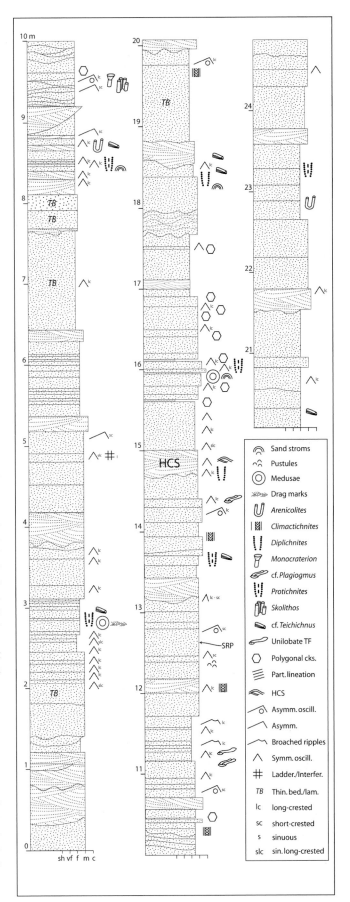

FIGURE 7—Composite measured section from the upper sandstone facies at Ausable Chasm. Section compiled from two sections measured on the east and west sides of the Ausable River between the spillway (Birmingham Fall) and Rainbow Falls. Medusae horizons at 2.85 and 15.85 m. Note the clustering of emergence indicators near these fossils, the overall paucity of mud in the section, and proximity of HCS and plane-laminated beds to the medusae-bearing horizon at 15.85 m. A near-permanent section reference point (SRP, arrowed) is at 12.6 m, where a large metal eyelet is anchored in the rock face on the east side of the chasm. Ripple types indicated in bottom half of legend.

general is rare in Phanerozoic sandstones (Seilacher *et al.* 1985; Seilacher and Pflüger, 1994). Thus, although the medusae at this locality are not well preserved and do not tell us much about the biology of pelagic Cambrian cnidarians, they are nonetheless important. They represent one of only two known jellyfish stranding deposits in the fossil record, and provide some basic information about the geographic and size distribution and community structure of Cambrian pelagic predators (Hagadorn and Belt, in press). The simple fact that gelatinous bags of "goo" can be fossilized in a relatively high-energy sandstone facies provides insights into the exceptional preservation of Late Cambrian intertidal to supratidal settings (Young and Hagadorn, in review). This preservation probably stems from the low levels of bioturbation and an abundance of microbial binding.

Although there are abundant discoidal structures preserved in the rock record and elsewhere in the Potsdam Sandstone (Kavanagh, 1888–1889; Hawley and Hart, 1934; Dietrich, 1953), the vast majority of these do not represent cnidarian medusae—rather, they represent inorganic, archeological, microbial, or other fossil structures (e.g., Jensen *et al.*, 2002; Mayoral *et al.*, 2004). Even in deposits that contain tens of thousands of medusae, most medusae rarely preserve sufficient anatomical detail to identify them to ordinal or lower levels (e.g., Hagadorn *et al.*, 2003).

However, there are four key criteria for the recognition of true medusae among this morass of "medusoids":

1) True medusae always display evidence of transport and deformation, because they are essentially hydrous clasts. Thus they are typically folded, twisted, torn, and/or tangled before, during, and/or after they come to lie on the substrate—processes that cause such deformation are also prevalent during deposition of the layers that bury medusae carcasses (Figure 8.2, 8.3).

2) True medusae often occur in great abundance (Figure 8.1) and on multiple bedding planes within similar depositional environments—rarely are they preserved only on one bedding plane.

3) Medusae always exhibit evidence of synoptic relief, even in low-energy deposits, where overlying burial layers and primary structures such as ripples deform around carcasses.

4) Medusae, if stranded, will often display evidence of desiccation and/or rehydration, and if stranded alive, will exhibit excavated moat-like rings around their periphery. These rings are formed by contractions of the bell as the medusae attempt to escape stranding during receding waters. As a result, most true medusae fossils are rarely radially symmetrical or preserved only at one bed interface. They typically have irregular outlines, are preserved in great abundance, may be concentrated into jelly-fish-"conglomerates" in deeper portions of topographic lows (e.g., abandoned tidal channels and pools), are often flipped over (e.g., subumbrella-up), and are sometimes associated with trace fossils made by predepostional dragging of medusae carcasses across bedding surfaces.

Medusae at Ausable dam.—The Potsdam medusae exhibit most of the features listed above (Figure 8), and occur on two horizons in the chasm (Figure 7). The lower horizon is only well exposed when water levels are low, and we will focus our attention on the upper surface on this field trip. This horizon bears

over a hundred medusae, over half of which were stranded while alive, and many others that were twisted and concentrated in a lag after death. The Potsdam medusae exhibit similar size ranges and morphologic and taphonomic characteristics as those from the Late Cambrian Elk Mound Group in Wisconsin (Hagadorn *et al.*, 2002; Hagadorn and Belt, in press), and show anatomical features that are known from extant scyphomedusae.

Microbial structures.—Siliciclastic microbial structures visible at Ausable include domal sand buildups [i.e., sand stromatolites (Figure 8.4); Hilowle *et al.*, 2000), sand shadow structures (York *et al.*, 2004), and breached ripples (Hagadorn and Belt, in press). On the upper medusae-bearing surface, the sand stromatolites mantle many of the medusae carcasses, including the escape troughs that rim some of the medusae impressions. This suggests that these surfaces were microbially bound after deposition and decay of the medusae bells. It is unknown what erosional resistance such mantling may have conferred, or if/how it mediated preservation of the medusae in this environment. However, it is worth noting that the medusae are overlain by plane-bed laminated sands. Sand shadow structures look like miniature drumlins on bedding planes, and are thought to form where sand accretes in the leeward margin of pustules or sand stromatolites. Sand may accumulate in downwind or downflow locations, and we know that the cores of these sand shadows were soft at the time of deposition (i.e., and thus do not represent shadows forming in the lee of concretions or nodules) because they are cross-cut by surface trackways. Sand shadows are not visible *in situ* in the spillway area at Ausable, but have been found on float blocks that spalled from the sides of the spillway and on *in situ* bedding planes lower in the section near the Ausable Chasm Resort boathouse. One of the most perplexing siliciclastic microbial structures at this stop are breached ripples—in which the surfaces of oscillation ripples have been eroded and undercut by post-rippling erosive events, and in which the cores of the ripples appear to have had less erosional resistance than their surface veneers. Could this reflect microbial mantling of these rippled surfaces, akin to the palimpsest ripples of Pflüger (1999) and Seilacher (1999)?

Trace fossils.—Trace fossils at this site are dominated by horizontally-oriented forms, such as the probable mollusk trails *Aulichnites* and *Climactichnites*, the arthropod trackways *Diplichnites* and *Protichnites*, and a burrow compared to *Teichichnus*. A few shallow, vertically oriented trace fossils, such as *Arenicolites* and *Skolithos*, are present. Many of the best exposures of the large traces are immediately below the spillway or on bedding planes that are not exposed except during low water. An exceptional specimen of *Protichnites* is on display in the Ausable Chasm Resort entrance. This slab was collected about 100–200 m lower in the section near the Ausable Resort boathouse, and is remarkable because it is not an undertrack, yet preserves the delicate bifid telson impressions of the trackmaker.

At end of Stop 2.6, retrace route to Rte. 9. Turn right (north) on Rte. 9, and continue to the State University of New York College at Plattsburgh campus.

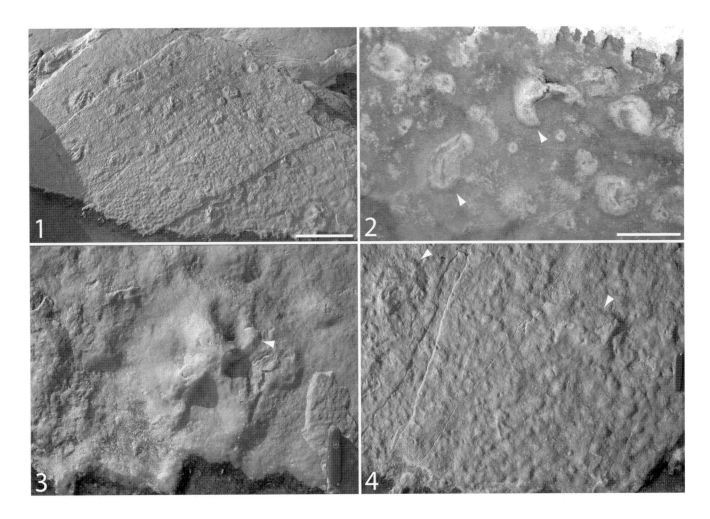

FIGURE 8—Field photographs of a portion of bedding surface at 15.85 m in the section below the dam on the Ausable River. *1,* Variety of small and large stranded medusae; note cluster of sand stromatolites at lower right and center of image. Many of these specimens exhibit the hallmark feature of scyphomedusae that were stranded while alive — a moat-like ring surrounding a central mound. A significant portion of this surface is submerged year-round due to groundwater that percolates through fractures in the rock; this portion of the surface is partially visible at the base of *1. 2,* Polarized light photograph of a portion of the submerged portion of this surface shows a concentration of medusae, some of which overlap one another, and many which exhibit folding (lower arrowhead) and twisting (upper arrowhead) of carcasses. *3,* Some medusae exhibit quasi-quadripartate symmetry, and often the distal radial lobes became twisted as the elevated central portion of the medusa bell rotated. The specimen here has been twisted clockwise, and one deformed lobe has been arrowed. *4,* Domal sand buildups or sand stromatolites, many of which mantle the margins of medusae (arrowheads). All specimens were photographed in low angle light emanating from the left or upper left. Scale bar in *1* is 50 cm; in *2,* 20 cm. Swiss army knife in *3* and *4* is 8.3 cm long.

AUGUST 1: ORAL AND POSTER PRESENTATIONS. KEY NOTE ADDRESS "REVIEW OF THE TIMING AND CONSTRAINTS ON THE NEOPROTEROZOIC–CAMBRIAN RECORD OF METAZOAN EVOLUTION" BY S. A. BOWRING (SEE ABSTRACTS, THIS VOLUME)

AUGUST 2: MIDDLE–UPPER CAMBRIAN SILICICLASTIC COVER OF THE NORTHWESTERN ADIRONDACK MOUNTAIN MASSIF, CLINTON COUNTY, NEW YORK

Overview

Today's stops emphasize new work on Cambrian stratigraphy and trace fossils of northeastern New York. The Potsdam Formation has long been regarded as the oldest Cambrian unit that overlies the middle Proterozoic rocks of the Grenvillian orogen in northwest New York and adjacent Ontario and Quebec. However, a poorly exposed, marine-deposited unit dominated by red silt shales and fine-grained sandstones with fossiliferous dolostones and marine trace fossils has now been recognized. This new unit, which underlies the Potsdam Formation, is tentatively designated the "Altona Formation," with the proviso that formations cannot be named in field trip guides or comparable reports and that formal proposal will require subsequent description in a peer-reviewed publication (North American Commission on Stratigraphic Nomenclature, 1983). The contacts of the "Altona Formation" with the underlying middle Proterozoic gneisses and Ediacaran–earliest Cambrian(?) mafic dikes and with the overlying feldspathic and current cross-bedded, lower Potsdam Formation (Ausable Member) will be demonstrated. Onlap of the "Altona Formation" during the latest Early–earliest Middle(?) Cambrian and the great thickness of the Potsdam Formation in Clinton County may have been related to the down-to-basin faulting close to the Ottawa aulocogen that produced the parautochthonous Franklin Basin in northwestern Vermont (Landing, preceding report, this volume; stops on August 3). On-going work on the upper (Keesville) member of the Potsdam shows that this shallow wave-dominated interval has an unexpectedly wide variety of facies-specific trace fossils at numerous localities. Excellent opportunities for study of Keesville lithologies and ichnofossils are possible in this region on the northeast flank of the Adirondack massif because of the extensive pavements of Potsdam bedding surfaces exposed in the "Flat Rocks" terrane of Clinton County (Figure 9).

Travel to Stop 3.1

The trip begins at the north parking lot at Hudson Hall on the SUNY Plattsburgh campus. Leave the parking lot and turn right (west) on Broad St.; travel for for 0.3 mi; continue through the Draper Avenue Intersection to Prospect Street. Turn right (north) onto Prospect Street, and proceed for 0.7 mi through the traffic light at Cornelia Street (0.09 mi) to the intersection with Tom Miller Road. Turn left (west) onto Tom Miller Road and proceed across the Northway (I-87) overpass. Continue west on Tom Miller Road for 2.5 mi through the traffic lights at Quarry Road, the entrance to the Champlain Center Mall and Smithfield Boulevard. Turn right onto Military Turnpike (Rte 190) and proceed northwest for 7.3 mi through the intersection with the Cadyville Expressway (Rte. 374) at 1.0 mi to Stop3.1. Military Turnpike crosses the Champlain border fault about 5.8 mi north-

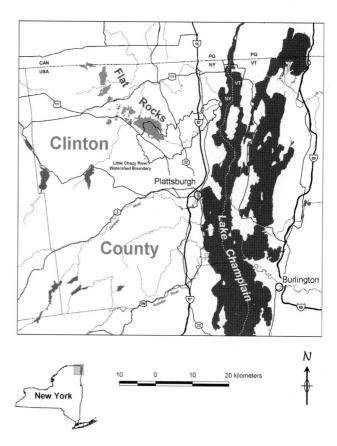

FIGURE 9—Map of Clinton County, New York, showing the locations of sandstone pavements, or Flat Rocks, and the drainage basin boundary of the Little Chazy River. Boundaries of the Flat Rock pavements are from Denny (1974).

west of the Cadyville Expressway, and rises over the fault-line scarp that forms the western margin of the Champlain Lowland. Stop 3.1 lies near the top of this fault-line scarp.

Stop 3.1, Rand Hill Dike Swarm

Late Proterozoic igneous and metamorphic rocks are exposed along both sides of Military Turnpike just southeast of the Murtagh Hill Road intersection. These rocks consist of gabbroic meta-anorthosite that is intruded by diabase, olivine-diabase, and trachyte porphyry dikes. The dikes comprise the Rand Hill dike swarm, one of the largest concentrations of dikes in the Adirondack region (Cushing, 1898; Hudson and Cushing, 1931; Isachsen *et al.*, 1988). The dikes range in width from a few decimeters to more than 5 m, and some can be traced laterally for more than 150 m (Isachsen *et al.*, 1988). The diabase dikes in this region do not cut the overlying clastic sedimentary rocks (Kemp and Marsters, 1893; Cushing, 1898), and several dates from the Rand Hill swarm range from 588 Ma to 542 Ma (Isachsen *et al.*, 1988). These early dates obviously provide a maximum age for the overlying "Altona Formation" and Potsdam Sandstone, and suggest that extension of the middle Proterozoic Adirondack basement and dike emplacement on the southwest margin of the Ottawa aulocogen extended into the earliest Cambrian.

Travel to Stop 3.2

Return to the vans, and continue northwest for 0.6 mi to Stop 3.2. Please pull the vehicles as far off the road as possible, and exercise caution when walking along the roadside. Military Turnpike is a very busy thoroughfare, and the shoulders of the road are very narrow at this location.

Stop 3.2, Middle Proterozoic–Cambrian nonconformity (15 minutes)

The "Altona Formation" is exposed in the drainage ditch on the southwest side of Military Turnpike. Wiesnet (1961) described the unit exposed at this location as a red shale and silt-stone lithofacies, whereas Fisher (1968) referred to the unit as the basal member of the Potsdam Formation and suggested a corre-lation with the so-called Allens Falls (Krynine, 1948) or Nicholville (Postel *et al.*, 1959) Formations. [Although named in the literature, an adequate description of either the Allens Falls or Nicholville Formations was never provided, and the litholo-gy, upper and lower contacts, and regional extent of these "units" were never described.] The "Altona Formation" crops out discontinuously along the northern flank of the Adirondack Upland, but is not found in the Plattsburgh and Rouses Point quadrangles of the northern Champlain Lowland to the east (see Fisher, 1968). The nonconformity is not exposed, and a ca. 3 m covered interval is present. The stop shows dark red to maroon (i.e., highly limonitic), dolomitic feldspathic sandstone and conglomerate in close proximity to the underlying Late Proterozoic meta-anorthosite near the base of the hill. Above the contact, the "Altona Formation" consists primarily of thin to medium bedded, red-brown to maroon dolomitic siltstone, sandstone and shale. Slabbing and formic acid-disaggregation of a large sample (ca. 6 kg) of dolomitic, limonitic feldspathic sandstone at this stop did not yield any evidence of trace or body fossils.

Travel to Stop 3.3

Return to the vans; continue northwest on Military Turnpike for 0.9 mi to Atwood Road. Turn right onto Atwood Road, and proceed 2.0 mi to Stop 3.3 at Atwood Farm. Atwood Road is an unimproved gravel road from Military Turnpike to a point near the Harvey Road intersection at 1.5 mi. Leave the vans at the entrance to a pasture on Atwood Farm, and walk to four small outcrops of the "Altona Formation" on the banks and in the bed the Little Chazy River. The vans will follow the road log to the last of the Atwood Farm outcrops and meet the group at that location.

Walk approximately 350 m north along a farm road to a small, east-flowing brook. Follow the brook downstream (about 70 m) to the Little Chazy River. The walking is easier in the field on the north side of the brook, but stay on the edge of the field to avoid damaging the crops.The first outcrop of the "Altona Formation" occurs about 20 meters upstream on the Little Chazy River.

Stop 3.3, "Altona Formation" at Atwood Farm (60 minutes)

The "Altona Formation" at the first outcrop location (Figure 10) consists primarily of maroon shale and fine-grained sand-stone with occasional thin (< 10 cm thick), dolomitic sandstone interbeds. A massive, pinkish weathering, light purple, dolomitic sandstone bed occurs below stream level. Large slabs

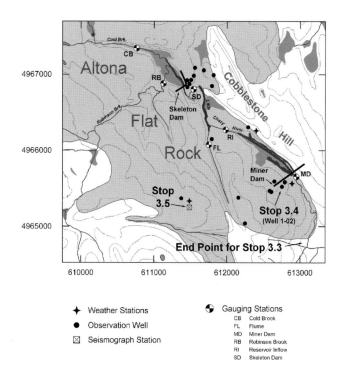

Figure 10—Map of the southeastern portion of Altona Flat Rock, showing the locations of Stops 3.3–3.5. Also shown: observation wells, stream-gauging stations, and weather stations that are part of the Little Chazy River hydrogeolog-ical research instrumentation network.

of this bed show show dewatering structures and dolomitic ghosts of highly abraded fossil fragments. However, no acid-resistant microfossils were recovered.

A second exposure approximately 130 m upstream is in medium-bedded (0.1–1.0 m thick) dark red-brown shale, dolomitic siltstone and sandstone, and dolostone. Mud or synaeresis cracks are present in the thin, fine-grained sandstone beds. A >1-m thick, yellowish gray to locally pink dolostone bed occurs at stream level, and caps a small waterfall at the down-stream end of the exposure. Slabs from the top of the dolostone show large intrastratal burrows and ghosts of brachiopod shells. Newly discovered trilobites (*Ehmaniella*) at the top of the expo-sure are early-middle Middle Cambrian.

Continue upstream along the Little Chazy River, first north-west, then west for approximately 730 m to a third outcrop. Small outcrops of the "Altona Formation" can be seen along the way. Dark red-brown, thin-bedded sandstone with shale and siltstone interbeds is exposed in a small stream cut on the south bank on the river. During a reconnaissance of this section, a small slab with poorly preserved specimens of *Cruziana* and *Rusophycus* that occur immediately under a dessication-cracked surface was collected. This location lies at the southeastern mar-gin of Altona Flat Rock (from which "Altona Formation" is derived), and is the highest occurrence of red-brown shale observed along the river.

Leave the river and follow the marked trail northward about 150 m from this location to the ruins of a hydroelectric power station built between 1910 and 1913 by the local millionaire-philanthropist William H. Miner. The power station was fed by a penstock from a dam located approximately 850 m upstream. The penstock trench exposes transitional facies that consist of thin- to medium-bedded sandstone, siltstone and shale between the "Altona Formation" and the overlying Ausable Member (cross-bedded, feldspathic sandstones) of the Potsdam Formation. Meet the vans at this location.

Travel to Stop 3.4

The following directions are for the van drivers who will pick up the field trip participants at the end of Stop 3.3 (Figure 10): Continue east for 1 mile on Atwood Road after the passengers disembark at Stop 3.3. Atwood Road ends at the intersection with Recore Road and West Church Street. Proceed east on West Church Street for 0.1 mi and turn left (north) on Barnaby Road. Barnaby Road ends in 1.0 mi, but the road continues north as Blaine Road, a seasonal gravel-surface road. Follow Blaine Road for 1.1 mi to the gate at the entrance to the Miner Institute property at Altona Flat Rock.

Proceed through the gate; follow the unnamed gravel access road for about 0.6 mi up the flank of Cobblestone Hill. At 0.05 mi, the road curves sharply left to a forked intersection with another gravel road about 0.1 mi from the gate. Low roadside excavations near this intersection expose cobble-gravel beach ridges that were deposited in proglacial Lake Fort Ann about 13,000 calendar years ago. Continue straight (left fork) over the crest of Cobblestone Hill to the bridge that crosses the Little Chazy River. Near the crest of the ridge, angular, 0.3 to 1.2 m diameter boulders that comprise the core of Cobblestone Hill can be observed at the surface. The remains of the "Million-Dollar Dam" can be seen to the right just southwest of the hill crest. Across the river, the road rises onto the exposed sandstone surface of Altona Flat Rock. Turn left a short distance past the bridge, and follow a small jeep trail south about 0.5 mi to the ruins of the former hydroelectric generating station to meet the group traveling up the Little Chazy River from Atwood Farm and Stop 3.3.

Return to the vehicles; follow the jeep trail 0.5 mi back to the access road near the Million-Dollar Dam. Turn left onto the access road; proceed west for about 0.4 mi to the groundwater observation well at Stop 3.4 (Figure 10).

Stop 3.4, Observation Well at Altona Flat Rock (20 minutes)

Altona Flat Rock setting.—The "Flat Rocks" in Clinton County are a discontinuous belt of exposed sandstone surfaces or "pavements" on the Potsdam Formation that were created by late-glacial breakout floods and lake outflow from Lake Iroquois and younger post-Iroquois proglacial lakes in the St. Lawrence and Ontario lowlands (Chapman, 1937; Denny, 1974; Clark and Karrow, 1984; Pair *et al.*, 1988; Pair and Rodrigues, 1993; Franzi *et al.*, 2002; Rayburn *et al.*, 2005) (Figure 9). The Lake Iroquois breakout originated at the international border near Covey Hill and released approximately 570 km³ of water stored in the Iroquois basin (Franzi *et al.*, 2002; Rayburn *et al.*, 2005). The flood water flowed southeast between the northeast flank of the Adirondack foothills and the receding ice margin before emptying into proglacial Lake Vermont in the Champlain Lowland. Flood discharge probably exceeded 90,000 m³/s (Rayburn *et al.*, 2005). The flow stripped the pavements of their surficial cover,

and cut deep bedrock channels and plunge pools into the Potsdam Formation sandstone. Large boulder bars were deposited on both sides of the flood channel where it entered Lake Vermont. The largest such bar, Cobblestone Hill, is an ice-contact deposit that marks the former ice margin at the time of the initial breakout. The date of the Iroquois breakout is bracketed by radiocarbon dates of approximately 13,400 and 12,800 calibrated years B.P. (Rayburn *et al.*, 2006). Cosmogenic ¹⁰Be dates from boulders on Cobblestone Hill and an exposed sandstone surface yielded slightly younger ages ranging from about 9,460 to 11,040 years B.P. (Rayburn *et al.*, 2007).

The sandstone pavements are nutrient-limited, drought-prone environments that are predominantly covered by low-diversity pine barren communities (Franzi and Adams, 1993; 1999). Jack pine (*Pinus banksiana*) dominates most of the sandstone barrens in the region, but other species including white pine (*P. strobis*), pitch pine (*P. rigida*), and red pine (*P. resinosa*) are common in areas where environmental conditions are less extreme. Sandstone pavement, jack pine barrens are globally rare, open-canopy woodlands on very shallow soils that develop on nearly level sandstone bedrock (Reschke, 1990). Jack pine is a relatively short-lived (<150 years), shade-intolerant, boreal species that maintains communities on the sandstone pavements because of its adaptations to fire and ability to survive in an area with thin (or absent), nutrient-poor soils (Franzi and Adams, 1999). Northern New York lies near the southern limit of the modern range of jack pine. Pine barrens are island ecosystems whose boundaries transition abruptly to northern hardwood and mixed hardwood-conifer forests at the margins of the pavement areas. A typical barren is dominated by a single tree species, jack pine, with virtually no subcanopy and few understory trees. Understory shrubs in the barrens are predominantly late low blueberry (*Vaccinium angustifolium*), black huckleberry (*Gaylussacia baccata*), black chokeberry (*Pyrus melanocarpa*), sweetfern (*Comptonia peregrina*), and sheep laurel (*Kalmia angustifolia*). Three species of lichen comprise most of the ground cover (*Cladonia uncialis, Cladina rangiferina,* and *Cladina mitis*). Other ground cover plants include haircap moss (*Polytrichum commune*), bracken fern (*Pteridium aquilinum*), and *Sphagnum* spp. (Stergas and Adams, 1989). Jack pine requires periodic crown fires for successful regeneration to occur (Ahlgren and Ahlgren, 1960; Cayford, 1971; Rowe and Scotter, 1973; Cayford and McRae, 1983; Rouse, 1986). Fire releases seeds from serotinous cones stored in the jack pine canopy, prepares a nutrient-rich ash seedbed, and reduces competition for the young seedlings. Fire is also an important environmental factor for many other plant species in the barren (Adams and Franzi, 1994).

The sandstone pavement jack pine barrens in northeastern New York are marginal communities in delicate equilibrium with existing hydrogeological and climatological conditions (Adams and Franzi, 1994; Franzi and Adams, 1999). The extensive ice storm that affected much of northern New York and New England in January 1998 severely damaged large portions of the pine barren, and left the future of this fragile ecosystem uncertain. In 1998, the Miner Institute contracted a logging company to complete a restoration cutting on approximately 60 ha of pine barren heavily damaged by the ice storm. The objectives were to reduce the hazardous fuel loadings to limit the risk of uncontrollable wildfires, and try to initiate regeneration of jack pine without fire.

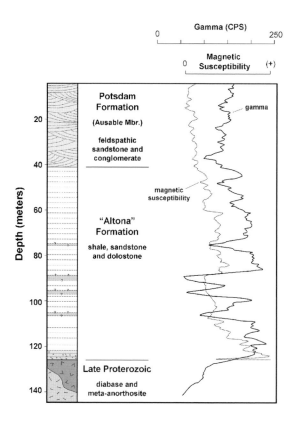

FIGURE 11—Borehole geophysical studies for Well 1-02 at Altona Flat Rock. Data courtesy of John Williams, U.S. Geological Survey, Water Resources Division, Troy, NY (adapted from from Williams et al., in review).

was never completed. The partially completed upstream dam was given the name "Skeleton Dam" because of its unfinished appearance (Dawson *et al.*, 1981). Mechanical problems at the generating station ultimately forced abandonment of the Flat Rock hydroelectric project after only seven years of intermittent use. Shortly after William Miner's death in 1930, a large hole was blasted at the base of the dam to allow the Little Chazy River to flow freely through the structure.

Miner Institute maintains its Altona Flat Rock land as a managed forest preserve that supports forestry, ecology and hydrogeology research. Twenty five 15-cm diameter observation wells, ranging in depth from about 10 to 142 m, were drilled near the abandoned hydroelectric dams on the southeastern portion of Altona Flat Rock as part of several hydrogeological research projects in the watershed.

Cambrian succession at Altona Flat Rock.—The deepest of the observation wells (Figure 11, Well 1-02) penetrated the following: 1) the lower Ausable Member of the Potsdam Formation, which forms the surface of Altona Flat Rock, 2) the entire thickness of the "Altona Formation," and 3) about 16 m into the underlying Late Proterozoic–earliest Cambrian(?) mafic dikes and gabbroic meta-anorthositic rocks (Figure 11, Table 1).

TABLE 1— Well 1-02 stratigraphy from drilling and borehole geophysical logs.

0–42 m,	Ausable Member, lower Potsdam Formation
42–126 m,	"Altona Formation"
126–135 m,	mafic dike
135–142 m,	meta-anorthosite

The Ausable Member ranges from feldspathic to subfeldspathic sandstone with lenses of conglomerate and interbeds of fine sandstone or shale and flat-pebble conglomerate (Wiesnet, 1961; Fisher, 1968). The eroded edges of truncated trough cross-beds, ripple marks, and solution pits are common minor bedding-plane features. The base of the Ausable Member is marked by a gradual increase in gamma radiation and magnetic susceptibility at approximately a 42 m depth in the borehole geophysical logs (Figure 11). From this point, the unit grades downward into the reddish brown or maroon, shale, siltstone and fine sandstone of the "Altona Formation." The first reddish brown well cuttings were observed at approximately 52 m in the drilling logs. Sharp decreases in gamma radiation at approximately 75, 88, 96, and 104 m and a general decrease in magnetic susceptibility in this depth range (Figure 11) may indicate the presence of dolostone interbeds, such as those observed in outcrops of the "Altona Formation" along the Little Chazy River at Atwood Farm (Stop 3.3), approximately 1.5 km downstream from Well 1-02. The nonconformity with underlying Late Proterozoic rocks at 126 m marks the base of the "Altona Formation." The total thickness of the "Altona Formation" at this location is approximately 84 meters.

Travel to Stop 3.5

Return to the vehicles and continue west on the access road. Bear left at the fork 0.31 mi from Well 1-02 and continue west

The William H. Miner Agricultural Research Institute owns more than 2,200 ha of forest land on and adjacent to Altona Flat Rock. The land was purchased in the early 1900s to provide protected drainage for hydroelectric power development. Construction of the hydroelectric dam (known locally as the Million-Dollar Dam) began in November 1910 (Gooley, 2005). When completed, the dam was more than 700 m long, had a maximum height of about 10 m, and had a storage capacity of approximately 3.5×10^6 m^3 (Figure 10). The gates were closed in March 1913, but the reservoir began leaking through the porous Cobblestone Hill boulder deposit, which forms much of the northeast slope of the reservoir basin. A slurry-trench wall was constructed at the base of Cobblestone Hill, and more than 16,000 m^3 of concrete grout was spread over 100,000 m^2 of the reservoir's northeast slope to mitigate against seepage losses (Gooley, 2005). Power generation finally began in January 1915, nearly two years after the dam was completed (Gooley, 2005; Dawson *et al.*, 1981), but the project was plagued by inadequate seasonal flow of the Little Chazy River and groundwater seepage through the grout or underlying sandstone. The Flat Rock generating station operated intermittently from 1915 to 1922 to supplement electric power generated by other stations in Chazy. Construction of a second dam approximately 2 km upstream from the Million-Dollar Dam was begun to provide a supplemental reservoir for the primary impoundment but this project toward Bear Hollow. The road follows the edge of a clear-cut that was made to reduce fuel-loading in the barren following a major ice storm in 1998. The mixed jack pine and pitch pine barren on the left side of the road shows the typical condition of an untreated pine barren after the storm. The clear-cut barren on the right shows some signs of regeneration, even with the exclusion of fire as a regenerative process.

Another observation well can be seen on the side of the road at 0.52 mi, after which the road crosses the Champlain Valley border fault-line trace, enters a wooded area underlain by late-glacial boulder gravel, and rises steeply up the fault-line scarp. The road bends north at the top of the fault-line scarp and enters another clear-cut area. The road crosses the terraced, cuesta-form edge of the Potsdam Formation for the next 0.3 mi. Flat-lying to very gently sloping road segments on bedding plane surfaces are punctuated by relatively steep rises where the road ascends to the next bedding surface. Wetlands of various sizes are interspersed throughout the barrens, especially in the locations where surface drainage or groundwater flow is controlled by bedrock structure and local hydrogeology (Franzi and Adams, 1999). Coles (1990) described "ledge bogs" as a wetland that forms at the base of terrace risers where soil depth is greater and water is more available. The road crosses an upland bog between 1.1 and 1.2 mi. Bogs and bog-like fens (poor fens) like this one are common on low-relief surfaces at Altona Flat Rock, with dominant plants including leatherleaf, tussock sedge, and blue-joint grass. Mature jack pines in this bog demonstrate the wide range of moisture conditions that this species can tolerate. Turn right onto a smaller trail just past the bog and proceed approximately 0.08 mi to Stop 3.5.

Stop 3.5, Altona Flat Rock overlook
(1 hour, includes lunch)

This location (Figure 10) lies near the crest of the upthrown fault block at the northern end of the Champlain border fault. Williams et al. (in review) estimate a fault-throw of about 60 m at this location based upon evidence from geophysical logs from nearby observation wells. Fault throw was considerably greater farther south where Late Proterozoic rocks of the Adirondack Uplands are exposed along a prominent fault-line scarp that forms the western boundary of the Champlain Lowland. The field instrumentation at this location includes a recording weather station that supports hydrogeological investigations in the Little Chazy River watershed and a broadband seismograph that is part of the LaMont-Doherty Cooperative Seismic Network (Scharnberger et al., 2006).

The view from this point overlooks the northern Champlain Lowland to the east and northeast and the St. Lawrence Lowland to the north. The city of Montreal, Quebec, and the Monteregian Hills (Mesozoic intrusions) of southern Quebec can be seen on the distant northern and northeastern horizons on a clear day. The Monteregian Hills are a roughly east–west trending series of alkaline igneous plutons, dikes, and sills that were emplaced between 240 and 90 Ma, coincident with the opening of the North Atlantic Ocean (Eby, 1987; see Landing, preceding report, this volume). Cobblestone Hill is the elongate ridge that forms the proximal horizon to the northeast. The hill is composed of coarse boulder gravel deposited against the ice front during the breakout of glacial Lake Iroquois about 13,000 years B.P. Two distinct baselevel controls are evident in the hill's

profile. Initial sedimentation was graded to the Coveville Phase of Lake Vermont in the Champlain Lowland, while later sedimentation was controlled by the lower Fort Ann Phase. Franzi et al. (2002) and Rayburn et al. (2005) suggested that propogation of the Lake Iroquois flood wave through the Champlain and Hudson lowlands breached the Coveville dam and was responsible for the drop to the Fort Ann lake level.

The remains of William Miner's Million-Dollar Dam can be seen in the near foreground. The unvegetated area is the "Scarpit," the concrete layer spread over the flank of Cobblestone Hill to mitigate against seepage losses from the impoundment upstream from the dam. A trench near the base of Cobblestone Hill marks the position of a grout curtain that was designed to prevent seepage under the boulder gravel.

Travel to Stop 3.6

Retrace the trip route back to Military Turnpike. Follow the access road approximately 1.8 mi back to the gate at the entrance to the Miner Institute property. Continue straight (bear slightly right) and follow Blaine Road 1.1 mi to Barnaby Road, and continue on Barnaby Road for 1.0 mi to West Church Street. Turn right on West Church Street and continue straight (right fork) onto Atwood Road at 0.1 mi. Follow Atwood Road for 4.1 mi to Military Turnpike. Note that Atwood Road is an unsurfaced gravel road for 1.5 mi from about Harvey Road to the Military Turnpike intersection. Turn right onto Military Turnpike and proceed northwest for 3.0 mi to the Rock Road intersection. Turn right onto Rock Road, and drive 2.2 mi north to Stop 3.6. The road crosses over the northwestern portion of Altona Flat Rock at about 1.1 mi north of the Military Turnpike intersection. The jack pine barren on this part of the sandstone pavement was damaged extensively during the great ice storm of January 1998.

Stop 3.6, Upper Potsdam Formation on Rock Road
(15 minutes)

Medium- to coarse-grained quartz arenite and subfeldspathic sandstone is exposed along the roadside at this location. These sedimentary rocks are compositionally more mature than the lower Ausable Member facies that form the pavement at Stops 3.4 and 3.5, but retain large-scale cross-bedding. These rocks may represent a transitional facies between the Ausable and Keeseville Members of the Potsdam Formation. Glacially polished surfaces and friction cracks can be observed on unweathered surfaces. The approximate exposure age of the surface from ^{10}Be dating of sandstone samples from this surface is 11,590 ± 190 yrs. B.P. (Rayburn et al., 2007).

Travel to Stop 3.7

Continue north on Rock Road for 0.5 miles to the intersection of Devil's Den Road. Proceed north (straight) on Devil's Den Road for 0.2 mi and turn left just past the bridge over the Great Chazy River into Feinberg Park.

Stop 3.7, Upper Potsdam Formation and trace fossils, Great Chazy River (30 minutes)

Setting.—The Keeseville Member of the Potsdam Formation can be observed along the Great Chazy River below LaSell Dam near Feinberg Park. This dam and the remains of the McGregor Powerhouse, approximately 360 m upstream, were part of two hydroelectric stations built by William Miner from 1921–1924.

The McGregor Powerhouse was fed by a 1.8 m-diameter pen-stock that originated at a dam on Miner Lake, approximately 1.6 km upstream on Ganienkah Territory. The interesting Spanish-mission-style powerhouse consists of six stories, the first three for plant operations and the upper three for apartments for the operators (Sullivan *et al.*, 1970). The power plant had an operating capacity of about 1,200 KW (Bell Hydropower, undated; Dawson *et al.*, 1981). The LaSell Powerhouse, constructed in the same Spanish style as the McGregor Powerhouse, was located approximately 3.6 km downstream. The LaSell Powerhouse had a generating capacity of 2,400 KW, twice that of the McGregor Plant (Bell Hydropower, undated; Dawson *et al.*, 1981). Power generation at these sites ceased around 1961.

Geology.—The Keeseville Member consists primarily of thin- to medium-bedded, medium- to fine-grained, quartz arenite and siltstone with lesser amounts of subarkose. Sedimentary structures typical of distal intertidal or proximal shelf environments include horizontal and ripple laminations, oscillation ripples, and hummocky cross stratification. Trace fossils will be seen at this location.

Travel to Stop 3.8

Leave Feinberg Park; turn left and continue north on Devil's Den Road for 1.0 mi through the village of Altona. Turn left onto Irona Road; proceed west 2.6 mi to the Alder Bend Road intersection. Irona Road crosses several small sandstone pavements northwest of Altona, and several low-relief exposures of the Potsdam Formation can be seen on both sides of the road. A 4 to 5 m-high exposure of thin- to medium-bedded sandstone occurs where the road crosses Park Brook in Irona. Turn right on Alder Bend Road and proceed north 1.3 mi to Rte. 11. Turn left on Rte. 11; proceed west 1.7 mi to the Cannon Corners Road. Turn right, and proceed north 2.3 mi to the entrance of the Gadway Pine Barren. Turn left onto the gravel access road, and drive 0.3 mi to where the gravel surface and hardwood forest end, and the road crosses onto Blackman Rock and the Gadway sandstone pavement jack pine barren. The corrugated surface of the rock road is created by mega–ripples with wavelengths of about 10–20 cm

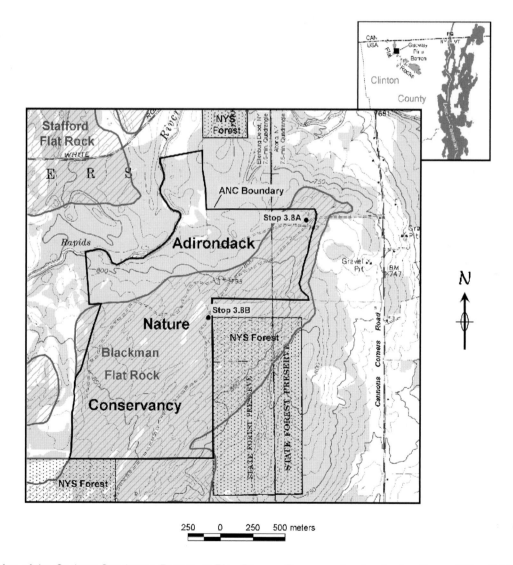

FIGURE 12—Map of the Gadway Sandstone Pavement Pine Barrens Preserve showing the locations of Stop 3.8A and 3.8B.

in the Keeseville Member of the Potsdam Formation.

The Gadway Preserve is owned and managed by the Adirondack Nature Conservancy for the purpose of maintaining a jack pine community capable of regeneration. As the Altona Flat Rock jack pine barren, the Gadway barren is a fire-adapted community. Prescribed fire is one of the management tools being considered for this site. Ice-storm damage in 1998 was less severe in the Gadway barren, and the stop provides an opportunity to observe a jack pine barren in a near-pre-storm condition. The first of two stops at this location is located about 0.08 mi from the entrance of the pine barren, and, if time is available, the second is located farther southwest on the faint, unimproved track that crosses the Potsdam (Figure 12, Stops 3.8A and 3.8B).

Stop 3.8, Upper Potsdam Formation trace fossils, Gadway Pine Barrens (20 minutes)

The Keeseville Member at this location (Figure 12) is composed of thinly bedded, light gray, medium- to fine-grained quartz arenite. Individual quartz grains are generally very well rounded and nearly spherical in shape. The sand is generally massive or horizontally laminated. Oscillation ripple marks with wavelengths ranging from about 1 to 2 cm are common, but large-scale mega-ripples (l ≈ 10–20 cm) may be found. Arthropod trackways (predominantly *Diplichnites* and *Protichnites* at Stop 3.8A), as well as the probable mollusk trackways *Climactichnites* and *Plagiogmus* (Stop 3.8B), are well preserved on some bedding surfaces (Figure 13).

Travel to Stop 3.9

Return to the vehicles and follow the Gadway preserve access road back to the Cannon Corners Road. Turn left, and proceed north over the English River at 0.5 mi to the Davison Road intersection at 0.6 mi. Turn right onto Davison Road and proceed east for 5.2 mi to where Davison Road ends at U.S. Rte. 11. Continue east on U.S. Rte. 11 through the village of Mooers. Turn left at the N.Y. Rte. 22 intersection (2.8 mi from Davison Road intersection), and drive east on U.S. Rte. 11. Continue east on U.S. Rte. 11 for 7.1 mi, crossing the I-87 overpass at 6.5 mi, to the intersection of U.S. Routes 11 and 9 and Main Street in Champlain. Turn right onto U.S. Rte. 9, and head south for 1.3 mi to the abandoned Clinton Farm Supply parking lot on the right (west) side of the road.

Stop 3.9, Upper Potsdam trace fossils, Clinton Farm Supplies locality (20 minutes)

The sedimentology and paleontology of the Keeseville Member at the Clinton Farm Supply Company site are detailed in several reports prepared as part of a field trip for the 65th New York State Geological Association meeting hosted by St. Lawrence University (Erickson, 1993a, 1993b; Erickson and Bjerstedt, 1993; Erickson *et al.*, 1993). The sandstone at this location is predominantly fine- to medium-grained quartz arenite, and contains such structures as asymmetrical ripple marks and trough cross beds indicative of relatively strong marine currents. Erickson *et al.* (1993) suggested that the sands were deposited in a complex tidal setting. An abundant and diverse assemblage of trace fossils is especially well preserved on bedding planes exposed along the north side of the parking lot. These traces include the U-shaped burrow *Arenicolites* and the radiating probes of the burrow *Phycodes* (Erickson *et al.*, 1993) (Figure 14).

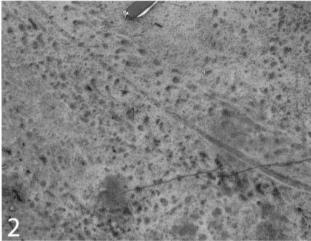

Figure 13—Field photographs of bedding surfaces of the Potsdam Sandstone, Gadway Nature Preserve, New York. *1,* Moderately bioturbated surface dominated by the probable mollusk burrow *Plagiogmus* (also known as *Psammichnites*). These burrows, one of which is labeled with a solid white arrow (center), are thought to have been produced just below the surface; the bilobed surface expression of the burrow represents sediment that was wedged upward during subsurface burrowing and bisected by the snorkel-like appendage of the tracemaker. Possible *Climactichnites* burrows may occur at lower left (open white arrow, lower left) and upper right of the image. *2,* Heavily bioturbated surface dominated by the epifaunal arthropod trackway *Protichnites*. Note continuous telson or tail drag mark in center of trackway and the eight or more sets of tear drop-shaped appendage marks arranged in overlapping arcuate sets. Did the animal move from the left side of this photograph toward the right? Or vice versa? Swiss army knife at middle left in *13.1*, and at top of *13.2* ca. 8.3 cm long.

Travel to Stop 3.10

Return to the vehicles; drive to Champlain via U.S. Rte. 9 (north), a distance of 1.3 mi. Proceed straight (north) through the U.S. Rte. 11–U.S. Rte. 9–Main Street intersection; follow Main

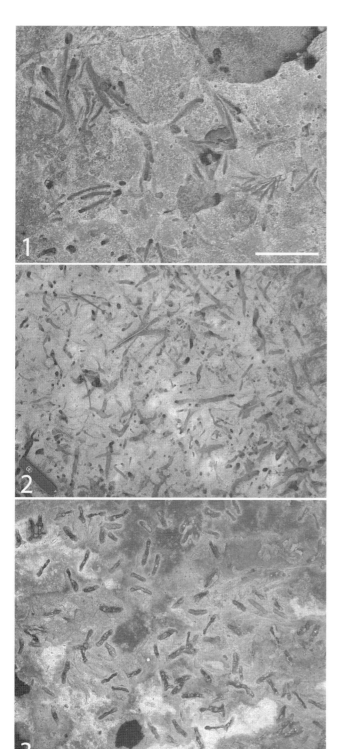

Street for 0.4 mi to the village center. Turn right onto Elm Street and cross the Great Chazy River. Elm Street bears right at the intersection with Oak Street and River Road. Follow Elm Street for 1.8 mi to its end at N.Y. Rte. 276. Turn left onto N.Y. Rte. 276 for about 0.3 mi to the entrance of a quarry in the Theresa Formation on the left (west) side of the road.

Stop 3.10, Theresa Formation (middle Lower Ordovician) (15 minutes)

The Theresa Formation in this quarry consists of interlayered medium and thick bedded, quartz-rich dolostone and quartz sandstone (Dawson, 2002). Cross bedding, intraformational conglomerates and ripple marks can be found. Bjerstedt and Erickson (1989) and Erickson and Bjerstedt (1993) described the trace fossils of the Theresa in detail, and *Skolithos* can be found on the south wall of this quarry.

The Theresa Formation has traditionally been considered an uppermost Cambrian or lowest Ordovician unit that conformably overlies the Potsdam Formation, and differs primarily from the Potsdam in having dolomitic sandstone beds (e.g., Fisher, 1968). However, this interpretation is incorrect, and conodonts from the Theresa Formation further north in Quebec indicate a middle Early Ordovician (*Macerodus dianae* Zone) and late Tremadocian age (Salad Hersi *et al.*, 2003). Indeed, the top of the Cambrian is a silcrete that marks an unconformity surface on the top of the Potsdam Formation (Salad Hersi *et al.*, 2002) on the southern limb of the Ottawa aulocogen. The post-Cambrian hiatus between the Potsdam and Theresa Formations is a long interval on the platform in northeasternmost New York north of Beekmantown village, and even the lowest Ordovician Tribes Hill Formation seen on days 1 and 2 of the field trip is absent north of Beekmantown village (Landing and Westrop, 2006) (see Landing, this volume, Figure 2). However, *Rossodus manitouensis* Zone conodonts recovered from an isolated dolostone outcrop in southern Quebec (Salad Hersi *et al.*, 2003) indicate that the Tribes Hill Formation apparently reappears as the lowest Ordovician unit under the Theresa in the Ottawa aulocogen.

Travel to Plattsburgh

Return to the vehicles; turn right at the quarry entrance, and proceed south on N.Y. Rte. 276 for 0.9 mi to U.S. Rte. 11. Turn right onto U.S. Rte. 11, and head west to the southbound ramp onto I-87 in Champlain, a distance of 1.6 mi. Turn left onto the southbound onramp after crossing the overpass, and proceed south to Plattsburgh.

FIGURE 14—Field photographs of bedding surfaces of the Potsdam Sandstone, Clinton Farm Supply, New York. *1*, Radiating arrays of the penetrative burrow *Phycodes*, thought to have been produced by the probing activities of an infaunal or epifaunal animal. *2*, Heavily bioturbated surface dominated by large and small arrays of *Phycodes*. Several tiers of burrows are visible; shallow tiers are holes or vertical shafts, and deeper portions of burrows are radiating, bedding-parallel arrays or galleries. *3*, Heavily bioturbated bed surface dominated by large (5–10 cm long) *Arenicolites* or *Diplocraterion*. Surface is dominated by U-shaped troughs of the burrow bottoms; paired vertical shafts are rare and burrow *Spreiten* are not visible. Scale bar in *3.1* ca. 6 cm. Swiss army knife at lower left in *14.2* and *14.3* ca. 8.3 cm long.

AUGUST 3: EPEIROGENIC AND EUSTATIC CONTROLS ON CAMBRIAN DEPOSITION IN THE DYSOXIC FRANKLIN BASIN, NORTHWESTERN VERMONT

Overview

The most fossiliferous Cambrian rocks in Vermont occur in a narrow N–S-trending belt just east of the Champlain thrust in northwestern and western Franklin County. This belt lies is part of the large overthrust called the Rosenberg slice (Clark, 1934), which was folded during the Taconian orogeny into the north-ward-plunging St. Albans synclinorium (see Shaw, 1958). The most significant faunas from this region include: 1) the terminal Lower Cambrian (upper *Olenellus* Zone s.l.) Lägerstatte from the lower Parker Formation east of Georgia, Vermont (e.g., Walcott, 1886, 1891a; Resser and Howell, 1938), and 2) the Upper Cambrian *Hungaia magnifica* assemblages (Rasetti, 1944) of Highgate gorge, which characterize Laurentian outer shelf and slope litho- and biofacies (e.g., Rowell *et al.*, 1973; Taylor, 1976, 1977).

The St. Albans synclinorium and the Lancaster, Pennsylvania, region are the only areas in eastern Laurentia that preserve essentially unfaulted Cambrian sections across the carbonate platform–upper slope transition (Rodgers, 1968). In northwest Vermont, the roughly E–W-trending Lemoile River valley marks the abrupt transition from the latest Early Cambrian–Ordovician deeper water facies of the Franklin Basin (Shaw, 1958) into the coeval platform succession of the Middlebury synclinorium (Stone and Dennis, 1964; Landing, this volume, fig. 3). This abrupt N–S transition will be crossed in the drive south to Burlington at the end of the day [see milepost 102.5 under *Travel to hotel* after Stop 4.7 (below)]. Despite being persistently dysoxic/anoxic from the late Early Cambrian through the Early Ordovician, the Franklin Basin succession in the St. Albans synclinorium has yielded abundant, allochthonous trilobite and microfossil collections from shales, bedded limestones, and debris flow blocks (e.g., Landing, 1983).

Today's trip emphasizes that the parautochthonous Cambrian–Lower Ordovician of the St. Albans synclinorium in northwestern Vermont underwent an abrupt transition from an underlying Lower Cambrian platform succession (i.e., Cheshire Quartzite and overlying Dunham Dolostone; Stops 4.5, 4.6) into a persistant dysoxic/anoxic upper slope facies. This abrupt transition took place in the late Early Cambrian [i.e., Early–Middle Cambrian boundary interval in terms of Gondwanan successions, see Geyer and Landing (2004)]. Newly recognized, wide-spread debrites of Dunham boulders at the base of the Parker Formation (Stop 4.7) suggest that down-to-basin block faulting on the southern margin of the Ottawa graben produced and maintained the persistently dysoxic/anoxic Franklin Basin facies (Stop 4.4) north of the E–W trending carbonate platform margin at the Lemoile River valley. The terminal Middle Cambrian–Lower Ordovician succession at Highgate gorge shows long-term dysoxia/anoxia in an upper slope facies, with the loss of prominent carbonate clast debris flows and quartz sand influx at the Cambrian–Ordovician boundary (Stops 4.1–4.3).

Travel to Stop 4.1

Plattsburgh–Chazy.—Depart conference hotel, enter on-ramp to the Northway (Interstate 87) and continue north towards the Canadian border. The topography along the route north is very subdued. Most of the bedrock is mantled by glacial till and overlying Champlain Sea deposits (ca. 11.5–12.0 Ka) that reflect marine incursion along the St. Lawrence River lowlands as a result of the ca. 125 m isostatic depression of the region by the late Pleistocene ice sheet (e.g., Occietti *et al.*, 2001). This incursion is reflected by the occurrence of mollusk shell accumulations (oysters and *Balthica macoma*), brackish foraminiferans and ostracodes, and whale remains (e.g., Howell and Richards, 1937). Gentle, roughly N–S-trending, broad ridges are barrier beaches that were formed in the Champlain Sea. At about milepost 158, enter Town of Beekmantown. Clarke and Schuchert (1899) named the post-Potsdam, carbonate-dominated, Upper Cambrian–Middle Ordovician Beekmantown Group. However, local outcrop is so limited in this nearly flat-lying succession, stratigraphic continuity so disrupted by normal faults (see Fisher, 1968), and fossils so rare in the "type" Beekmantown that the reference standard for the group lies across Lake Champlain in the Champlain slice near East Shoreham, Vermont (Brainerd and Seely, 1890; see Landing and Westrop, 2006). The first outcrops along the north lane of the Northway north of Plattsburgh are in dolostones of the uppermost Middle Ordovician Providence Island Formation (Fisher, 1968).

Chazy–Rouses Point village.—Chazy, New York, marked by the exit sign at about milepost 161, is the type area for the Chazy Group—a carbonate-dominated, terminal Middle–lower Upper Ordovician interval that unconformably overlies the Beekmantown Group. The Chazy Group has representatives of Earth's oldest (early Caradocian) bryozoan-coral reefs. Comparable and coeval low-diversity bioherms generally dominated by one or two species of bryozoans, corals, or sponges occur along the eastern margin of Laurentia in Tennessee, adjacent Quebec, and western Newfoundland (e.g., Raymond, 1924a; Pitcher, 1964; Batten Hender and Dix, 2006). A small Chazy section occurs in a roadcut at about mile 166. The best Chazy Group sections are seen in ornamental limestone ("marble") quarries and on lakeshore cliffs in the northernmost Lake Champlain lowlands; patch reefs in the Chazy locally form knolls in pasture sections in this area. The numerous broken trees at about milepost 170 resulted from an ice storm in 1998.

Take Exit 42 from Northway, and drive east on Rte. 11 to Rouses Point village. At T-intersection in village, continue north on Rte 11 and drive through village to intersection with Rte. 2.

Rouses Point–Swanton, Vermont.—Take Rte. 2 bridge across northernmost Lake Champlain (actually the north-flowing Richelieu River at this point) to Vermont; note ruins of Fort Montgomery on the west side of the Richelieu River and just south of the Canadian border. The east side of the bridge is on the Alburg Tongue, a large peninsula with its northern end in Quebec. At the intersection with Rte. 78 (marked by a yellow caution light), turn left onto Rte. 78 East. Follow Rte. 78, and take bridge across Missisquoi Bay on northeastern Lake Champlain at East Alburg, Vermont. On the east side of the lake, Rte. 78 traverses the lowland of the Missisquoi River delta, a classic bird-foot delta with swampy woodlands that comprise the Missisquoi National Wildlife Refuge. Any positive topography is again largely defined by Champlain Sea beach ridges.

Swanton–Highgate gorge.—Follow Rte 78 through Swanton, Vermont; black, fine-grained sandstones and silt shales under the bridge and below the dam in the Missisquoi River are synorogenic, late Caradocian deposits of the Taconian orogeny, and are overthrust by the upper Lower Cambrian Dunham Dolostone in the eastern outskirts of Swanton (see Shaw, 1958). Travel about four miles on Rte 78 to the hamlet of Highgate Center, turn right (south) onto Rte 207. Immediately descend into "Highgate gorge" on the Missisquoi River and cross new bridge across river. Make first right (west) onto Baker Road (unpaved); drive past power plant, and park near last house on road. Walk the unimproved track west and then north between the properties to low sandstone ledges exposed on the south bank of the river.

Stop 4.1, Marjuman Stage through Cambrian–Ordovician boundary in slope deposits at Highgate gorge, and "early" *Cordylodus* elements (60 minutes)

Geologic setting—The "Highgate gorge section" (Schuchert, 1937) is a highly condensed continental-slope package that dips upstream along the Missisquoi River. The Gorge and overlying Highgate Formations represent more proximal, debris-flow- and sandstone-bearing vs. more distal, black siliciclastic mudstone-dominated facies, respectively (Landing, 1983). Stop 4.1 includes four overlapping sections (A–D) measured along the south shore of the Missisquoi River below the Swanton, Vermont, municipal power plant (Landing, 1983; Figure 15).

Section A.—Section A is the longest, and includes a lower interval of unfossiliferous, medium gray, brownish weathering, massive, lenticular, dolostone pebble–cobble debris aprons and dolomitic quartz arenites (Figure 16, unit 1). Clast imbrications in the debris aprons indicate current and mass movement direction to the north, and directly away from the shelf–slope break ca. 30.4 km to the SSW along the south side

of the Lemoile River valley (e.g., Rodgers, 1968).

Steptoean–Sunwaptan hiatus in lower section A.—Thinner-bedded (2–20 cm), arenaceous dolostones and dolomitic quartz arenites of unit 4 exposed on the riverbank at low water (Figure 16) yield lower Upper Cambrian (Steptoean Stage) trilobites of the *Dunderbergia* Zone (Gilman Clark and Shaw, 1968a). Upper unit 4 yields the biostratigraphically problematical, lower *Hungaia magnifica* trilobite assemblage (i.e., "zone 1" of Raymond, 1923–1924, 1924, 1937; Gilman Clark and Shaw, 1968b) from Highgate gorge and abundant rooted dendroids [*Dendrograptus hallianus* (Prout, 1851)].

"Zone 1" taxa include such forms reported as *Acheilus macrops* Raymond, 1924b; *Apatokephaloides clivosus* Raymond, 1924; *Aasphiscus inornatus* Raymond, 1924b; *Dikelocephalus insolitus* Raymond, 1924; *Plethometopus convergens* (Raymond, 1924b); *Pseudosalteria laevis* Raymond, 1924b; *Richardsonella laeviuscula* Raymond, 1923–1924; and *Stenopilus pronus* Rasetti, 1924. Associated conodonts from upper unit 4 include *Proconodontus muelleri* Miller, 1968, and suggest a correlation with the upper Sunwaptan Stage (Landing, 1983) [e.g., upper *Rasettia magna*–lower *Saukiella junia* Subzones of the middle *Saukia* Zone of the south-central Laurentian platform (e.g., Stitt, 1977)]. The lengthy hiatus within unit 4 remains unexplained (Figure 17), but may reflect either protracted non-deposition and/or erosion or presence of a sedimentary decollement (i.e., slide) surface in this slope environment.

***Depositional environment of upper* Hungaia magnifica *assemblage of upper section A and B.*—**Trilobites and conodonts are unknown from units 5–13, but conodonts re-appear in unit 14 near the base of the alternating debris flows and bedded arenaceous limestones (units 13–21) that compose the cliffs west of

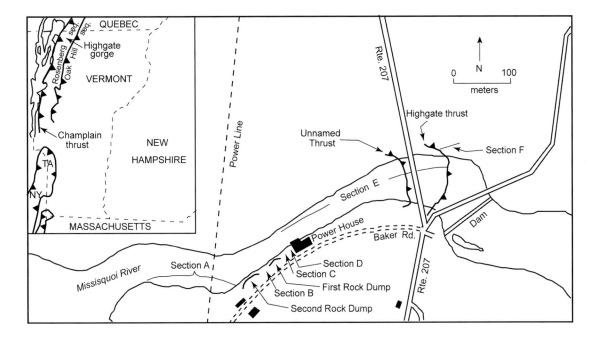

FIGURE 15—Highgate gorge, northeastern Vermont. Location of sections A–F at the type sections of the Gorge and Highgate Formations at Highgate gorge, Franklin County, Vermont. Inset shows location of detailed map. (Figure modified from Landing, 1983, fig. 1).

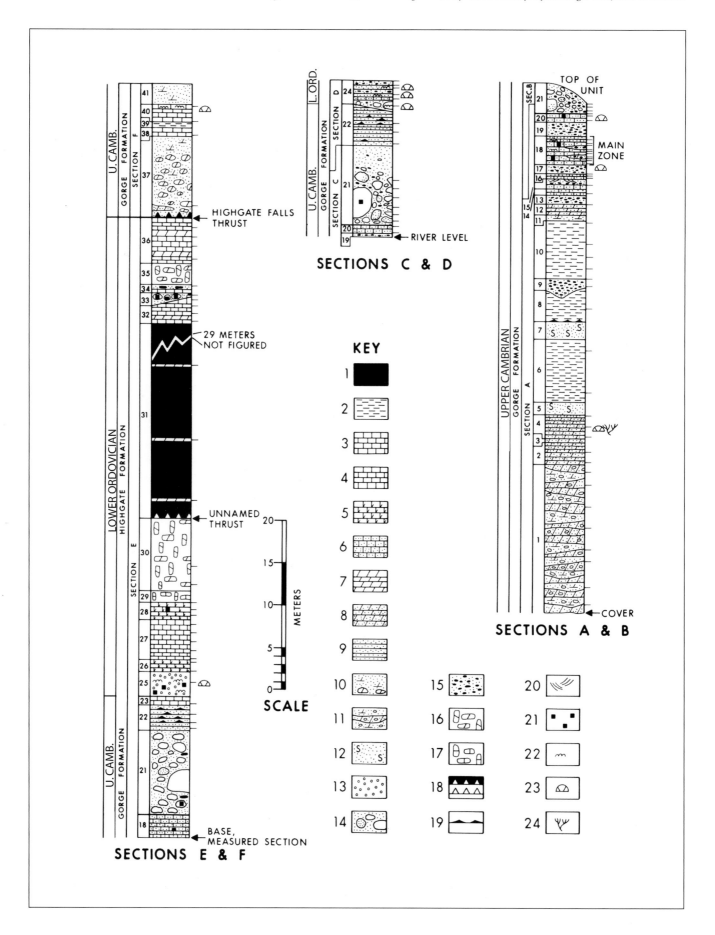

SECTIONS C & D

KEY

SECTIONS A & B

SECTIONS E & F

FIGURE 16—Measured sections of the Gorge and Highgate Formations at Highgate gorge on the Missisquoi River, Franklin Co., Vermont. Overlaps of section A with B and section C with D indicated to left of sections. Key: 1, siliciclastic mudstone or slate, dark gray–black, weakly calcareous, with silty laminae; 2, dolomitic silt-shale with arenaceous dolostones in lenticular, graded, 2–4 cm-thick beds, dark brown; 3, lime mudstone and intercalated siliciclastic mudstone, dark gray–black, light gray weathering, in 0.5–1.0 cm beds; 4, as lithology 3 but in 1–4 cm beds; 5, dolomitic lime mudstones, dark gray–black, orange-gray weathering; 6, sandy lime mudstones with lime mudstone granule and trilobite wacke- to grainstone lenses, dark gray–black, weathering buff-gray, in 3–10 cm beds; 7, silty dolostone, finely laminated to micro-crossbedded, dark gray, weathering orange, in 5–40 cm beds; 8, arenaceous, sucrosic dolostone and dolomitic quartz arenite, dark gray, weathering light gray, in 2–20 cm beds (unit 13 is 50 cm thick); 9, calcareous quartz arenites, dark gray, weathering light gray, in 0.5–15 cm beds; 10, massive, dolomitic quartz arenite (unit 41) to dolostone pebble–cobble debris apron with dolomitic quartz arenite matrix (unit 37); 11, as lithology 10 but in massive (0.5–1.0 m) beds; 12, siliceous quartz arenite, massive, light buff; 13, debris flow with lime mudstone and granule intraclast grainstone pebbles–cobbles with lime mudstone matrix (unit 25); 14, polymict debris apron with lime mudstone (white) and calcareous quartz arenite (stippled) granules–cobbles derived from platform margin (unit 21); 15, debris apron, arenaceous dolostone pebbles–cobbles in unsorted arenaceous dolostone matrix; 16, tectonic breccia, large blocks of slaty, silty dolostone in silty, calcareous slate, weathering gray brown; 17, tectonic breccia, boudinaged lime mudstone and intraclast pebble packstone, in 2–5 cm beds, in chocolate-brown, silty slate; 18, thrust fault, indicated by white sawteeth when at base of dark gray–black slate; 19, rippled surface; 20, trough crossbedding; 21, echinoderm debris; 22, trilobite fragments; 23, trilobite collections; 24, rooted dendroids. Conodont sample horizons indicated by horizontal lines to right of columns. (Figure modified from Landing, 1983, fig. 2).

the two rock dumps (i.e., top section A and section B) (Figures 15, 16). Trilobites re-appear as allochthonous, current-transported associations in unit 18, where they occur in lenticular, coarse-grained, normally graded, echinoderm-trilobite hash pack- and grainstones that occur with thin-bedded, planar to microcrossbedded, CDE and DE turbiditic limestones (Landing, 1983).

The absence of burrow churning in the limestones and black color of the interbedded shales are consistent with dysoxic/anoxic bottom conditions. However, this slope facies was likely not particularly deep, as indicated by the oscillation (wave) ripples on the top of unit 7 and within unit 22. As suggested by Landing (1983, p. 1163), the assumption of a 1° slope from the shelf–slope break at the Lemoile River suggests that deposition of the Gorge Formation accumulated at a water depth of ca. 90 m.

Trilobites and conodonts of upper **Hungaia magnifica** *assemblage.*—The trilobites of unit 18 comprise the relatively high-diversity (ca. 40 species) "main zone" *Hungaia magnifica* trilobite assemblage [Schuchert (1937); =zones 2 and 3 of Raymond (1923–1924, 1924b)]. Sparse conodonts from units 14 and 16 are comparable to those from unit 4, and most suggestive of the *Proconodontus muelleri* Subzone and a correlation into the middle *Saukia* Zone on the Laurentian platform. The appearance of *Eoconodontus (E.) notchpeakensis* (Miller, 1968) in lower unit 18 further suggests a correlation of the "main zone" with the middle *Saukia* Zone (e.g., Miller, 1988).

Cordylodus *from upper* **Hungaia magnifica** *assemblage.*— Landing (1983) reported a few elements of *Cordylodus proavus* Müller, 1959, from the middle of unit 18, and argued that this demonstrated an early occurrence of the species before its "expected" lowest occurrence as known in platform successions worldwide [e.g., with the conodont and trilobite biomere at the base of the *Eurekia apopsis* Zone on the Laurentian platform (Figure 17)].

Taylor *et al.* (1991) objected to this supposedly "early" occurrence of *Cordylodus proavus*, and attributed the report to mis-correlations between the alternating debris flows and bedded limestone intervals that form the cliffs of sections A and B. They resampled Landing's (1983) intervals 14–24, and concluded that correlations between the two rock dumps based on the apparent comparison of bedded limestone-dominated intervals and debris flows was incorrect (Figures 18 and 19). EL agrees with their stratigraphic re-evaluation.

However, far more important and pertinent to the key thesis of Taylor *et alii*'s (1991) report is an issue not addressed by them. This is the fact that the reported *C. proavus* elements from Landing's (1983) sample B18C2-0.2 occur with a characteristic sub-*E. apopsis* trilobite assemblage [*Apatokephaloides clivosus*; *Bowmania americana* (Walcott, 1884); *Eurekia* sp., *Stenopilus pronus*; saukiid indet., *Tatonaspis* sp.; identifications by R. Ludvigsen *in* Landing (1983, p. 1160)]. In addition, unidentified saukiid fragments occur in unit 20 (Landing, 1983, p. 1160) indicate a sub-*Eurekia apopsis* equivalency of unit 20 and unit 18. Similarly, Taylor *et alii*'s (1991) correlation of unit 20 also indicates a sub-*Eurekia apopsis* equivalency (Figure 18). So, what do the *Cordylodus* specimens from unit 18 mean?

It is now understood that *Cordylodus* appears below the lowest Ibexian Series (i.e., *E. apopsis* Zone and correlative strata) in unrestricted marine settings, where it is represented by *Cordylodus andersi* Viira and Sergeeva *in* Kaljo *et al.* (1986) in the cool-water successions of Baltica and western Gondwana (Szianiawski and Bengtson, 1998; Landing *et al.*, In press). *Cordylodus andersi* resembles *C. proavus*, but differs primarily by having a deeper basal cavity. As *C. andersi* was proposed in 1986, and well after Landing's (1983) report, the *Cordylodus* elements with deep basal cavities from unit 18 reported by Landing (1983) were mistakenly referred to *C. proavus* (the earliest cordylodan than known), and actually belong to *C. andersi*.

Section C.—Section C is dominated by a massive, polymict debris flow (unit 21) with boulders (to 2 1/2 × 2 m diameter) of shelf-derived, white, intraclast granule packstones with vadose cavity-fills and well sorted quartz arenites (Figures 15, 16). At least 3.5 m of underlying strata were cut out during deposition of unit 21. Unit 21 thins and has smaller clasts where it forms the

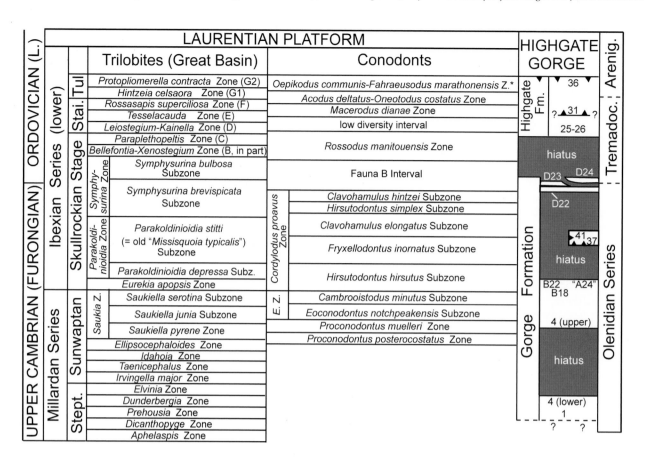

FIGURE 17—Correlations of Gorge and Highgate Formations at Highgate gorge. Great Basin trilobite zonation from Ross *et al.* (1997). Designation "*Oepikodus communis-Fahraeusodus marathonensis* Zone" replaces "*Oepikodus communis* Zone" of Ross *et al.* (1997) (see Landing and Westrop, 2006), and base of *O. communis-F. marathonensis* Zone correlates into upper *Hintzeia celsaora* Zone (unpub. data of EL from Garden City Formation, northernUtah–southern Idaho; compare Ross *et al.*, 1997). Abbreviations: *E. Z., Eoconodontus* Zone; L., Lower; Paibai., Paibaian Series; Stai., Stairsian Stage; Step, Steptoean Stage; Subz., Subzone; Tul, Tulean Stage; Z., Zone. Figure modified from Landing (1983, fig. 4).

highest unit at the top of sections A and B (Figure 16). Conodonts from boulders in unit 21 include low diversity assemblages with *Cordylodus proavus* that could be referable to the terminal Cambrian (i.e., terminal Sunwaptan–lowest Ibexian) or lowest Ordovician, and do not include sub-Ibexian assemblages. Landing (1983) followed Keith (1924, p. 116) in referring unit 21 and several higher units (22–24) to the top of the Gorge Formation. Landing's (1983) justification of this assignment was to assign successions with prominent debris flows and quartz sandstones to the Gorge Formation.

Section D and the terminal Cambrian.—Section D shows that the highest beds of the type section of the Gorge Formation range into the highest Cambrian. Conodonts, including *Monocostodus sevierensis* (Miller, 1969) and presently undescribed trilobites from unit 24 indicate a correlation with the upper *Symphysurina brevispicata* or lower *Symphysurina bulbosa* Subzones on the Laurentian platform (see Stitt, 1971, 1977). The trilobites include *Geragnostus* sp., *Hystricurus* sp., and *Symphysurina* sp. (large specimens with heavy spine at genal angle) from sample D24B-0.7 and *Symphysurina* sp. (with

rounded genal angles) and *Hystricurus* sp. from sample D24D-0.1 (R. J. Ross, Jr., *in* Landing, 1983, p. 1160).

Cambrian–Ordovician boundary and Gorge–Highgate interformational unconformity.—Strata above unit 24 in section D are obscured by the foundation of the power plant. However, unit 25, a lime mudstone granule–pebble debris apron with abundant trilobites in its lime-mudstone matrix [tectonically deformed specimens of *Leiostegium* sp. and *Rossaspis*? sp.; R. J. Ross, Jr., *in* Landing (1983, p. 1162)] unconformably overlies unit 23 on the north bank of the Missisquoi River. Unit 25 is the basal bed of the Highgate Formation, and its *Leiostegium-Kainella* Zone D trilobite assemblage (see Ross, 1951; Hintze, 1953) indicates a terminal upper lower Tremadocian equivalency (e.g., Landing *et al.*, 2003a) (Figure 17). Thus, the Gorge–Highgate contact in Highgate gorge is physically an unconformity as it shows erosional cut-out of the upper Gorge Formation between sections D and E. In addition, the hiatus represented by this unconformity can be biostratigraphically bracketed as uppermost Cambrian–terminal upper lower Tremadocian.

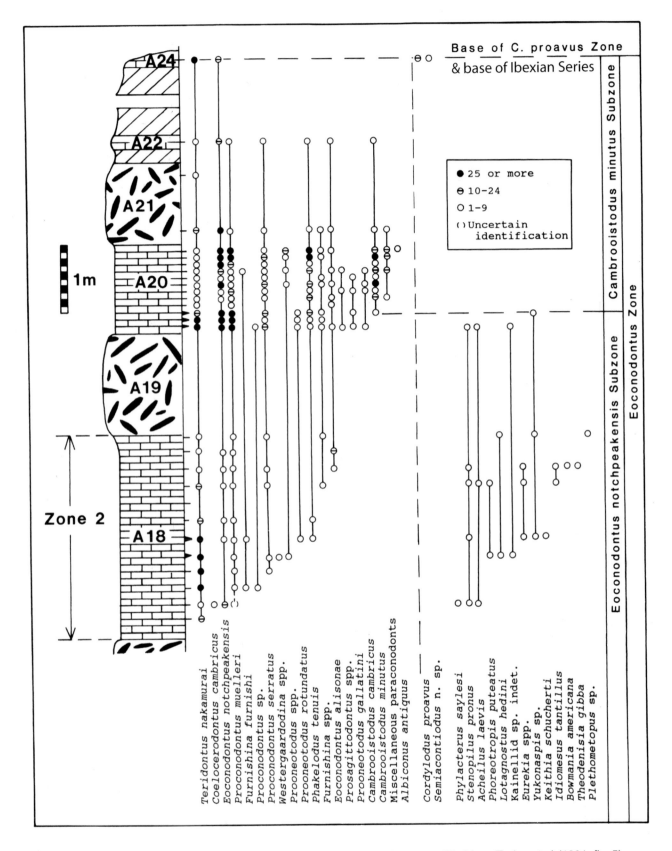

Figure 18—Faunas and lithology of upper section A at Highgate gorge. Figure modified from Taylor *et al.* (1991, fig. 5).

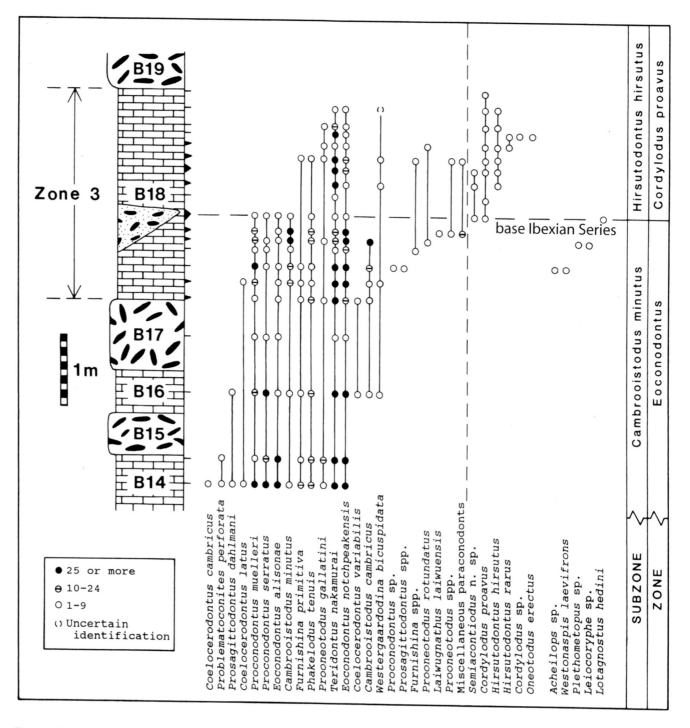

FIGURE 19—Faunas and lithology of section B at Highgate gorge. Figure modified from Taylor *et al.* (1991, fig. 4).

Travel to Stop 4.2

At end of stop, return to bus. Return to Rte 207, turn right (north). Park at north end of bridge; walk ca. 100 m east along canoe portage trail to point midway between old and new bridges, descend at lowest point in path to riverbed at Highgate Falls thrust.

Stop 4.2, Lower Ibexian (lower Skullrockian) and type *Parakoldiniodia stitti* (i.e., "*Missisquoia typicalis*") assemblage at Highgate gorge (15 minutes)

Stratigraphy and stratigraphic nomenclature.—The Highgate thrust (Figure 15) brings 15+ m of Upper Cambrian debris flows with dolostone clasts, massive sandstones, and minor bedded limestones and black silt shales of the Gorge Formation (section F, Figure 16) across the Lower Ordovician Highgate Formation. Shaw (1958) and Shaw and Gilman Clark (1968) referred to these rocks above the Highgate thrust as the type section of the Highgate Formation, because they used a chronostratigraphic, not lithologic basis to define the Gorge as an Upper Cambrian interval, and defined the Highgate as Lower Ordovician. This convention also reflected the early convention to assign the Laurentian *"Missisquoia* Zone" to the lowest Ordovician.

Landing (1983) followed Keith (1932), Schuchert (1937), and Shaw (1951) in regarding the black mudstone-dominated interval under the Highgate thrust as the type section of the Ordovician Highgate Formation, and saw the Gorge Formation as a Cambrian interval dominated by debris flows and turbiditic sandstones.

"Missisquoia typicalis" type locality. — The type locality of the upper Upper Cambrian trilobite *"Missisquoia typicalis"* Shaw, 1951 [now *Parakoldinioidia stitti* Fortey, 1983], lies in poorly exposed lime mudstones in unit 40 (Figure 16). Current-disarticulated, allochthonous trilobites reported from this horizon (R. J. Ross, Jr., *in* Landing, 1983) include *Geragnostus* sp.; *Parakoldinioidia stitti; Symphysurina minima* Shaw, 1951; *Parabolinella?;* and *Terranovella?* sp. (see also Shaw, 1951, 1931, 1955a, 1958). *Fryxellodontus lineatus* Miller, 1969, a conodont restricted to Stitt's (1971) *"Missisquoia typicalis"* Subzone and lower *Symphysurina brevispicata* Subzone (Miller, 1980) in the Great Basin and south-central United States, occurs in sample F40-01 (Landing, 1983).

Travel to Stop 4.3

At the end of Stop 4.2, walk downstream. Cross Highgate thrust, and walk down through east-dipping section in type section of Highgate Formation to the lower part of unit 31 under the new bridge.

Stop 4.3, Dysoxic/anoxic Tremadocian–lower Arenigian of the Highgate Formation at Highgate gorge (15 minutes)

The purpose of this walk stratigraphically downward through the Highgate Formation is to emphasize that the dysoxic/anoxic conditions characteristic of Gorge Formation deposition from the Middle through Late Cambrian persisted through the Early Ordovician in the franklin Basin.

Type section of the Highgate Formation. — This completely exposed section in the Highgate Formation along the north bank of Highgate gorge is dominated by slaty, dark gray to black siliciclastic mudstones and silt shales with carbonate clast debris flows and thin-bedded carbonates (Figure 16, left column). Conodonts provide only a very limited biostratigraphic resolution (probably upper Tremadocian–lower Arenigian; Landing, 1983) to units 31–36 of the Highgate Formation. However, the highest outcrops of the Highgate Formation only range into the lower Arenigian in the St. Albans synclinorium (Landing, 1983, unpub. data), and much of the formation is probably represented in the section. Upper lower Tremadocian trilobites [*Leiostegium–Kainella* (D) Zone of Ross (1951) and Hintze (1953)] and Fauna D conodonts come from the matrix of a debris flow (unit 25) at the base of the Highgate Formation that cuts out the *Symphysurina*–bearing sandstones (unit 24) at the top of the Gorge Formation in section D.

Early Ordovician upper slope dysoxia/anoxia and diagenetic dolostone. — The black mudrocks of the Highgate Formation are laminated and show almost no evidence for burrowing or any *in situ* benthic organisms in this strongly dysoxic/anoxic slope facies. Many of the bedded and nodular limestones were weakly to strongly dolomitized by the low pH conditions in the dysoxic muds, and are now weakly to strongly orange in color on weathered surfaces. This orange color reflects weathering of an iron-bearing dolomite. Comparable deep-water dolostones are known from many ancient and modern marine settings with low-oxygen, organic-rich environments (e.g., Garrison *et al.*, 1984).

Travel to Stop 4.4

At end of stop, return to the bus. Drive 2.7 miles south on Rte. 207 along the western limb of the St. Albans syncline to the cross road with Woods Hill. The low ridge visible to the east of Rte. 207 about 1.5 miles south of the bridge over Highgate gorge is underlain by the resistant, Lower Cambrian Cheshire Formation (Stop 4.5) on the east limb of the St. Albans syncline. This Cheshire Formation ridge is immediately west of the higher-grade metamorphic Cambrian rocks of the Oak Hill thrust sheet. The distant eastern skyline, visible if the weather is clear, is the north end of the Green Mountain anticlinorium [i.e., Sutton Mountain anticlinorium across the border in Quebec]. Turn right (west) on Woods Hill Road. Low road cut on north side of Woods Hill Road 0.4 miles west of Rte 207 is in orange-weathering debris flow consisting of arenaceous (coarse-grained) dolostone with small arenaceous dolostone clasts in the middle of the Skeels Corners Formation. Almost half of the Skeels Corners Formation (Howell, 1939) is composed of sandy dolostone and dolostone debris flows (e.g., Shaw, 1958, fig. 7), with the remainder of this upper Middle Cambrian unit (upper Marjuman Stage, *Cedaria* Zone) consisting of dark gray–black shales with thin quartz arenites.

Turn right (north) on Donaldson Road 0.7 miles west of intersection of Woods Hill Road with Rte. 207; travel 0.6 miles north on Donaldson Road, park next to long road cut in Parker Formation on east side of Donaldson Road.

Stop 4.4, Dysoxic/anoxic Parker Formation (Middle Cambrian) on Donaldson Road (15 minutes)

The road cut is in the upper part of the Parker Formation (Keith, 1932) and lies a short stratigraphic distance below the massive Rugg Brook Dolostone [Schuchert (1933), type section redefined by Schuchert (1937)]. The Rugg Brook, an unfossiliferous, rusty weathering, massive, lenticular (3–90 m-thick) interval of sandy dolostones and dolomitized debris flows that separates the Parker Formation from the overlying St. Albans Formation [ca. 80 m of dark gray–black mudstones with rare thin limestones and limestone clast debris flows], lies just to the east, but is not visible from the road (see Landing, this volume, fig. 3).

The road cut shows ca. 8 m of gently east-dipping (15°), dark gray–black, muddy siltstones and fine-grained sandstones with orange-weathering, coarse-grained, dolomitic sandstones that show flutes and B–D turbidite structure. Burrowing is limited to small, horizontal, meanders. Sedimentary structures and the near-absence of a benthic fauna are consistent with a dysoxic/anoxic habitat on the upper slope. This low-oxygen facies appears with the initial deposition of the Parker Formation (upper *Olenellus* Zone), and, as seen at Highgate gorge, persists through the Lower Ordovician in the Franklin basin.

Fossils have not been recovered in an examination of the ca. 25 m of section beginning in the road cut and continuing into the wooded slopes above the road cut. However, this interval of upper Parker Formation lies a relatively short distance stratigraphically below Schuchert's (1937, locality XVIII) and Shaw's (1954, 1957, locality SA-EC-1) lower Middle Cambrian (*Albertella* Zone) assemblage from the Donaldson quarry [e.g., *Kootenia boucheri* Shaw, 1957; *Mexicella stator* (Walcott, 1916), *Orriella* sp., *Syspacephalus cadyi* Shaw, 1957; *Nisusia* spp., "*Finkelnbergia*" sp. (brachiopods); *Hyolithes americanus*? (Hall, 1847) (hyolith); *Coreospira*? *raymondi* Shaw, 1957 (helcionellid); and echinoderm columnals].

Travel to Stop 4.5

Donaldson Road–Sheldon Springs, Vermont.—At end of Stop 4.4, return to Woods Hill Road, turn left (east) and return to intersection with Rte. 207. Continue straight (east) through intersection on Woods Hill Road. The low hills on the skyline are underlain by resistant Dunham Formation and underlying Cheshire Formation on the east margin of the St. Albans synclinorium. The intervening lowland with limited exposures along the axis of the synclinorium is largely occupied by a thrust slice of the Lower(?)–Upper(?) Ordovician Morses Line Slate (Shaw, 1951; dark green and gray slate with thin bedded limestones and carbonate clast debris flows). [The "Morses Line" is lithologically identical and should be regarded as a synonym of the Stanbridge Slate across the border in Quebec.]

At stop sign at intersection with Rte. 205, continue northeast on Rte. 205. Within a mile, pass low wooded ridge of gently east-dipping, overturned lower Dunham Formation (on west) and upper Cheshire Formation (on east) just right (south) of road. In this section near the road, Shaw (1951, p. 1034, locality SA-SE-3) reported, but did not illustrate, a small Lower Cambrian assemblage from dark-gray quartzites of the uppermost Cheshire Formation on this ridge [*Hyolithes*? sp. (hyolith), *Hyolithellus*? (phosphatic problematicum), "and many indeterminable organic fragments"].

Sheldon Springs–Shawville, Vermont.—Within a mile, enter village of Sheldon Springs, Vermont; pass intersection with bike path, and turn north on Shawville Road. Follow meandering Shawville Road north past the mill, cross narrow bridge across Missisquoi River. [The trace of the Oak Hill thrust was crossed just before we entered Sheldon Springs, and the gorge immediately downstream from the bridge is in highly deformed Cambrian phyllites of the Oak Hill slice.]

Shawville Road ends at a T-intersection with Rte. 78; turn left (west) onto Rte. 78. Travel 0.3 miles west, and park alongside road just east of low road cuts. BEWARE OF FAST TRAFFIC! Examine cut on north side of road.

Stop 4.5, Pre-Franklin basin deposition: Cheshire Quartzite at Shawville, Vermont (10 minutes)

Geologic setting.—Despite its resistance to erosion, exposures of the Cheshire Quartzite are limited in the St. Albans synclinorium, and this road cut is one of the most readily accessible sections for a large group. As noted above, the overlying

Dunham Formation is the oldest unit above the Champlain thrust on the west side of the St. Albans synclinorium. On the east side of the synclinorium, exposures of Cheshire tend to be heavily overgrown, and neither the base of the formation nor underlying units are exposed. However, the Oak Hill slice immediately east in Vermont and north into Quebec shows a downward succession from 1) a phyllitic Cheshire to 2) dark gray phyllites of the West Sutton Schists, 3) marble of the White Brook Dolostone carbonate platform, and 4) green metawacke and phyllites of the Pinnacle Formation (rift facies) with underlying greenstones of the Tibbit Hill volcanics (Clark, 1934) (see brief review by Clark and Eakins, 1968). [Identical units, unfortunately with a somewhat different nomenclature, will be seen tomorrow north of Rutland Vermont.]

Cheshire Formation road cut.—The ca. 3 m-high road cut consists of east-dipping, sheared dark green-gray weathering, medium gray quartz arenites with silty interbeds and quartz-filled tension gashes. Fossils have not been noted in this roadcut, and sedimentary structures are limited to planar laminations and low angle cross beds in the quartz arenites.

Cheshire and "Gilman".—Shaw (1954, 1958) applied Clark's (1934) term "Gilman Quartzite" for the sub-Dunham interval in the St. Albans synclinorium. "Gilman Quartzite" was a designation proposed for the thick quartzite interval in the Oak Hill succession. Shaw (1958, p. 523) noted that the "Gilman" was the lateral equivalent of the Cheshire Formation (Emerson, 1892) further south in Vermont and Massachusetts, but considered the Cheshire to be a whiter, better-sorted and -washed quartzite. However, the Cheshire Formation is not a monofacial unit, and mottled gray and white quartz arenite, darker colored, more argillaceous facies and mudstone beds and dolomitic beds occur in the unit in central and southern Vermont (e.g., Cady, 1945, p. 528; Brace, 1953). For this reasons, "Gilman Quartzite" and Jacobs' (1935) informal "Brigham Hill Graywacke" are regarded as junior synonyms of the regionally extensive Cheshire Formation.

At the few localities that yield body fossils, the Cheshire yields the lowest fossils on the east Laurentian platform [i.e., upper Lower Cambrian (lowest faunas of the *Olenellus* Zone s.l.]. Walcott (1888, p. 285) recovered *Hyolithes* and *Olenellus* from the Cheshire near Bennington in southern Vermont; Clark (1936, p. 146) recorded the inarticulate *Kutorgina* near Scottsboro, Quebec, and Shaw (1951) noted *Hyolithes* and the problematica *Hyolithellus* and *Salterella* with unidentifiable trilobites from the St. Albans synclinorium (discussed above and below).

Travel to Stop 4.6

Shawville–Highgate Center.—At end of stop, continue west on Rte. 78 back to Highgate Center. After sharp turn in East Highgate village, note outcrops of "Morses Line" Formation in rapids of Missisquoi River just south of road. Drive through Highgate Center.

Highgate Center–Swanton Junction.—On west side of Highgate Center, turn left (south) on Rte. 207. Follow Rte. 207 for 2.9 miles; turn right (west) on Woods Hill Road, and drive west past intersection with Donaldson Road (Stop 4.4) and under Vermont Turnpike (Rte 89) overpass to T-intersection with Rte. 7. Turn left (south) on Rte. 7 and drive along trace of the Champlain thrust [generally with low ridge of Lower

Cambrian Dunham Dolostone on east (left) and lowland of Upper Ordovician synorogenic sedimentary rocks on west (right)]. Travel 1.3 miles south of Woods Hill Road-Rte. 7 intersection; stop at gentle curve in road, and park on wide gravel parking area close to railroad tracks. This site marks the abandoned hamlet of Swanton Junction. BEWARE OF FAST TRAFFIC! Carefully cross Rte. 7 to road cuts in Dunham Dolostone.

Stop 4.6, Pre-Franklin basin deposition: Dunham Dolostone at Swanton Junction (20 minutes)

Geologic setting.—The Dunham Dolostone (Clark, 1934) defines the base of the Champlain thrust in northwestern Vermont. This resistant, very widespread, readily recognizable unit extends south from its type area in southern Quebec to southern Vermont. Shaw (1958) recorded thicknesses of the Dunham up to 900 m thick in northwestern Vermont, although the lower part of the formation is truncated by the Champlain thrust at most localities, and continuous sections down to the underlying Cheshire Formation are absent everywhere along the western margin of the St. Albans synclinorium.

Swanton Junction road cut in upper Dunham Dolostone.— The road cut at Swanton Junction lies just above the Champlain thrust, and only a thin succession through the upper Dunham Formation is present. The rocks of the road cut (ca. 8 m) are almost flat-lying, thin- to medium-bedded, grayish weathering, pink-colored, medium-grained sucrosic dolostones with thin, pink, dolomitic shale laminae. Stylolitization along the dolostone laminae may explain the somewhat nodular appearance of many of the beds. Body fossils (rare brachiopod valves) and limited evidence of burrowing suggest restricted marine (probably elevated salinity) depositional environments. Shaw (1958) noted the occurrence of orange through red and violet dolostones above lower gray dolostones in the "carbonate facies" of the Dunham Formation. This stop is in the upper part of the "carbonate facies" of the Dunham.

South of the Missisquoi River, the "carbonate facies" is overlain by a thin (10–25 m-thick) "sandy facies" of dolomitic quartz arenite, quartz arenite, red feldspathic sandstone, and black shale that thickens northward (Landing, this volume, fig. 3). The Dunham is represented only by the "sandy facies" north of the Missisquoi River (Shaw, 1958).

Biostratigraphy.—Trilobites from localities in the "calcareous" and "sandy facies" of the Dunham Formation are uncommon, and have not received modern study. *Antagmus typicalis* Resser, 1937; *A.? simplex* Resser, 1937; *Billingsaspis adamsi* (Billings, 1861); *Bonniella desiderata* (Walcott, 1891); and *Ptychoparella teucer* (Billings, 1861) indicate a reference of the Dunham to the *Olenellus* Zone s.l. Older *Olenellus* Zone assemblages occur in the underlying Cheshire Formation in southern Vermont (Walcott, 1891), and uppermost *Olenellus* Zone assemblages occur in the lower part of the overlying Parker Formation (Shaw, 1954, 1957). Mehrtens and Gregory (1984) recovered *Salterella conulata* Clark, 1924, from open-shelf facies of the middle Dunham Dolostone, and used the occurrence to support a correlation with the upper *Olenellus* Zone s.l.

Travel to Stop 4.7

At the end of Stop 4.6, continue south on Rte 7. At 0.8 miles, pass low outcrops and road cuts in east-dipping Parker Formation. Pass by commercial strip and enter St. Albans; at 4.4

miles, turn right (west) onto Lower Newton Road at four-way stop light in northern St. Albans, and drive an additional 1.8 miles. Park on graveled area at transformer station on south side of Lower Newton Road; walk ca. 270 m south on railroad tracks to low overgrown railroad cut on west side of tracks. Examine this cut and more extensive cuts to south on east side of tracks.

Stop 4.7, Epeirogenic development of the Franklin basin and Schuchert's "mushrooms" (25 minutes)

History of study.—Schuchert (1937, p. 1025, 1034, fig. 8) correlated the sharp lithologic break from the carbonates of the Dunham Formation into the mudstone-dominated Parker Formation with a "distinct erosion interval." Stop 4.7 is Schuchert's (1937) locality VII and Shaw's (1954) locality SA-C-5, where this erosion is supposedly best exemplified by erosive, ca. 3 m-deep channels on the Dunham. Schuchert's (1937, fig. 8; Figure 20) drawing of the Dunham–Parker contact shows the presence of mushroom-like domes of Dunham at the contact. The presence of *Olenellus* Zone s.l. faunas from the upper Dunham and lower Parker has been cited as evidence of a short hiatus (e.g., Shaw, 1958).

FIGURE 20—Schuchert's "mushrooms" at Stop 4.7. Schuchert's (1937, fig. 8) illustration of a deeply eroded unconformity surface on the Dunham Dolostone (the "Mallett dolomite" of the figure) at the Dunham–Parker Formation contact is reinterpreted on this field trip. The dolostone "pedestals" are massive clasts of Dunham Formation within the basal Parker Formation that were transported as debris flow blocks from a fault scarp(s) to the south.

Re-evaluation of Dunham–Parker unconformity.—Re-examination of the succession at Stop 4.7 shows no evidence for erosive channeling on the Dunham Formation. Rather, the succession shows a lower conglomerate overlain by about a meter of dark green to dark gray mudstone. The characteristic dolomitic strata of the Dunham Formation are not exposed.

The section begins with a conglomerate that consists of brown-weathering dolostone blocks derived from the "sandy facies" of the upper Dunham Formation (Shaw, 1958, discussed above). These cobble- to boulder-sized dolostone blocks float in an unsorted matrix comprised of dolostone fragments (sand- to pebble-sized) and quartz sand. One of the dolostone blocks on the west side of the tracks is 1.2 m x 0.7 m x 0.4 m in size. Exposures of this conglomerate are at least 10 m thick on the east side of the tracks, and the dolostone blocks are up to 2.0 m in diameter. Deposition of the conglomerate was in a marine environment, and Shaw (1954, locality SA-C-5) described a small, upper *Olenellus* Zone fauna from the matrix of the conglomerate [*Bonnia capito* (Walcott, 1916) and *Ptychoparella teucer* (Billings, 1861) (trilobites); *Nisusia festinata* (Billings, 1861) and *N. transversa* (Walcott, 1886) (brachiopods); probable echinoderm plates]. The conglomerate is overlain by less than a meter of dark green sandstone composed of quartz and dolomite sand, and then by ca. 0.5 m of silty, green and dark gray mudstone.

The re-interpretation of the succession at Stop 4.7 is that a marine-deposited debris flow(s) with blocks of Dunham dolostone, an overlying allodapic dolomite sandstone, and a short interval of dark mudstone comprise the lowest Parker Formation. Schuchert (1937) and Shaw (1954) likely regarded the very large blocks of dolostone as mushroom-like erosional pinnacles on a subaerial erosion surface on the Dunham because mechanisms by which submarine pebbly mudstone and rockfall deposits are deposited were only understood after their work (e.g., Gorsline and Emery, 1959; Bourcart, 1964). Interestingly, Rodgers (1968, fig. 10-1 caption) noted reports of a dolostone conglomerate at the Dunham–Parker contact, but did not discuss the significance of this succession.

***Epeirogeny and origin of the dysoxic/anoxic Franklin Basin on the east Laurentian platform.*—**Reconnaissance of the Dunham–Parker contact shows that this conglomerate is widespread in the Franklin basin (E. Landing, unpub. data). As noted below, a second outcrop of this basal Parker Formation conglomerate will be seen immediately east of the intersection of Rte. 7 with the access road to interchange 19 on Interstate 89. The coincidence of this widespread, basal Parker conglomerate at the transition from the shallow-water Dunham platform into the persistent dysoxic facies of the Franklin basin suggests that it marks an epeirogenic episode on that part of east Laurentia that lay close to the southern margin of the Ottawa graben. The suggestion is that formation of the Franklin basin resulted from epeirogenic re-adjustments along the cooling margin of east Laurentia. These adjustments apparently included the geologically abrupt formation of a sharp shelf–basin break, perhaps by faulting, that allowed collapse and mass-movement of boulders derived from the platform margin into deeper-water, dysoxic/anoxic facies of the newly formed Franklin basin.

Landing and Bartowski (1996) and Landing *et al.* (2002) had earlier proposed that the abrupt vertical transition from the platform carbonates of the Dunham Formation into the black mudstones of the Parker Formation was the local expression of eustatic onlap in the Lower–Middle Cambrian boundary interval following the Hawke Bay regression. Although this lithofacies transition from carbonate platform into black mudstone basin took place at about the same time as the terminal Lower Cambrian Hawke Bay regression (see Landing *et al.*, 2006), this interpretation is no longer acceptable because the primary cause of the vertical lithofacies change was epeirogenic.

Travel to hotel

***Stop 4.7–St. Albans.*—**At end of Stop 4.7, return east on Lower Newton Street to Rte. 7. Aldis Hill directly ahead (east) of the stop light at Rte. 7 is a thrust slice with west dipping lower Dunham and upper Cheshire Formations (Shaw, 1958). Shaw (1954, p. 1034, locality SA-SE-3) reported, but never illustrated, "three imperfect specimens" of the agglutinated conoidal problematicum *Salterella* Billings, 1861, and unidentifiable trilobite fragments from beds "which are probably 100 feet below the top of the Gilman" [= Cheshire Formation] on the northeast slope of Aldis Hill.

***Roadcut through Dunham–Parker unconformity.*—**Turn right (south) on Rte. 7, and follow road for 1.1 miles through St.

Albans. At access road to Interstate 89, turn left (east). The east-dipping section immediately at the west end of the access road includes: 1) Dunham Formation—gray weathering, medium- to thick-bedded, arenaceous dolostones and dolomitic quartz arenites of the "sandy facies" of the upper Dunham Formation (Shaw, 1958) and 2) Parker Formation—several meters of sheared debris flows with orange weathering dolostone cobbles and boulders in greenish weathering matrix [best exposed on north side of access road] and several meters of greenish weathering slate. Directly in front of the vehicle is St. Albans Hill, a thrust slice of resistant Cheshire Formation.

***Interstate 89–Lemoile River.*—**Exit access road to Interstate 89 south to Burlington. From mile post 117 and the Town of Fairfax border, the Adirondack Mountains first become visible to the right (southwest). Road cuts from a mile north of Exit 18 to Exit 18 (to Georgia Center) are in Dunham Formation. Milepost 105 lies near dark mudstones and thin sandstones of the Skeels Corners Formation (upper Middle Cambrian, upper Marjuman Stage, *Cedaria* Zone).

***Franklin Basin slope–platform break.*—**At milepost 102.5, begin passing a half-mile-long series of high road cuts in sheared, probably Middle Cambrian mudstones, and cross bridge over Lemoile River. These mudstones lie at the southern margin of the Franklin basin, and the Lemoile River marks the approximate transition to the Cambrian–Ordovician platform succession of the Middlebury synclinorium (Stone and Dennis, 1964). As in the St. Albans synclinorium, the parautochthonous, north–south-trending Middlebury synclinorium also lies above and east of the Champlain thrust. The Middlebury synclinorium forms the western margin of the Lake Champlain lowlands, and is structurally overlain by the Taconic allochthon in southern Vermont–western Massachusetts–east central New York [see Zen, 1967, for an early, thorough synthesis of the structural relationships of the Taconic allochthon and the underlying Middlebury synclinorium.]

***Platform succession from Lemoile River–Shelburne, Vermont.*—**The first road cuts south of the Lemoile River are in lower Middle Cambrian sandstones of the Monkton Formation; road cuts in the Monkton again appear from mileposts 97 to 94.5, with the southern road cuts showing the red sandstones of the upper part of the formation. The Monkton reappears in road cuts from mileposts 92.5–92, and the overlying massive, yellow-weathering beds of the Middle Cambrian Winooski Dolostone appear in road cuts as Exit 16 (to Winooski) is approached and further south across the Winooski River.

Take Exit 13 to Interstate 189; drive short distance west to Rte 7. Turn left (south) on Rte 7 and drive 1.7 miles to large hotel complex in Shelburne, Vermont.

AUGUST 4: LOWER–MIDDLE CAMBRIAN BOUNDARY INTERVAL OF THE EASTERN PLATFORM IN VERMONT AND EDIACARAN(?)–CAMBRIAN OF THE WESTERN GREEN MOUNTAIN ANTICLINORIUM

Overview

The trip begins with a stop just south of the hotel that shows the local expression of the Lower–Middle Cambrian boundary interval Hawke Bay "event" [see summary of eustatic history of this "event" in Landing *et al.* (2006) and in Landing (this volume)]—the regressive, terminal Lower–early Middle Cambrian(?) Monkton Quartzite (Keith, 1923) and overlying Winooski Dolostone (Cady, 1945) in the Middlebury synclinorium, western Vermont (Stop 5.1).

Stops further south along the west flank of the Green Mountain anticlinorium near Pittsford Mills, Vermont, complement the Franklin Basin succession to the north (Stops 4.1–4.7, above) by illustrating the Cheshire Formation and underlying units in a succession deposited close to the eastern margin of the Laurentian platform. Correlative units deposited off the Laurentian platform and on the east Laurentian continental slope will be seen on August 5.

The middle Proterozoic core of the Green Mountains [Mount Holly Complex (Whittle, 1891)] is nonconformably overlain on the west flank of the Green Mountain anticlinorium by a low-grade metamorphic succession [Pinnacle (greenish siliciclastics, Stops 5.4, 5.5)–Forestdale (dolomite marble, Stops 5.2C–5.4)–Moosalamoo (black phyllite with beds of white quartzite, Stop 5.2B)–Cheshire (quartzites with beds of black phyllite low in the formation, Stop 5.2A)]. This conformable succession is apparently all referable to the upper Lower Cambrian (*Olenellus* Zone s.l.) (Landing, preceeding report, this volume), and represents the oldest sedimentary rock locally deposited on the cooling and subsiding margin of east Laurentia following the late Proterozoic rifting of the Rodinia supercontinent. The Forestdale Marble is the oldest carbonate platform lithosome in east Laurentia. The post-Cheshire succession on the west limb of the Green Mountain anticlinorium continues up through the mixed carbonate-siliciclastic platform succession of the east Laurentian platform (Stop 5.6).

Travel to Stop 5.1

Turn left (south) from hotel complex onto Rte 7; travel 2.3 miles and turn right onto side road that allows left-hand turns across Rte 7 and onto Webster Road. Park at long road cut along side road.

Stop 5.1, Winooski Dolostone and Hawke Bay eustasy (15 minutes)

The stop features ca. 10 m of north-dipping, thin- to medium-bedded, light gray to pinkish dolostone that characterize the lower Winooski. The dolostones at the stop locally have abundant quartz sand, show sparse burrowing, and have planar laminations. A black mafic dike, likely related to the Mesozoic intrusions that extend along much of the Middlebury synclinoriun, at the north end of the cut shows baked contacts.

The facies at Stop 5.1 is distinguishable from the upper Winooski, which is characterized by medium gray dolostone (e.g., Welby, 1961). Red sandstones of the Monkton Quartzite are exposed a short stratigraphic distance below this section in road cuts on Rte. 7 immediately south of Stop 5.1.

Travel to Stops 5.2A–C

Shelburne–Mount Philo.—At end of stop, continue south on Rte. 7—the distances listed below are miles from the hotel. Exposures of red quartz arenite along Rte 7 just south of Stop 5.1 are in upper Monkton Formation. Cross Otter Creek and note additional exposures of red quartz arenites of Monkton.

Pass through village of Shelburne, Vermont, at 3.5 miles. At 5.3 miles, enter Charlotte township; note "dual exposure" of

middle Proterozoic (Grenvillian orogen) in Adirondack Mountains (to west) and high peaks of Green Mountains (eastern skyline). Lake Champlain becomes visible to southwest with descent of hill (7.6 miles).

Series of black shale road cuts on east side of Rte 7 (7.6–9.0 miles) are in Late Ordovician Stony Point Shale (Ruedemann, 1921)—the Stony Point and overlying Iberville Shale (Clark, 1934) are black mudstones correlative with the Utica Shale. They are supposedly distinguished by being calcareous and noncalcareous, respectively (e.g., Welby, 1961), and are the first siliciclastic-dominated deposits of the Taconian orogeny. The contortion visible in these cuts of Stony Point Shale reflect deformation under the Champlain thrust with westward movement of the Middlebury synclinorium slice.

Mount Philo in Mount Philo State Park visible to east of road (10.8 miles) lies on the Champlain thrust. This butte-like hill has a cap of Lower–Middle Cambrian boundary interval Monkton Formation that structurally overlies Late Ordovician synorogenic mudstone and sandstone; gray weathering Monkton Formation is visible on the western crest of Mount Philo.

At 14.8 miles, large road cut in Stony Point Shale on east side of road shows contorted black shales with quartz-filled tension gashes. Enter outskirts of Ferrisburg, Vermont (15.4 miles).

Mount Philo–Middlebury, Vermont.—At 17.2 miles, low road cut on east shows thin-bedded, light gray weathering limestones in black shale of the Glen Falls Formation—the Upper Ordovician Glens Falls Formation (top of the Trenton Group) underlies the Iberville Shale, and represents the last Ordovician limestone deposition in eastern New York and western Vermont.

Intersection of Rte. 7 with Rte. 22A (17.7 miles); continue southeast on Rte. 7. Just southeast of intersection, note low dip slope in Glens Falls Formation limestones several hundred meters beyond intersection on right side (south) of Rte. 7. Climb hill over internally thrust-repeated, Glens Falls–Stony Hollow succession (19.5 miles), low hills directly ahead that form skyline ahead (southeast) of vehicle are formed of parautochthonous rocks of Middlebury synclinorium.

At 23.3 miles, intersection with Vermont Rte. 17; continue south on Rte. 7. Note spectacular scenery in Green Mountains to east (e.g., cirques with high walls and U-shaped valleys formed by mountain glaciers in latest Pleistocene). At 27.7 miles, cross New Haven River.

Middlebury–Brandon, Vermont.—Enter outskirts of Middlebury, Vermont (29.9 miles); continue through city on Rte. 7. The older buildings in Middlebury, including those of Middlebury College, are constructed of locally derived, gray weathering Middlebury Limestone. The Middlebury Limestone is a tectonically significant unit. With loading and subsidence of the eastern margin of Laurentia by the westward moving Taconian alloththon, the Middlebury was deposited in the Middlebury synclinorium succession as a deeper-water, turbiditic limestone deposit. The Middlebury is an allodapic limestone unit correlative with the reef-bearing facies of the lower Upper Ordovician Chazy Group further west in the Champlain valley and on the stable platform. As the Taconic allochthon advanced further west and the Middlebury synclinorium succession began to be thrust, more interior parts of the east Laurentian margin were depressed, and the younger (middle Late Ordovician) Glens Falls Limestone records deepening in front of the advancing allochthon.

After leaving Middlebury, road cut (33.3 miles) on both sides of Rte. 7 in sandy dolostones is referable to the lower Upper Cambrian Galway Formation [in the Middlebury synclinorium, a mixed dolostone-quartz arenite termed the "Clarendon Springs Formation" (Keith, 1932) is a junior synonym of the Galway Formation]. At 35.2 miles, junction with Rte. 125 on west side of East Middlebury, Vermont; enter Town of Salisbury (36.7 miles). At 41.4 miles, cross creek and pass outcrops of thin bedded, white-weathering (bleached?) limestone.

At 45.0 miles, the ridge forming the skyline directly in front of the vehicle marks the eastern margin of the Taconic allochthon.

Brandon–Stop 5.2A–C.—During the drive southward through Brandon (entered at 46.9 miles), the west skyline is formed by the Taconic Range and the eastern skyline is defined by the Green Mountains. The intervening lowland, or "Vermont valley," is underlain by Cambrian–lower Upper Ordovician carbonates of the Vermont marble belt.

Pass through Brandon, Vermont; the high peak visible southeast of the intersection with Rte. 73 is Mount Nickwacket, just east of Stops 5A–C (Figure 21). A series of road cuts and a quarry just southeast of Brandon (48.7 miles) are probably in Upper Cambrian Little Falls Formation. The high peaks of the Taconic Range appear southwest of the road.

Exit Rte. 7 at Citgo station (50.8 miles) onto McConnell Road. Continue north on McConnell Road for 1.1 miles; turn right on Birch Hill Road (dirt) (52.4 miles) and ascend hill. At stop sign at T-junction with North Birch Hill Road (53 miles), turn right (south). Follow North Birch Hill Road for about 1.2 miles, and park about 100 m west of the old green house on the right (south) and 300 m east of the sharp south bend on North Birch Hill Road (Figure 21).

Stops 5.2A–C, Terminal Proterozoic?–Lower Cambrian near Birch Hill Road–North Birch Hill Road intersection (25 minutes)

Stops 5.2A–C are made during a walk east to the sharp turn on North Birch Hill Road (Figure 21). This section from the lower Cheshire through the underlying Mossamaloo Phyllite and down into the Forestdale Marble is poorly exposed, but outlines the sequence. [Stops 5.2A–C correspond to Osberg's (1959) Stops 1–3.]

Stop 5.2A.—The lithologies of the lower Cheshire Formation are observable from loose boulders on east slope of the crest of the low hill on the north side of the road. The lithologies range from white, well sorted, massive, coarse-grained "supermature" siliceous quartz arenite to thin-bedded, medium bedded, greenish quartz arenite.

At the end of Stop 5.2A, walk east, and begin gentle descent down hill ca. 50 m east of old green house. The peaks of Mount Nickwacket are visible directly to the east.

Stop 5.2B.—This section of the walk features low exposures of the Moosamaloo Phyllite on the north side of the road. Black phyllite and rare thin-bedded, black, medium-grained, argillaceous sandstone beds with large pyrite cubes occur in the grass where the road margin has been cut back. These low exposures extend for ca. 175 m, and almost reach the sharp bend on North Birch Hill Road. Deposition of the Moosamaloo Formation took place in anoxic/highly dysoxic environments

prior to deposition of the shallow water, high energy facies of the Cheshire Formation.

Stop 5.2C.—This part of the walk features very limited outcrops of the middle facies (sandy dolostone) of the Forestdale Marble at the base of the high cut on the west side of North Birch Hill Road. These limited outcrops are at road level, and located ca. 50 m south of the sharp bend on North Birch Hill Road.

Travel to Stop 5.3

At end of Stop 5.2C, drive south on North Birch Hill Road. Low road cut on left 0.8 miles south of the sharp bend shows east-dipping (overturned) sandy member of the Forestdale Member and more massive lower member further east in trees. At 1.1 miles south from Stop 5.2C is a second sharp bend to the east and a fresh road cut in the Forestdale Marble. Park close to road cut.

Stop 5.3, Forestdale Marble (15 minutes)

Approximately 30 m of west-dipping (not overturned), light gray, medium-grained marble is exposed in the road cut. The western part of the cut shows tight, small parasitic folds. Primary sedimentary structures include bi-directional tabular cross beds 2 m above the base of the cut. These cross beds are defined by light and light-medium gray layers, and probably reflect the original color of the limestone. These cross beds indicate that the marble was originally composed, at least in these beds, of sand-sized material that was moved around in relatively shallow marine water. In short, the Forestdale Marble and apparently coeval, sub-Cheshire marbles on the west limb of the Green Mountain anticlinorium [White Brook Marble and Battell Member in northern Vermont and southern Quebec] and east limb of the anticlinorium in eastern Vermont [Plymouth Marble and Sherman Marble] represents the oldest carbonate platform lithosome in east Laurentia. The Forestdale is relatively well exposed and weakly deformed on the west flank of the Green Mountain anticlinorium, and may yield acid-resistant microfossils that would help refine its age (project undertaken by EL).

Travel to Stop 5.4

At end of Stop 5.3, continue south on North Birch Hill Road. At 1.3 miles south of Stop 5.3, pass high (8 m) cut in white and light pink Forestdale Marble. This gently east-dipping section is overturned. The medium-bedded marbles are very fine-grained, with interbeds of "argillaceous" green marble. Slabbed samples taken in a preliminary study of the cut show only a vaguely developed planar lamination.

Additional exposures of Forestdale include a large moss covered surface just east of the road (2.2 miles south of Stop 5.2C) and a large ridge (2.6 miles). Stop 3.3 miles south of Stop 5.2C opposite low, northeast-dipping outcrops in woods on east side of road.

Stop 5.4, Pinnacle–Forestdale contact (15 minutes)

This stop [Stop 7 of Osberg (1959)] shows the contact of the Forestdale Marble with the underlying Pinnacle Formation. Gray and white dolostone marble with local cross bedding of the Forestdale is exposed close to the road, and lies in a tight, westerly overturned syncline. The Pinnacle is exposed further east in the trees, and includes lower light gray, quartz-

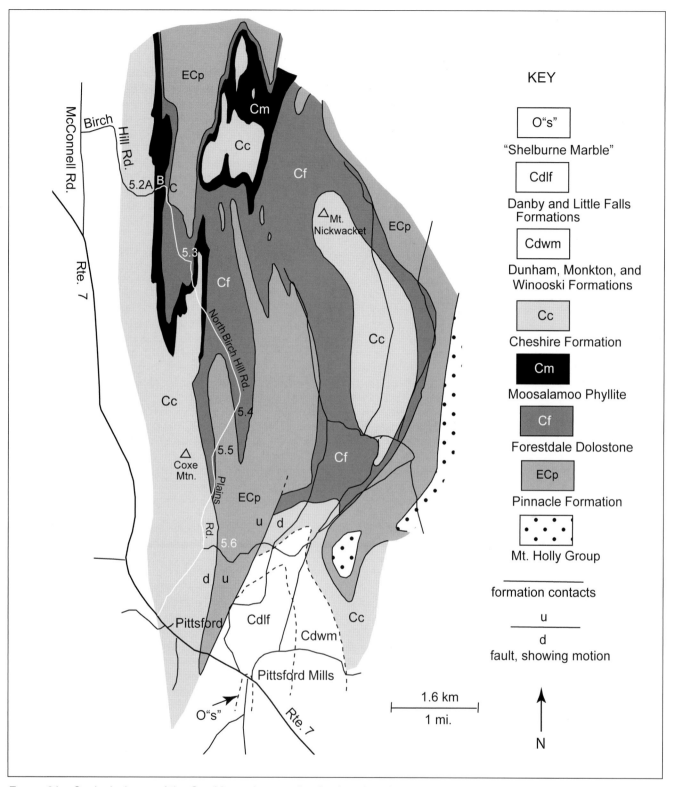

FIGURE 21—Geological map of the Cox Mountain area showing location of stops 5.2A–5.6. Figure modified from Osberg (1959, pl. F-2). The Danby Formation (dolomitic quartz arenites and arenaceous dolostones) is the outer platform equivalent of the Potsdam and Galway Formations on the inner platform in eastern New York and southwest Vermont. "Little Falls Formation" replaces the traditional Vermont term "Clarendon Springs Formation" [these "units," as well as the "Whitehall Formation" further south, are lithologically comparable, coeval (late Late Cambrian) carbonate units, with "Little Falls Formation" being the senior synonym (Landing, 2002; Landing *et al.*, 2003a)]. The traditional designation "Shelburne Marble" is only a slightly metamorphosed variant of the Tribes Hill Formation of eastern New York and southern Vermont.

muscovite-feldspar gneiss with relict quartz and feldspar grains. A generalize fining-up succession is indicated by the presence of upper light green, quartz-muscovite-chlorite schist (ca. 20 m east of road) in contact with the Forestdale Formation.

Travel to Stop 5.5

At end of stop, continue south on North Birch Hill Road. Climb hill and stop near crest 3.8 miles south of Stop 5.2C.

Stop 5.5, Pinnacle Formation (10 minutes)

The low cut on the east side of the road features low outcrops of light green phyllite with thin sandstone laminae of the upper Pinnacle Formation. Across the road on the west is a high ridge of Forestdale Marble and overlying Cheshire Formation on its west side.

Travel to Stop 5.6

At end of stop, continue south. Park at 5.0 miles at T-junction of Sugar Hollow Road (North Birch Hill Road has this name at its south end) and Plains Road. Walk about 150 m east along Plains Road, and walk north up first driveway north from Plains Road.

Stop 5.6, Pinnacle–Cheshire contact (20 minutes)

At this stop [Stop 8 of Osberg (1959)] on the east side of the driveway, nearly vertical, light to medium, gray-green quartz-biotite-feldspar-muscovite schist of the Pinnacle Formation is in contact with poorly exposed Cheshire Formation. The Cheshire is best represented by rounded boulders of white and light gray quartzite, with some of the blocks composed of conglomeratic quartzite and dolomitic, feldspathic sandstone. Osberg (1959) considered the convergence of the Cheshire with the Pinnacle in the Cox Mountain area (Figure 21) to reflect an angular unconformity, and considered the base of the Cheshire to be a disconformity in the Green Mountain anticlinorium (Osberg, 1952; also Keith, 1932, and Fowler, 1950). However, limited exposure and the likelihood that the resistant Cheshire provided a focus for bedding-parallel faulting and decollement suggest that local sub-Cheshire "unconformities" are simply faulted contacts.

Travel to Stop 5.7

At end of stop return to vehicles. Turn left onto Plains Road and drive to intersection with Hitchcock Road. Turn right on Hitchcock for a short distance, then left onto Furnace Road. Drive up hill to intersection with Adams Road; turn right onto Adams. Drive south on Adams Road for 1.4 miles toward Pittsford Mills, note High Peaks of Taconic Range to west; the route is down an axis of a syncline that begins in the Cheshire Formation and includes Lower Ordovician in its core south of Pittsford Mills. At intersection with Oxbow Road, turn right and follow Oxbow Road to T-intersection with Rte 7. Park vehicle at end of Oxbow Road, and climb down stream bank to section under bridge.

Stop 5.7, "Shelburne Marble" (Tribes Hill Formation) (20 minutes)

A 15 m-thick, vertical section in light yellowish gray, buff weathering dolostone of the "Shelburne Marble" is exposed under the bridge Osberg (1959). As discussed above, the

"Shelburne" is a junior synonym of the Tribes Hill Formation. A reconnaissance sample (6.0 kg) taken in 2006 by EL 1.5 m above the base of the section did not yield conodont elements.

Travel to hotel

At end of stop, turn left (south) on Rte. 7. Follow Rte. 7 for ca. 9 miles through Rutland, Vermont; turn right into hotel just north of exit to Rte 4 (west).

AUGUST 5: CAMBRIAN OF THE TACONIC ALLOCHTHON, EASTERN NEW YORK—CONTINENTAL SLOPE MUDSTONE COLORS, EUSTASY, AND BOTTOM-WATER OXYGENATION

Overview

The last day of the field trip illustrates the latest rift–drift (passive margin)–convergent margin facies succession that comprise the Cambrian–Ordovician of the Taconic allochthon in eastern New York. This condensed succession was deposited off the eastern margin of the Laurentian platform, and represents the deepest-water succession on the trip. The most coherent (i.e., weakly tectonically deformed) stratigraphy preserved in the Taconic allochthon crops out in the structurally low, western Giddings Brook slice. Almost all known fossil localities and all slate production occur in the Giddings Brook slice. Natural exposures, quarries, and road cuts in the Giddings Brook slice allow examination of the complete Cambrian–Ordovician succession in a series of localities in northern Washington County to Columbia County, New York (Figure 1, localities 6.1–6.10).

The Giddings Brook succession (see Landing, this volume, fig. 5) includes feldspathic, turbiditic sandstones (Bomoseen Member) referable to the end of the end of rifting and subsidence of the east Laurentian margin. Lithologic similarities exist between the Bomoseen–Truthville Slate succession (Stops 6.1, 6.7) and the Pinnacle Formation on the west flank of the Green Mountain anticlinorium, while recovery of trilobite sclerites (this report) suggest an upper Lower Cambrian correlation of the Zion Hill quartzites at the top of the Bomoseen. Overlying Cambrian units feature two black–green mudstone macroscale alternations that are interpreted to be a proxy for major eustatic changes. The black, dysoxic/anoxic Browns Pond Formation, with one or two thick, coarse-grained quartzites in its lower part that resemble those of the Cheshire Formation, and lower *Elliptocephala asaphoides* assemblages in its upper part, is equated with the Cheshire–Dunham eustatic high (Stops 6.2, 6.5). The succeeding green mudstone-dominated, oxic facies of the Middle Granville Formation is equated with the Hawke Bay regression (Stops 6.2, 6.5, 6.10), while the terminal Lower Cambrian–lowest Ordovician Hatch Hill Formation (black mudstones and sandstones) is considered to reflect a long interval of generally high eustatic levels (Stops 6.3, 6.4, 6.10). Macroscale black (anoxic)–green (oxic) mudstone alternations continue through the Lower–lower Upper Ordovician (Stops 6.3, 6.9), and are a proxy for high and low eustatic levels, respectively. Although not yet recognized in the Cambrian of the Taconic allochthon, microscale black–green–buff mudstone alternations known as Logan cycles in the Lower Ordovician of the Taconic allochthons from eastern New York to eastern

Quebec may reflect climate variations in the Milankovic band (Stop 6.8), and should be searched for in Cambrian upper slope successions elsewhere.

Travel to Stop 6.1

Hotel–base of High Taconic Range.—Leave hotel, turn south on Rte. 7, almost immediately turn right (west) onto exit ramp to Rte. 4 (west). On entering Rte. 4, the high ridge directly ahead that forms the skyline and the western margin of the Vermont valley is the High Taconic Range (Bird Mountain slice). Cross Otter Creek (1.2 miles). Pass exit to West Rutland; begin ascent of lower slopes of High Taconic Range.

Pass road cut in sheared Upper Ordovician mudstone that underlies the Taconic allochthon [mudstones, frequently comprising a wildflysch with tectonized blocks of Taconic siliciclastics, Vermont valley-type carbonates, and even Grenville metamorphic rocks, crop out all around the margins of the Taconic allochthon; see Zen (1967, p. 35–40)].

High Taconic Range (Bird Mountain slice).—Above the Upper Ordovician mudstone, the route ascends the northern end of of the Bird Mountain slice. The Bird Mountain slice is largely composed of Lower Cambrian green phyllites and low grade schist seen in a series of long road cuts beginning 5.0 miles from hotel. The Adirondacks become visible as the western skyline at 7.0 miles with the descent down the western slope of the High Taconic Range. Pass rest area at 8.0 miles; enter town of Castleton (8.8 miles); additional road cuts of green phyllites of Bird Mountain slice occur at 10.0–10.8 miles near exit to Castleton State College.

Eastern Giddings Brook slice–New York border.—Pass into lower grade metamorphic rocks of the Low Taconics of the Giddings Brook slice near the exit to Castleton, Vermont; note road cuts in Lower Cambrian, purple and red slates of Middle Granville Formation at 12.2 miles and just before Exit 4 (13.6 miles).

Upper Ordovician black shales with bedded limestone in road cut at 14.4 miles may be caught at base of Pine Pond slice within the Giddings Brook slice.

Cross southern end of Lake Bomoseen (15.3 miles) and pass road cuts in Lower Cambrian(?) Bomoseen Formation (Stops 6.1, 6.7) and Lower Cambrian green and purple slate (15.8–16.0 miles). Exit to Fair Haven (16.6 miles) with cut in interbedded black shale and thin micrites ("ribbon limestones") of upper Lower Cambrian Browns Pond Formation (Stops 6.2, 6.5; below). Pass Exit 2 (17.6 miles) and road cut in green Lower Cambrian slates (18.0).

New York border–Washington Co. Rte. 18 intersection.—Cross bridge across small Poultney River, and enter New York (19.3 miles) (the mileages for the remainder of the trip are measured from the New York–Vermont line). [Notice how road maintenance, road width, and property maintenance abruptly diminish as New York is entered.]

The first part of the route across the border in New York (through 3.9 miles) is in the Giddings Brook slice—dark road cut on right (0.4 miles) is in upper Lower Cambrian Browns Pond Formation in core of small syncline (Fisher, 1984, pl. 1); at 0.6 miles, the road cuts on left (south) are in light gray-green overlying Middle Granville Slate on east limb of large syncline; Middle Granville Slate is in road cut at curve in road (1.6 miles)

on west limb of same syncline. At 1.7, miles enter Town of Whitehall. At 1.8 miles near core of large syncline, note small cut on north side of road with spectacular, contorted, thin micrite beds ("ribbon limestones") in black mudstone (upper Hatch Hill Formation, uppermost Cambrian or lowest Ordovician). Immediately to the west, the small quarry to the north with trailers (1.9 miles) is also in upper Hatch Hill Formation.

With descent through the normal, west limb of the large syncline, the exposures in the descending succession include the Middle Granville Slate (road cuts at 2.2, 2.4, 2.5 miles in gray green slate) and Bomoseen Formation (road cuts in resistant greenish sandstones with intercalated green mudstones on both sides of road, 2.7–3.4 miles).

At ca. 3.9 miles, cross Taconic masterthrust, and enter Upper Ordovician, Taconian wildflysch belt (at the end of the woods and with the appearance of subdued, flatter topography). Note low peaks of middle Proterozoic Adirondack Mountains directly to west beyond village of Whitehall; to the northwest is east slope on terminal Middle Cambrian–lower Lower Ordovician Laurentian platform rocks of Skene Mountain (Stops 2.1, 2.2).

Washington Co. Rte. 18–Stop 6.1.—Make hard left (5.0 miles) from Rte. 4 onto Washington Co. Rte. 18. Immediately climb low slope and pass large antiques shop (on left) and cemetery (on right) underlain by cratonic upper Lower Ordovician Fort Cassin Formation of the carbonate platform. Light gray weathering rubbly outcrop in field on left (ca. 150 m from road) is small klippe of Potsdam Formation thrust on the Fort Cassin Formation; this small klippe of Potsdam immediately underlies the Taconian wildflysch (Fisher, 1984, pl. 1).

At ca. 5.5 miles, road descends to ESE as Taconic wildflysch belt is crossed—the forested low hills directly to the east are underlain by resistant Lower Cambrian Bomoseen Formation, and mark the leading edge of the Taconian allochthon. Interesction with Beckwith Road on left (6.2 miles).

At 6.6 miles, stop at exposure of Taconic masterthrust on left (north) side of Washington Co. Rte. 18.

Stop 6.1, Lower Cambrian Bomoseen Formation and Taconic masterthrust (5 minutes)

This is a brief stop for orientation and photography. The thin- to medium-bedded, light gray-weathering, cephalopod-bearing limestone at the base of the overgrown outcrop is a giant Wildflysch block of lower Upper Ordovician Isle la Motte Limestone (Emmons, 1842) of the Black River Group in the Forbes Hill wildflysch. The Wildflysch block is structurally overlain by brownish weathering, east-dipping, sheared sandstones of the Lower Cambrian(?) Bomoseen Formation.

Travel to Stop 6.2

At end of Stop 6.1, continue southeast and then east on Washington Co. Rte. 18. Intersection with Beckett Road to right (6.9 miles); at 7.2 miles, road cut on both sides in Bomoseen Formation. Stop at cross road in hamlet of East Whitehall (8.0 miles), turn right [temporary road cut in upper Hatch Hill Formation (Theokritoff, 1959) ca. 50 m to north on east side of road yielded turbidity current-disarticulated fragments of early meraspid, lower Upper Cambrian olenid trilobites (E. Landing, unpublished data)]. Low, grassy cuts on east side of road are in upper Hatch Hill Formation thin sandstones and black mudstones.

Greenish slates at 8.4 miles are in Deep Kill Formation [Ruedemann, 1902]; Lower–lower Middle Ordovician] in core of syncline. Descend section in adjacent anticline; road cuts on right (south) (8.6, 8.7 miles) in back rusty weathering, dolomitic sandstones and black mudstones in Hatch Hill Formation; gray green slates of upper Lower Cambrian Middle Granville Slate at 8.8 miles.

At Y-intersection with Holcombville Road (9.6 miles), bear right on Holcolmbville Road and drive south past road cuts in black slates and thin sandstones in east-dipping, overturned, upper Lower Cambrian Browns Pond Formation. Overlook of Browns Pond at 10.1 miles; park (10.7 miles) just north of road cuts on both sides of Holcombville Road near southeast end of Browns Pond.

Walk to road cut on east side of road. After inspection of this road cut, we will examine the overlying debris flow of the uppermost Browns Pond Formation on the west side of the road, and then examine the lowest green slates of the Middle Granville Formation in the pasture immediately northwest.

Stop 6.2, Late Early Cambrian Browns Pond dysoxic/anoxic interval and lower *Elliptocephala asaphoides* assemblage (15 minutes)

Browns Pond dysoxic interval. — This section may be regarded as the "type locality" for the late Early Cambrian Browns Pond dysoxic/anoxic interval on the east Laurentian slope (Landing *et al.*, 2002). The Browns Pond dysoxic/anoxic interval is recognized throughout the external thrusts of the Taconic allochthon in New York–Vermont and in Taconian Québec (Landing, this volume, fig. 5).

Faunas and lithology of the Browns Pond Formation. — This overturned section (30° E) in the upper Browns Pond Formation shows 2.5 m of dark gray, fine-grained sandstones (to 10 cm-thick) and slates with thin (decimeter-thick), lensing, sandstone pebble debris flows on the east side of the cut. Small-scale current cross-bedding in the orange-weathering, dolomitic quartz aenites shows that the section is overturned. Although centimeter-wide grazing trails occur on the top of some of the sandstone beds, burrows are rare, and fine lamination and other primary structures are not disturbed. Rare burrows, absence of a shelly fauna, and dark gray (carbonaceous) sediments are all consistent with deposition under dysoxic conditions (e.g., Sagemann *et al.*, 1991).

Debris flow cap of Browns Pond Formation. — The west side of the road cut is dominated by a thick (3.0+ m) limestone pebble to (rare) boulder clast debris flow with dolomitic sandstone matrix. The limestone clasts yield trilobites, archaeocyathans, mollusks, and calcareous and phosphatic problematica of the lower *Elliptocephala asaphoides* assemblage (see Landing and Bartowski, 1996) at this locality (Theokritoff, 1964).

None of the clasts show derivation from the carbonate platform. The clasts include nodular lime mudstones and bedded fossil packstones that are interpreted as allodapic clasts that initially accumulated as limestone on the upper slope, and were subsequently transported down slope. Pyrite-infilled and phosphate-replaced, calcareous conoidal fossils in these clasts (E. Landing, unpublished data) is consistent with the deposition/lithification of these limestones in a strongly dysaerobic environment that developed on the upper slope (see Landing

and Bartowski, 1996; Landing *et al.*, 2002).

Debris-flow conglomerate lenses are common as the cap unit of the Browns Pond Formation, and some have received local stratigraphic names (e.g., Ashley Hill Conglomerate in Landing, 1984). Locally, allodapic fossil hash packstones and debris lenses are the cap unit of the Browns Pond where the debris flow cap lenses out (e.g., Landing and Bartowski, 1996) (Stop 6.4, below). In either case, the conglomerates or bedded limestones are directly overlain by a green/green gray or locally purple or red siliciclastic mudstone unit in the Taconic allochthon.

Middle Granville Formation. — The lowest black–green transition in the late Early Cambrian is seen at Stop 6.2 immediately above the conglomerate with an abrupt transition into the lower green slates of the Middle Granville Slate. These green slates form low outcrops in the pasture to the west. Stops 6.5 and 6.6 (below) further illustrate this interval of improved oxygenation on the east Laurentian slope and relate the improved oxygenation to the latest Early Cambrian Hawke Bay regression of Palmer and James (1979). Sea-level still-stand and progradation of the shelf margin or sea-level fall at the onset of the Hawke Bay regression are mechanisms to explain the carbonate clast debris flows and allodapic limestones at the top of Browns Pond dysoxic/anoxic facies.

Travel to Stop 6.3

At end of Stop 6.2, continue south on Holcombville Road along strike of Browns Pond Formation. Turn left (west) on Tanner Hill Road (11.2 miles); almost immediately after turn, pass outcrops of overlying green-gray Middle Granville Slate on right (north). At 11.5 miles, park at foot of hill near base of high cuts in brownish weathering sandstones with black shales.

Stop 6.3 involves a ca. 0.5 mile walk along the north side of Tanner Hill Road from the base of the section through the lower Upper Ordovician Indian River Slate; the Hatch Hill–Deep Kill formational contact is at 11.7 miles, and the Deep Kill–Indian River contact at 11.8 miles on the upper west slope of the hill.

Stop 6.3, Hatch Hill dysoxic/anoxic interval (terminal Early Cambrian–earliest Ordovician) through early Late Ordovician paleo-oceanographic changes) (20 minutes)

The superb Tanner Hill section was first described by Rowley *et al.* (1979); the following comments are modified from Landing (2002). The walk up hill crosses the overturned east limb of a large syncline and ends in the syncline axis.

Hatch Hill Formation deposition. — Dolomitic quartz arenites; conglomeratic sandstones; and interbedded, minor dark gray and black siltstones and shales of the Hatch Hill Formation form the lowest part of the section. The medium- to massively bedded, coarse, lensing, conglomeratic sandstones and conglomerates that characterize the lowest part of this interval have typically been compared to submarine channel-fill deposits in reports on Taconic geology (e.g. Keith and Friedman, 1977, 1978; Friedman, 1979; Rowley *et al.*, 1979). However, significant erosion at the base of purported channels and vertical stratigraphic successions characteristic of channels have never been described in the Taconic regions. Thus, these coarse-grained sandstones and conglomerates may simply represent sand- and debris-sheet deposits that originated at many places along the shelf–slope break and upper slope, rather than from a persistent point source (submarine canyon head).

The sandstones of the Hatch Hill Formation become thinner-bedded and finer-grained higher in the section, and black mudstones become dominant. This entire interval with black mudstones up to an abrupt transition into the green-gray mudstones of the overlying Deep Kill Formation is the Hatch Hill Formation. The Hatch Hill records a long interval of persistent dysaerobic deposition on the east Laurentian continental slope (terminal Early Cambrian–lowest Ordovician [lowest Tremadocian] Hatch Hill dysoxic/anoxic interval) (see Landing, 1993; Landing *et al.*, 2002).

However, the changes in relative oxygenation of slope waters through this long interval are admittedly poorly known at present. Indeed, the development of three important Upper Cambrian "Grand Cycles" on the northeastern Laurentian shelf (Chow and James, 1987) should have been accompanied by sea-level and climate fluctuations recorded by changes in relative oxygenation on the continental slope. One explanation for the lack of any apparent record for changes in relative oxygenation through this interval may be that the transport and deposition of the thick sandstones that characterize the lower Hatch Hill served to erode and obscure much of the record of relative oxygenation that is recorded elsewhere in the Taconic succession by mudstones of various colors. Even with a maximum estimated thickness of 200 m (Rowley et al., 1979), the 20 m.y. interval bracketed by the Hatch Hill Formation indicates that it is a condensed unit that may have a number of unconformities produced during the transport and deposition of thick sand sheets. These sand sheets may have been emplaced primarily during eustatic lows.

Sandstones disappear in the upper Hatch Hill in the Tanner Hill section. The upper Hatch Hill corresponds to the interval of earliest Ordovician dysoxic/anoxic mudstone deposition that has been termed "Poultney A" (abandoned designation, Landing, 1988b) by Theokritoff (1959; Zen 1964).

Deep Kill Formation.—A sharp transition from the Hatch Hill Formation into the overlying green-gray mudstones of the Deep Kill Formation is present in the drainage ditch on the north side of Tanner Hill Road. Limited outcrop of the Deep Kill Formation likely explains the apparent absence of the black mudstone-limestone mesoscale intervals characteristic elsewhere of the formation (Landing, this volume, fig. 5).

Indian River Formation.—The transition into the lowest synorogenic sediments of the Taconic allochthon is observable just west of the crest of the hill with the appearance of low outcrops of the red, thin (ca. 50 m) Indian River Slate. Fisher (1961) attributed the red color of the Indian River to off-slope transport of lateritic sediments produced on the platform during development of the Knox unconformity. However, the rapid development of bacterial films on sediment grains with their transport into marine regimes regularly leads during early burial to a grayish sediment color, and an alternative explanation for the color of the Indian River must be found.

Landing (1988b) noted three lines of evidence in proposing that the Indian River reflects very slow deposition on an oxygenated sea-floor and long sediment residence time at the sediment-water interface. These lines of evidence include: 1) occurrence of radiolarian cherts and thin volcanic ashes undiluted by background argillaceous sediment; 2) thorough burrow-homogenization of much of the unit; and 3) presence of large, up to 3 cm-wide burrowers that were active on a well-oxygenated bottom).

Indian River Formation: oldest synorogenic deposit of Taconic orogeny.—The cherty, red slaty mudstones of the Indian River Slate mark an important stage early in the Taconic orogeny. As detailed by Landing *et al.* (1992), comparable red mudstones are widespread in a number of orogens, where they always underlie green mudstones and higher flysch (e.g., in the Taconian allochthons from New York to western Newfoundland, southern Uplands of Scotland, Hercynian Rheinisches Schiefergebirge and Hart Mountains, and Jurassic of Japan).

These data suggest that red, cherty, oxygenated shales in collisional orogens reflect the following history: 1) passage of a peripheral bulge through passive margin successions; 2) consequent flexural uplift and restriction of sedimentation on the peripheral bulge to slowly deposited pelagic muds, radiolarian cherts, and thin volcanic ashes of the Indian River-type; and 4) final flexural down-warping and increased rates of deposition as sediment provenance changes to the emergent accretionary prism (initial cherty green mudstones of Mount Merino-type and overlying Austin Glen flysch). The transition into the green-dominated, synorogenic mudstones of the overling Mount Merino and then into Austin Glen Formation flysch are present in the core of the Tanner Hill syncline.

Travel to Stop 6.4

At end of Stop 6.3, drive northwest along Tanner Hill Road. Begin descend hill through west (normal) limb of syncline (12.0 miles); Deep Kill outcrops on right (north) of road at 12.2 miles. Park (12.6 miles) opposite high, vegetated outcrop on left (south) side of road in thin, gently east-dipping (not overturned) sandstones and black shales of upper Hatch Hill Formation.

Stop 6.4, Cambrian–Ordovician boundary interval in upper Hatch Hill dysoxic/anoxic interval (15 minutes)

Graptolite and conodont biostratigraphy.—The Cambrian-Ordovician boundary occurs in the upper Hatch Hill Formation in northern and southern localities in the Taconic allochthon (Landing, this volume, fig. 5). An understanding of the Cambrian–Ordovician boundary interval in the Taconics came from a re-examination of three supposed "Upper Cambrian" dendroid graptolite genera that had been repeatedly cited at Stop 6.4 (Berry, 1959, 1961; Bird and Rasetti, 1968; Fisher, 1984).

Examination of these specimens in the NYSM Paleontology Collection showed the assemblage was not Upper Cambrian because it is comprised exclusively of rhabdosomes of the earliest Tremadocian form *Rhabdinopora flabelliformis praeparabola* Erdtmann, 1982 (Landing, 1993). This monospecific, lowest Tremadocian dendroid assemblage was re-located in a shaly interval (42.9–43.4 m) near the top of this cut on Tanner Hill Road (Figure 22). Twelve samples were processed for conodonts, but only a sample at 22.8 m yielded conodont elements—an upper Sunwaptan Stage fauna [*Eoconodontus notchpeakensis* Zone with *E.* (*E.*) *alisoniae* Landing, 1983; *E.* (*E.*) *notchpeakensis* (Miller, 1969); *Proconodontus muelleri* Miller, 1969]. These limited biostratigraphic data indicate that the base of the Ordovician lies in the interval 22.8 to 42.9 m, an interval without any evident stratigraphic break or lithofacies change (Figure 22).

Lithostratigraphy and regional comparisons.—The Stop 6.4 succession in the upper Hatch Hill Formation is dominated by thin- to medium-bedded dolomitic quartz arenites and dark

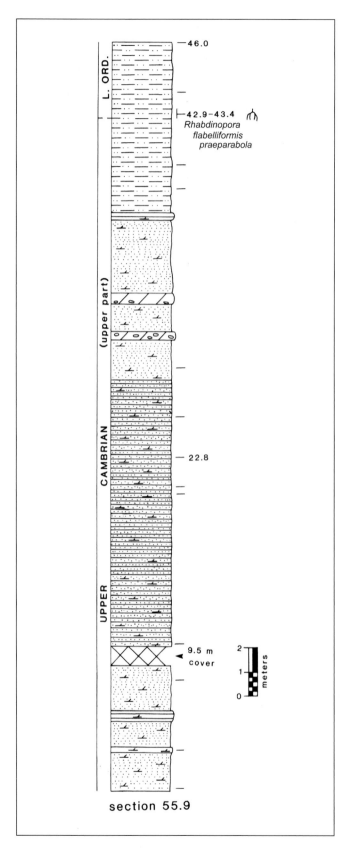

FIGURE 22—Cambrian–Ordovician boundary in the Hatch Hill Formation at Stop. 6.4. Figure modified from Landing (1993, fig. 2).

gray silt shales with debris flows with pebble-sized dolomitic sandstone clasts. By comparison, bedded limestones and carbonate clast debris flows dominate the Cambrian–Ordovician boundary interval at a locality approximately 160 km south in the southern Taconics near Hudson, New York (Landing, 1993). As in the late Early Cambrian (Landing and Bartowski, 1996), southern localities in the Giddings Brook thrust seem to have occupied a somewhat higher position on the continental slope, and have more prominent limestone in the form of bedded limestones and debris flows (Landing, 1993).

Travel to Stops 6.5 and 6.6

At end of Stop 6.4, return south on Tanner Hill Road to overturned limb of syncline. At T-intersection (14.0 miles), turn right (south) on Holcombville Road. Drive a short distance, and park (14.5 miles) between two small, abandoned quarries on that lie almost along strike on the west side of Holcombville Road.

Walk to small ramp to water's edge on east side of the northern quarry (Stop 6.5). At end of Stop 6.5, walk ca. 150 m south along Holcolmville Road, and examine large blocks of purple and green slate that have been stacked to form a wall immediately west of the road (Stop 6.6).

Stop 6.5, Browns Pond dysoxic/anoxic interval–Hawke Bay regression oxygenated facies (10 minutes)

Browns Pond Formation.—Rowley *et al.* (1979) first provided a description of Stop 6.5. The overturned section begins with 2.0 m of black siliciclastic mudstones with light gray, nodular lime mudstones. The black mudstones are capped by a 30–40 cm-thick, white weathering, light gray, conglomeratic pack- to grainstone composed of limestone sand–small intraclast pebbles and trilobite fragments with black phosphatic sand grains. This ca. 2.4 m of section is the top of the Browns Pond Formation, and the top of the upper Lower Cambrian dysoxic/anoxic macroscale cycle on the east Laurentian continental slope. The 30–40 cm-thick limestone is the apparent lateral equivalent of the thick debris flow at Stop 6.2. Micro- and macrofaunal elements of the lower *Elliptocephala asaphoides* assemblage occur in this top limestone of the Browns Pond Formation (E. Landing, unpub. data).

Middle Granville Formation.—A very abrupt change into the gray-green mudstones of the Middle Granville Formation takes place right at the top of the 30–40 cm-thick limestone. The lower part of this greenish macroscale interval formed by the Middle Granville Formation has several beds of nodular lime mudstone. A thin limestone clast debris flow (less than 1.0 m-thick), which may be visible if the water level is low, is composed of slumped fragments of these nodular limestones. All of the thin Middle Granville Slate is exposed in the quarry. Several beds of purple slate in the Middle Granville Formation are present higher in the quarry.

Hatch Hill Formation.—A transitional interval from the Middle Granville Formation into the Hatch Hill Formation is seen in the west wall of the quarry, where the Middle Granville changes color into a grayish hue. Black, pyritiferous mudstone of the lower Hatch Hill Formation [i.e., the Hatch Hill interval, or terminal Lower Cambrian–lowest Ordovician dysoxic/ anoxic macroscale interval (Landing *et al.*, 2002)] appears ca. 5 m higher. Finally, beds of dolomitic quartz arenite characteristic of the Hatch Hill Formation are found not more than 10 m stratigraphically above the west wall of the quarry.

Stop 6.6, Oxygenated Middle Granville Slate and the Hawke Bay regression (15 minutes)

Trace fossils.—The following description of the southern Holcolmbville Road quarry is modified from Landing (2002). The wall composed of large slate slabs on the west side of the road and the large large pile of brownish red and minor green slate on the east side came from the small flooded quarry in the Middle Granville Formation. If the light is good, dense *Planolites* and large grazing traces up to 2 cm-wide can be seen on many of the bedding plane-parallel cleavage surfaces of the green and reddish slate. The abundance of burrows, which led to the general absence of primary depositional structures in the slate, and its reddish color (produced by traces of ferric iron) are consistent with deposition of the Middle Granville Slate under a more oxygenated slope-water mass than the underlying Browns Pond Formation. Evidence for skeletalized metazoans is not present in the reddish, purple, and green mudstones of the Middle Granville Formation. Either these metazoans were not present on the bottom, or their calcareous remains were dissolved away during diagenesis.

Hawke Bay regression.—Landing *et al.* (2002) noted that the uppermost Lower Cambrian (upper but not uppermost *Olenellus* Zone) on the New York and Québec portions of the eastern Laurentian slope is composed of red and green siliciclastic mudstones. This interval of improved oxygenation of slope waters is equated with the presumed lowered sea-levels, cooler climates, and deeper circulation of oxygenated surface waters during Palmer and James' (1971) Hawke Bay regression. Subsequent sea-level rise and the re-establishment of dysaerobic slope facies (e.g., Hatch Hill Formation and Hatch Hill dysoxic/anoxic interval) took place in the terminal Early Cambrian. This Lower–Middle Cambrian boundary interval eustatic rise and climate amelioration led the actual movement of poorly oxygenated slope water onto the continental shelf in such widely separated areas as northern Vermont (Parker Slate) and eastern California (Mule Springs Formation) (Landing and Bartowski, 1996).

Travel to Stop 6.7

At end of Stop 6.6, continue south of Holcombville Road, at intersection with DeKalb Road (15.3 m), turn left (southeast), then turn almost immediately right (south) (15.4 miles) onto Middleton Road (dirt). At Y-intersection (15.7 miles), bear right (southwest) on Middleton Road. At 16.6, cross small creek and drive along north bank of Mettawee River. At intersection with Truthville Road (16.8 miles), turn left and cross bridge to village of Truthville [A well exposed section from the Bomoseen Formation through the lower Hatch Hill Formation begins on the north bank of the Metawee River about 600 m west of the bridge (Rowley *et al.*, 1979).]

At T-intersection in Truthville (17.0 miles), turn right (west) and drive through Truthville. At intersection (17.2 miles) with Rte. 22, drive straight across (south) and park near north end of Dorn Road. BEWARE OF VERY FAST MOVING TRAFFIC ON RTE. 22! Walk across Rte. 22 to north side of road; step over steel road barrier, be sure the barrier protects you from fast traffic as you walk ca. 50 m east past the western end of the road cut.

Stop 6.7, Early Cambrian Bomoseen–Truthville Members: the oldest units in the Giddings Brook slice (20 minutes)

Stratigraphic succession.—The Rte. 22 cut exposes the lowest units in the Giddings Brook slice. This overturned, east-dipping (30°) succession includes ca. 100 m of Bomoseen Formation (planar to micro-cross laminated gray sandstones with minor greenish silt-slate intervals) that fine into ca. 2.0 m of greenish silt-slates at their top. A distinctive 1.6 m-thick interval of 5–15 cm-thick, light gray weathering, dark gray, pyritiferous quartz arenites with trough cross beds lies at the top of these silt-slates. This quartz arenite is lithically comparable to the lenticular Zion Hill Quartzite [Ruedemann *in* Cushing and Ruedemann, 1914; see discussion by Zen, 1964] at localities further south in the Giddings Brook slice. The highest rocks of the Rte. 22 cut are 3.0 m of gray green mudstones of the Truthville Slate (Fisher, 1984).

Age and regional correlations.—The age of the Bomoseen–"Zion Hill"–Truthville interval has long been questionable. Body fossils have not been reported below the upper Lower Cambrian, lower *Elliptocephala asaphoides* assemblage of the upper Browns Pond Formation. As a result, most reports have only tentatively included the Bomoseen–"Zion Hill"–Truthville interval in the Lower Cambrian (e.g., Rowley *et al.*, 1979; Fisher, 1984). However, preliminary work has led to recognition of a trilobite sclerite (a "Jacob's crook") on a slabbed section of the lowest bed of the "Zion Hill" at Stop 6.7 (E. Landing, unpub. data). As trilobites only appeared more than half-way through the Early Cambrian (ca. 519 Ma; Landing *et al.*, 1998), this indicates that the "Zion Hill"–Truthville Slate is unequivocally Lower, but not lowest, Cambrian, and further suggests that the underlying Bomoseen Member is also likely Lower Cambrian.

Stop 6.7 supports regional correlations of Lower Cambrian rocks that reflect the geologic evolution and sea-level history of the east Laurentian margin. Indeed, the fining-up sequence of the Bomoseen–Truthville Slate is lithically comparable to the fining-up succession within the Pinnacle Formation (Stops 5.5, 5.6), and suggest that cooling of the rifted margin of this part of east Laurentia allowed subsidence and marine onlap, not in the latest Proterozoic, but only within the Early Cambrian. Landing and Bartowski (1996; also Landing *et al.*, 2002) equated the lower *Elliptocephala asaphoides* assemblages of the upper Browns Pond with carbonate lithosomes, such as the Dunham Formation, that overlie quartz arenite units, such as the Cheshire Quartzite, along the Appalachians. Interestingly, one or two, thick (up to 10 m-thick), coarse-grained, gray to whitish quartz arenites [Mudd Pond Quartzite; Zen (1961), see Zen, 1964)] are intercalated in the black mudstone-dominated, lower Browns Pond Formation (e.g., Rowley *et al.*, 1979, stop 5A).

As noted above (Stops 5A–C), coarse quartz arenites of the Cheshire Formation are intercalated with black mudstones and overlie black mudstones of the Moosalamoo Formation on the west flank of the Green Mountain anticlinorium. In short, a correlation of the Pinnacle–Dunham interval on the outer Laurentian platform with the Bomoseen–Browns Pond interval on the Taconian continental slope seems likely. In both regions, the Lower–Middle Cambrian boundary interval regression of the Hawke Bay event is marked by a distinctive lithofacies, the Monkton Formation and Middle Granville Slate, respectively (Landing and Bartowski, 1996; Landing *et al.*, 2002).

Travel to Stop 6.8

At end of stop, turn left on Rte. 22. Travel through village of North Granville—note locally quarried, Lower Cambrian, green and purple slate tiles (Middle Granville Slate) used on the roofs of many buildings. Bright red slates on some buildings are from the lower Upper Ordovician Indian River Formation.

Cross from Taconic allochthon into belt of structurally underlying Late Ordovician wildflysch in middle of village of North Granville (e.g., Fisher, 1984, pl. 1). At junction with Rte. 40 (18.8 miles), turn left (south) on Rte. 40. On its route south to Troy, New York, Rte. 40 roughly parallels the western margin of the Taconic allochthon—with the hills to the left (east of Rte. 40) marking the western margin of the allochthon, and the lowland to the west developed on the wildflysch or, locally as far south as the village of Middle Falls, on Laurentian platform carbonates.

Follow Rte. 40 south; park (21.4 miles) on road side opposite high cut on east side of road.

Stop 6.8, Logan cycles: mesoscale cycles in the Milankovitch band (15 minutes).

Logan cycles.—This is one of the most accessible outcrops that shows the color alternations characteristic of Logan cycles (Landing and Benus, 1985; Landing *et al.*, 1992) on the Early–early Late Ordovician continental slope of east Laurentia. Though not yet recognized in the Cambrian of the Taconian allochthons from eastern New York to eastern Quebec, Logan cycles are reviewed on this excursion, as they may prove to be present in upper slope Cambrian deposits elsewhere.

Logan cycles (Figure 23) are asymmetrical, mesoscale redox cycles that can consist of up to three (A–B) intergrading siliciclastic mudstone units: A) a lower black, laminated (unburrowed), noncalcareous, siliciclastic mudstone; B) a middle green to green gray, weakly calcareous, siliciclastic mudstone with abundant burrows; and C) an upper buff-weathering, dolomitic mudstone with abundant burrows. The tops of Logan cycles are sharp, and remane sediment grains (garnet and large quartz grains) suggest sedimentary condensation/erosion intervals before deposition of a superjacent cycle. "Complete" A–C cycles frequently alternate with incomplete base- or top-absent (i.e., BC and AB cycles, respectively). Top-absent cycles may result from sedimentary decollements on the slope, while base-absent cycles may reflect failure to develop the more strongly dysoxic/anoxic bottom waters suggested by the lithofacies of the A and B units.

Well preserved Logan cycles that extend through a completely exposed section of the Arenigian Series at Levís, Québec, appear to have an average period of < 100 k.y. (Landing *et al.*, 1992). Logan cycles are evident as the dominant depositional motif in the deeper-water, organic-rich, Miocene petroleum source rocks on the southern margin of the Mediterranean (Landing *et al.*, 1992).

Stop 6.8 succession.—The section lies at the leading edge of the Taconic allochththon and is structurally complex. It is overturned and dips ca. 70 degrees dip. About four Logan cycles are present in this ca. 6 m-thick section. Most of the cycles are BC cycles, and lack the lower black mudstone that appears in many, but not all, Logan cycles (Figure 23). The uppermost part of the section (about at waist level) shows the highly burrowed, buff-weathering C-unit of a Logan cycle sharply over-

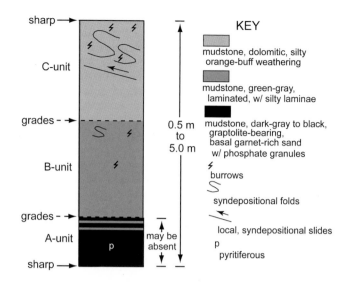

FIGURE 23—Stop 6.8: internal stratigraphy of Logan cycles (mesoscale cycles in the Milankovitch band). Contacts with under- and overlying Logan cycles are "sharp;" vertical transitions between units A–C of a Logan cycle are transitional ("grades"). Modified from Landing *et al.* (1992, fig. 8)

lain by black mudstones with thin sandstones (A-unit) of an overlying Logan cycle.

Travel to Stop 6.9

Stop 6.8–Argyle, New York.—At end of Stop 6.8, continue south on Rte. 40. [If time is available, we will examine (Stop 6.9) the classic lower Lower Ordovician outcrop at Schaghticoke gorge on the Hoosic River. This structurally complex section features the black shale and limestone macroscale interval that records the late early Tremadocian dysoxia/anoxia of the Laurentian continental slope from eastern New York to easternmost Quebec, and which correlates with the strong onlap that led to deposition of the Tribes Hill Formation (Landing *et al.*, 1992).]

Stop light in village of Argyle, New York (37.4 miles); turn left (south) and continue on Rte. 40. Shortly after turn, note prominent Logan cycles in cut in Deep Kill Formation on left side of road (37.7 miles).

Bald Mountain block.—45.3 miles, pass by intersection with Bald Mountain Road on right (west). The old Bald Mountain limestone quarry was developed in a giant block in Late Ordovician wildflysch at the western margin of the Taconic allochthon (see Zen, 1967, p. 31, 32, 36). The white weathering, massive Bald Mountain Limestone has a mollusk-dominated fauna (e.g., Cushing and Ruedemann, 1914, p. 75–80). This macrofauna and its conodonts (E. Landing, unpub. data) indicate a late Early Ordovician age, and allows interpretation of the Bald Mountain limestone as a massively bedded block of Fort Cassin Formation torn off the outer carbonate platform by Taconian thrusting. The block lies under the Taconic masterthrust in early Late Ordovician wildflysch.

Beekmantown–Trenton contact (not the "Knox unconformity"!).—Enter village of Middle Falls (51.2 miles); then, turn left (south) to continue on Rte 40 (52.1 miles). For the next several miles, Lower Ordovician carbonate platform units under the Taconic allochthon are exposed in low cuts along the east side of Rte 40.

At 54.7 miles, note cut in vertical beds of lower Trenton Group limestones on east side of road and opposite wide dirt pull-off on west side of road. This is a good place to bring class trips for two reasons:

1) The meaning and typically casual definition of the trans-Laurentian Upper Ordovician "Knox unconformity" can be investigated at the very north end of the outcrop. The "Knox unconformity" is the base of the trans-Laurentian Tippecanoe sequence of Sloss (1963), and by definition lies at the base of the lower Upper Ordovician Chazy Group and its equivalents. However, in eastern New York, an amalgamated unconformity that consists of the record of the eustatic Knox unconformity, an unconformity at the base of the Black River Group caused by passage of the Taconic peripheral bulge (Landing, 1988b), and a third, epeirogenically caused unconformity at the base of the Trenton Group. An unconformity that separates the top of the Beekmantown Group from the overlying Trenton Group, as seen at this outcrop, is commonly termed the "Knox unconformity" in the local literature. This is a mis-application of the term "Knox unconformity."

The road side outcrop shows the contact of relatively proximal, brachiopod-dominated limestones of the Trenton Group with underlying, brown-weathering dolostones (age presently undetermined but possibly early Middle Ordovician and referable to the Providence Island Dolostone).

2) The stop also provides a panorama that includes the Devonian of the Catskill high peaks to the south, the Proterozoic Grenvillian hills of the southernmost Adirondacks to the west, and the Lower Cambrian of the Taconic allochthon on the hillcrest immediately east.

Schaghticoke village.—At 65.9 miles, stop light; continue straight on combined Rtes. 40 and 67 into village of Schaghticoke. At 66.8 miles, turn right onto School Street (parallels Rte. 40 at its southern end), and park near red brick church. Walk ca. 100 m south along Rte. 40 and descend to Schaghticoke gorge on the Hoosic River on steep paths under the bridge.

Stop 6.9, Schaghticoke gorge, upper lower Tremadocian dysoxic interval (40 minutes, optional stop)

Geologic setting.—The section is in a tectonically isolated slice of green and black slate at the leading edge of the Taconic alloththon. This is the type locality of the lowest Ordovician "Schaghticoke Shale" (Ruedemann, 1903; term abandoned; Landing, 1988b), and features the structural duplication of a thin (ca. 4 m) black mudstone-limestone mesoscale alternation in greenish-gray slaty mudstones. These facies are referable to the lower Deep Kill Formation (Landing, 2002).

Biostratigraphy.—Graptolites from the black mudstones (Ruedemann, 1903) are representative of the Lower Ordovician "Matane" dendroid faunas known along the leading edges of the Taconian allochthons in Québec (Bulman, 1950). "Matane" dendroid assemblages are upper lower Tremadocian (e.g., Cooper, 1979), and associated conodonts indicate a correlation with the Tribes Hill Formation and equivalent platform units across Laurentia (Landing *et al.*, 1986). However, conodonts are limited to stratigraphically long-ranging protoconodonts

[*Phakelodus tenuis* (Müller, 1959)] at Schaghticoke (Landing, 1976; E. Landing unpublished data).

Late early Tremadocian macroscale dysoxic interval.—The lithology of this upper lower Tremadocian black shale-limestone macroscale alternation is remarkably similar to the coeval black shale-limestone macroscale alternation exposed for 400 km along the south shore of the St. Lawrence River in Québec (Landing *et al.*, 1986). This interval of climate and intensified dysaerobia on the Taconic continental slope is equated with the eustatic rise that led to deposition of the Tribes Hill Formation and coeval units across the Laurentian platform (Stops 1.1, 2.3).

Travel to Stop 6.10

Continue south on Rte. 40; cross bridge over Hoosic River. Cross bridge over Tomhannock Creek (67.2 miles). At rise in road (72.7), note views of High Peaks of Catskill Mountains [lower Upper Devonian terrestrial facies (red beds)] to south, and southern foothills of middle Proterozoic Adirondack Mountains massif to west. Enter village of Melrose (73.6 miles).

Deep Kill type section.—At 74.3 miles, begin descent to valley of the Deep Kill ["kill," which evokes the Dutch heritage of eastern and southeastern New York, means "stream." Sadly, environmental activists in the late 1990s petitioned to have the village of Fishkill, near the southern end of the Taconic allochthon in Dutchess County, renamed as "Fishsave." A little appreciation of history was needed then.]. Village of Grant Hollow is at bottom of descent. The type section of the Deep Kill Formation lies along the Deep Kill ca. 300 m east of Grant Hollow. The Deep Kill type section has classic middle Lower–lower Middle Laurentian faunal province graptolites (Ruedemann, 1902; Berry, 1962) and North Atlantic province (i.e., unrestricted marine) conodonts (Landing, 1976). As the section at Schaghticoke, the Deep Kill type section is a slice at the leading edge of the Taconic allochthon. Rice Mountain, the high hill that forms the eastern skyline, is composed of Lower Cambrian rocks that were overthrust across the Deep Kill klippe.

Upper Ordovician synorogenic flysch.—At 75 miles, pass high road cut in Upper Ordovician, black synorogenic mudstones and thin sandstones (flysch) on both sides of the road that structurally underlie the Taconic allochthon; additional road crops of this flysch also occur at 75.1, 75.4, 75.5, and 76.1 miles.

Enter village of Spiegelton (76.2 miles). Pass large, overgrown quarry in Upper Ordovician flysch on right (76.9 miles).

Taconic overthrust in Troy.—Enter city of Troy, New York (78 miles); intersection with Rte. 142 at traffic light (78.1 miles); turn right and bear left on combined Rtes. 142 and 40.

At 78.2 miles, pass low road cut in buff weathering, Lower Cambrian debris flow in upper Browns Pond Formation on left (south side of Rte. 142); the route is back on the Taconic allochthon. At intersection and traffic light (78.3 miles), turn left (south) onto Rte. 40 (south) (Oakwood Avenue).

Drive south parallel to N–S-trending ridge underlain by amalgamated Lower Cambrian debris flows of Browns Pond Formation. Pass driveway into Oakwood Christian School (79.6 miles); the driveway had exposures of black shale with decimeter-thick trilobite packstones (lower *Elliptocephala asaphoides* assemblage) of the upper Browns Pond Formation during its construction (E. Landing, unpublished data). Debris flow blocks at entrance were derived from the highest part of the Browns Pond Formation.

Pass Oakwood Cemetary with large crematory chimney on left (west) of Rte. 40 (80.3 miles).

Begin descent from Taconic allochthon at Frear Park (81.2 miles); Albany skyline visible to south. Intersection with Rte. 7 at traffic light (81.7 miles); turn right (west) onto Rte. 7 [cuts of Upper Ordovician synorogenic flysch that structurally underlie the Taconic allochthon lie just uphill]. Continue in middle lane across the Collar City Bridge and cross Hudson River. ["Collar City Bridge" evokes the industrial heritage of Troy, NY—the Cluett Peabody Company was once world famous for its acetate shirt collars.]

Troy–Albany.—The Troy dam visible to the north of the "Collar City Bridge" marks two features: 1) the "fall line" and northernmost extent of diurnal tides on the Hudson River, and 2 the first lock on the Erie and Champlain canals. These canals extend, respectively, west across New York to Lake Erie and north, via Lake Champlain, to Montreal and the St. Lawrence River.

Bear left on entrance ramp to Interstate 787 south (82.6 miles), and pass through city of Watervliet. Lower Cambrian rocks at the leading edge of the Taconic allochthon (and Giddings Brook slice) form the upper part of the N–S-trending bluff in the city of Troy to the left (east). The foreground and Interstate 787 are underlain by Upper Ordovician synorogenic flysch. Enter city of Menands (87.1 miles).

Enter city of Albany (87.9 miles). From right to left the prominent buildings to the southwest include the high Corning Tower [these are state offices; at 50 stories, they are the tallest building between New York City and Montreal]; a lower building with a greenish glass dome [houses the Comptroller's office; termed the "Taj MaCall" by wags for Carl McCall, the comptroller (ret.) under whose tenure it was built]; and a lower, whitish, ornate castle-like building that is the headquarters of the State University of New York [this building, copied from an Austrian castle, was the local headquarters of the defunct New York Central Railroad—it is said that the railroad built the building to shield a view of the tracks from the State Capital building at the top of the hill].

Albany–Rensselaer.—Take exit 3A to Rte. 20 (east) (at 90 miles). Take bridge across Hudson River. The forested hill to the northeast is Rysedorf Hill, which has abundant blocks of very fossiliferous, Upper Ordovician Chazy and Trenton Group limestones in Wildflysch at the base of the Taconic allochthon (e.g., Ruedemann, 1912).

Enter city of Rensselaer on east side of Hudson River (90.8 miles), and continue east and up hill. Exit onto Rte. 9J (91.7 miles); drive south past Port of Rensselaer. [Rensselaer was settled early (ca. 1628), and was part of Rensselaerswijck, a huge patent which included Rensselaer and Albany Counties, that Kiliaen Van Rensselaer received from the Dutch West Indies Company (WIC) in 1630. New Netherlands, the name for the holdings of the WIC, included eastern New York and the Caribbean islands of the Netherlands Antilles. Fort Crailo in Rensselaer was the site of Van Rensselaer's mansion.]

From 92–102.5 miles, drive south on Rte. 9J along eastern margin of Hudson River flood plain. The route is underlain by recessive, Upper Ordovician synorogenic flysch, with the ridge immediately east forming the western margin of the Taconic allochthon. Much of the flood plain is covered with alien switch grass that has displaced native cat tails.

Synorogenic Wildflysch south of Rensselaer.—Pass long cut (92.9–93.1 miles) in east-dipping, Upper Ordovician synorogenic sandstones on east side of Rte 9J; this outcrop supplied the first graptolites (*Cornoides americanus* Zone) that were used to date the Taconic orogeny (Berry, 1962).

Second cut immediately south (93.2–93.3 miles) is a Wildflysch with pebbles–boulders of exotic limestone sheared from the east Laurentian platform with movement of the Taconian allochthon (the large, white boulder in the middle part of the cut is Upper Cambrian) intermixed with contorted flysch.

Glacial Lake Albany.—Pass large pit in Glacial Lake Albany varved clays in left at intersection with Hays Road (95 miles). Glacial melt waters filled the lower Hudson River valley shortly after ca. 20.18 Ka with melting of the continental ice cap and damming of melt water, presumably at Hell Gate, in northern New York City. "Glacial Lake Albany" is defined as the later stage in this proglacial lake, when the lake waters extended north of the Hudson Highlands. The complex history of the lake included its progressive northern extension as the ice margin melted back, with interruptions by glacial re-advances, until it filled the Hudson and lower Mohawk River valleys, and finally extended into the southern Lake Champlain valley. At ca. 11.60 Ka, the barrier to the south was breached, and the Hudson River cut its canyon through the Glacial Lake Albany sediments (e.g., Connally and Cadwell, 2002).

Schodack and Papscanee Island history.—Enter Town of Schodack (95.5 miles); the area called "Schodack" included the traditional council fire of the Mahican Indians (traditionally spelled "Mohican"), one of the westernmost tribes that was part of the Algonquin language group. Many of the Mahicans were driven east after 1628 as a result of a war with the Mohawks—the easternmost tribe of the Iroquois language group (Huey, 1992–1993).

Pass Papscanee Island Nature Preserve (south entrance) (95.9 miles). Papscanee Island and nearby islands along the east bank of the Hudson River were associated with the Mahican Indians, whom Henry Hudson encountered on his first trip up the river in 1609. On September 17, 1609, Hudson's ship, the Half Moon, ran aground in the vicinity. His mate went ashore the next day, and visited "an old Savage, a Governour of the Country," whose house was at modern Castleton or, possibly, on Papscanee Island. Excavations on Papscanee and small adjacent Cuyper Island showed evidence of a prehistoric (i.e., pre-European contact), 15th–16th century firepit; historic Mahican occupation; contact with Europeans in the 16th or early 17th centuries; and later Dutch farmsteads. "Papscanee" was derived from Papsickene, a Mahican leader, whose heirs sold the island to Kiliaen van Rensselaer in 1637. The Dutch immediately farmed the fertile island by using the extensive corn fields earlier cleared by the Mahicans (Dunn, 1994; Huey, 1996).

Note tidal creeks on right (96.3 miles); the diurnal tidal range ranges up to one meter along this stretch of the river.

Moordener Kill.—Cross bridge over Moordener Kill (97.8 miles). Ruedemann (1912) recovered diverse Upper Ordovician faunas from limestone blocks in Wildflysch below the Taconic masterthrust just upstream of the road. The structurally overlying Lower Cambrian Middle Granville Formation provided Walcott (1894) with some of the first specimens of *Oldhamia, O. occidens* Walcott, 1894, found in Laurentia.

Castleton-on-Hudson–Schodack Landing.—Enter village of Castleton-on-Hudson (98 miles); railroad and Thruway (Interstate 90) bridges over Hudson River visible to south. Pass entrance to Schodack Island State Park (99.7 miles); cross under high railroad and Rte. 90 bridges (100.5 and 100.6 miles).

Enter village of Schodack Landing (102.1); pass long cut in Upper Ordovician synorogenic flysch (103 miles), and ascend hill above Hudson River flood plain. Enter Columbia County (103.4 miles), and pass road cut in sheared flysch.

Pass road cut in east dipping, Lower Cambrian rocks of Middle Granville Formation (green mudstones and ribbon limestones that form intervals 2 and 3 of Stop 6.10) at western margin of Taconic allochthon (104.2 miles). Almost immediately (104.3 miles), turn left into dirt road, and park near Rte. 9J. Walk east to Vermont Central Railroad tracks, and then walk about 100 m north along the tracks. BEWARE OF TRAINS!

Stop 6.10, Schodack Landing: upper *Elliptocephala asaphoides* assemblage and onset of terminal Early Cambrian–earliest Ordovician Hatch Hill dysoxic/anoxic interval (25 minutes)

This section along the Vermont Central Railroad tracks shows the second green–black (oxic–dysoxic/anoxic) transition in the Taconic allochthon. Bird and Rasetti (1968, p. 24–26) outlined the stratigraphy of this important section south of Schodack Landing that lies at the western margin of the Taconic overthurst.

Ford (1884; also Goldring, 1943, and Landing, 1974) noted the occurrence of Lower Cambrian fossils (i.e., upper *Elliptocephala asaphoides* assemblage in intervals 3 and 5). Ford also used the fossils to show that the succession is faulted over the Upper Ordovician synorogenic mudstones exposed from the banks of the Hudson River to the base of the cliff on the west side of Rte. 9J. Bird and Rasetti (1968) reported an upper *E. asaphoides* assemblage from interval 2.

As outlined below [description modified from Bird and Rasetti (1968, p. 24, 25)], this well exposed section extends from the oxic mudstones of the upper Middle Granville Formation through a transitional contact with dysoxic/anoxic, black silt-shales of the lower Hatch Hill Formation. The section lacks the slaty cleavage present in most sections in the Giddings Brook slice. Units 2–12 will be examined. DO NOT HAMMER ON OR COLLECT FROM THE DEBRIS FLOW (INTERVAL 5). From top to bottom, the Schodack Landing section includes:

Hatch Hill Formation (lower)

12. Silt-shale, black, with thin, fine-grained sandstone and limestone				4.5+ m
11. Quartz arenite, dolomitic, massive coarse-grained				1.5 m
10. Quartz arenite, black silt-shale, sandy limestone				1.5 m
9. Quartz arenite, massive bed, dolomitic, with limestone pebbles				0.9 m
8. Silt-shale with thin, dolomitic quartz arenites and sandy limestones. *Botsfordia caelata* (Hall, 1847), 4 m from base				6.0 m
7. Silt-shale, dark gray				8.0 m

Middle Granville Formation (upper)

6. Silt-shale to siliclastic mudstone, green gray				1.0 m
5. Debris flow, lenticular, pebble–boulder-sized clasts of lime mudstone to fossil pack- to grainstone. Diverse upper *E. asaphoides* assemblage				0–1.2 m
4. Siliciclastic mudstone, green gray, lower part with diagenetic limestone nodules				5.5 m
3. Lime mudstone, thin-bedded (3–8 cm), light gray weathering, with very thin, green gray silt-shale interbeds. Ford (1884) reported *Serrodiscus speciosus* Ford, 1884				4.2 m
2. Silty mudstone, green, with beds and lenses of gray lime mudstone with inarticulates, *Coleoloides, Hyolithellus micans* (Billings, 1872), *Discinella micans* (Billings, 1872), *Elliptocephala asaphoides* Emmons, 1844				13.5 m
1. Shale, green, base faulted against Upper Ordovician				18+ m

Travel to Albany.—At end of Stop 6.10, return north on Rte 9J to Albany.

AUGUST 6: PLENARY SESSION IN NEW YORK STATE MUSEUM

ACKNOWLEDGMENTS

Early research on the Cambrian of eastern New York and Vermont was completed by EL under National Science Foundation (NSF) grant EAR76-10601. More recent study was supported by the New York State Museum; scanning microscopy of microfaunas has been done under NSF grant 0116551 at the Electron Microscopy Unit, Center for Laboratories and Research, New York State Health Department (via W. Samsonoff). P. Drooker and G. Hamill (NYSM) supplied references on the archeology of the Papscanee Island area.

REFERENCES

The following list also includes references cited throughout this volume.

ADAMS, F. D., AND A. E. BARLOW. 1913. Excursion A-2—Haliburton–Bancroft area of central Ontario, p. 5–98. *In* Guide Book No. 2, Excursions in the Eastern Townships of Quebec and the eastern part of Quebec. International Geological Congress, Geological Survey of Canada, 139 p.

ADAMS, K. B., AND D. A. FRANZI. 1994. The Clinton County (New York) pine barrens: glacial catastrophe, historical wildfires, and modern uniquity. Wildflower 10:30–33.

ADRAIN, J. M., AND S. R. WESTROP. 2005. Sunwaptan (Late Cambrian) ptychaspidid trilobites from the Notch Peak Formation, western Utah. Geological Magazine 142:377–398.

AHLGREN, I. F., AND C. E. AHLGREN. 1960. Ecological effects of forest fires. Botanical Review, 26:483–533.

BABCOCK, L. E., S. C. PENG, G. GEYER, AND J. H. SHERGOLD. 2005. Changing perspectives on Cambrian chronostratigraphy and progress toward subdivision of the Cambrian System. Geosciences Journal, 9:101–106.

BARRANDE, J. 1881. Systéme Silurien du centre de la Bohême. Volume 6, Acéphales. Paris and Prague, 342 p.

BATTEN HENDER, K. L., AND G. R. DIX. 2006. Facies, geometry and geological significance of Late Ordovician (early Caradocian) coral bioherms: Lourdes Formation, western Newfoundland. Sedimentology, 53:1361–1379.

BELL HYDROPOWER. Undated. Altona hydrogeneration reconnaissance report. Excerpts from a report submitted to the Town of Altona, 9 p.

BENISON, K. C., AND T. K. LOWENSTEIN. 1997. Carbonate-hosted mineralization of the Lower Ordovician Ogdensburg Formation: evidence for a Paleozoic thermal anomaly in the St. Lawrence lowlands of New York and Ontario, p. 207–218. *In* I. Montanez, K. Shelton, and J. Gregg (eds.), Basin-wide fluid flow and associated diagenetic patterns: integrated petrologic, geochemical, and hydrologic considerations. SEPM Special Publication 57.

BERRY, W. B. N. 1959. Graptolite faunas of the northern part of the Taconic area, p. 61–70. *In* E. Zen (ed.), Stratigraphy and structure of west central Vermont and adjacent New York. Guidebook for the Fifty-First Annual Meeting of the New England Intercollegiate Geological Conference, October 17, 18, 1959, Rutland Vermont.

BERRY, W. B. N. 1961. Graptolite fauna of the Poultney Slate. American Journal of Science, 259:223–228.

BERRY, W. B. N. 1962. Stratigraphy, zonation, and age of the Schagticoke, Deepkill and Normanskill Shales, eastern New York. Geological Society of America, 73:695–718.

BILLINGS, E. 1861. Palaeozoic Fossils, Volume 1, Part 1. Canada Geological Survey.

BILLINGS, E. 1872. On some new species of Palaeozoic fossils. Canadian Naturalist, New Series, 6:213–222.

BIRD, J. M., AND F. RASETTI. 1968. Lower, Middle, and Upper Cambrian faunas in the Taconic sequence of eastern New York: stratigraphic and biostratigraphic significance. Geological Society of America, Special Paper 113, 66 p.

BJERSTEDT, T. W., AND J. M. ERICKSON. 1989. Trace fossils and bioturbation in peritidal facies of the Potsdam–Theresa Formations (Cambrian–Ordovician, northwest Adirondacks. Palaios, 4:203–224.

BRACE, W. F. 1953. The geology of the Rutland area, Vermont. Vermont Geological Survey, Bulletin 6, 124 p.

BRAINERD, E., AND H. M. SEELY. 1890. The Calciferous Formation in the Champlain valley. American Museum of Natural History Bulletin, 3:1–23.

BOURCART, J. 1964. Les sables profonds de la Méditerranée occidentale, p. 145–155. *In* A. H. Bouma and A. Brouwer (eds.), Turbidites. Developments in Sedimentology, 3.

BULMAN, O. M. B. Graptolites of the *Dictyonema* shales of Quebec. Quarterly Journal of the Geological Society of London, 106:63–99.

CADY, W. M. 1945. Stratigraphy and structure of west-central Vermont. Geological Society of America Bulletin, 56:515–558.

CAMERON, B. Stratigraphy of upper Bolarian and lower Trentonian limestones: Herkimer County, p. 16.1–16.29. *In* J. M. Bird (ed.), Guidebook for field trips in New York, Massachusetts, and Vermont. New England Intercollegiate Geological Conference, 61 Annual Meeting, State University of New York at Albany.

CAPUTO, M. 1998. Correlating Ordovician–Silurian glaciations and sea-level change, p. 15–25. *In* E. Landing, and M. E. Johnson (eds.), Silurian cycles—linkages of dynamic stratigraphy with atmospheric, oceanic, and tectonic changes. James Hall centennial volume. New York State Museum Bulletin, 491, 327 p.

CAYFORD, J. H. 1971. The role of fire in the ecology and silviculture of jack pine. Proceedings of the Tall Timbers Fire Ecology Conference, 10:221–224.

CAYFORD, J. H. AND D. J. MCRAE. 1983. The ecological role of fire in jack pine forests, p.183–199. *In* R. W. Wein and D. A. MacLean (eds.), The Role of Fire in Northern Circumpolar Ecosystems, John Wiley and Sons, New York.

CHADWICK, G. H. 1919. The Paleozoic rocks of the Canton quadrangle. New York State Museum Bulletin, 217–218, 238 p.

CHAPMAN, D. H. 1937. Late-glacial and postglacial history of the Champlain Valley. American Journal of Science, 5th Series, 34:89–124.

CHERICHETTI, L., B. DOOLAN, AND C. MEHRTENS. 1998. The Pinnacle Formation: a late Precambrian rift valley fill with implications for Iapetus rift basin evolution. Northeastern Geology and Environmental Sciences, 20:175–185.

CLARK, P. U., AND P. F.KARROW. 1984. Late Pleistocene water bodies in the St. Lawrence Lowland, New York, and regional correlations. Geological Society of America Bulletin, 95:805–813.

CLARK, T. H. 1924. The paleontology of the Beekmantown Series at Levis, Quebec. Bulletins of American Paleontology, 10, 136 p.

CLARK, T. H. 1934. Stratigraphy and structure of southern Quebec. Geological Society of America Bulletin, 45:1–20.

CLARK, T. H., AND P. R. EAKINS. 1968. The stratigraphy and structure of the Sutton area of southern Quebec, p. 163–173. *In* E. Zen, W. S. White, J. B. Hadley, and J. B. Thompson, Jr. (eds.), Studies of Appalachian Geology: Northern and Maritime. Interscience Publishers, New York.

CLARKE, J. M. 1903. Classification of the New York series of geologic formations. New York State Museum, Handbook 19, 28 p.

CLARKE, J. M., AND C. SCHUCHERT. 1899. The nomenclature of the New York series of geological formations. Science, 10 (New Series):876, 877.

COLLINS-WAIT, D., AND T. K. LOWENSTEIN. 1994. Diagenesis of Cambro-Ordovician Beekmantown Group carbonates, southern Champlain valley. Geological Society of America, Abstracts with Programs, 26(3):11, 12.

COLPRON, M. 1990. Rift and collisional tectonics of the Eastern Townships, Humber Zone, Brome Lake area, Quebec. Unpub. M.Sc.

thesis, University of Vermont, Burlington, 287 p.

CONNALLY, G. G., AND D. H. CADWELL. 2002. Glacial Lake Albany in the Champlain valley, p. B8-1–26. *In* J. McLelland and P. Karabinos (eds.), Guidebook for field trips in New York and Vermont. New England Intercollegiate Geological Conference 94th Annual Meeting and New York State Geological Association 74th Annual Meeting, Lake George, New York.

COOPER. R. A. 1979. Sequence and correlation of Tremadoc graptolite assemblages. Alcheringa, 3:7–19.

COOPER, R. A., G. S. NOWLAN, AND S. H. WILLIAMS. 2001. Global stratotype section and point for base of the Ordovician System. Episodes, 24:19–28.

CREATH, W. B., AND A. B. SHAW. 1966. Paleontology of northwestern Vermont. XIII. *Isochilina* from the Ordovician Highgate Formation. Journal of Paleontology, 40:1312–1330.

CUSHING, H. P. 1898. Syenite porphyry dikes in the northern Adirondacks. Geological Society of America Bulletin, 9:239–256.

CUSHING, H. P. 1905. Geology of the northern Adirondack region. New York State Museum Bulletin, 95:271–449.

CUSHING, H. P., AND R. RUEDEMANN. 1914, Geology of Saratoga Springs and vicinity. New York State Museum Bulletin 169, 177 p.

DALE, T. N. 1893. The Rensselaer Grit plateau in New York. U. S. Geological Survey, 13th Annual Report, Part 2, p. 301–340.

DALE, T. N. 1904. Geology of the Hudson valley between the Hoosic and the Kinderhook. U. S. Geological Survey Bulletin, 242, 63 p.

DALZIEL, I. W. D., L. H. D. SALADA, AND L. M. GAHAGAN. 1994. Paleozoic Laurentian–Gondwana interaction and the origin of the Appalachian–Andean mountain system. Geological Society of America Bulletin, 106:243–252.

DAWSON, J. C. 2002. Early Paleozoic continental shelf to basin transition rocks: selected classic localities in the Lake Champlain valley of New York State, p. A5/1–A5/23. *In* J. McLelland and P. Karabinos (eds.), Joint Meeting of the New England Intercollegiate Geological Conference (94th Annual Meeting) and New York Geological Society (74th Annual Meeting), Guidebook for Field Trips in New York and Vermont.

DAWSON, J. C., J. F. HEINTZ, C. FRIEDRICHS, AND L. WEST. 1981. William H. Miner and hydroelectric power development for Heart's Delight Farm, Chazy, New York (1907–1930), p. 3–22. *In* J. C. Dawson (ed.), Proceedings 1981 Eighth Annual Lake Champlain Basin Environmental Conference, Miner Center, Chazy, New York, June 9, 10, 1981.

DENNY, C. S. 1974. Pleistocene geology of the northeastern Adirondack region, New York. U. S. Geological Survey Professional Paper 786, 50 p.

DEWEY, J., AND K. BURKE. 1973. Tibetan, Variscan and Precambrian basement re-activation: products of continental collision. Journal of Geology, 81:683–692.

DIETRICH, R.V. 1953. Conical and cylindrical structures in the Potsdam Sandstone, Redwood, New York. New York State Museum Circular 34, 19 p.

DOOLAN, B., T. MOCK, AND AND A. MCBEAN. 1987. Stratigraphy and structure of the Camel's Hump Group along the Lemoile River transect, northern Vermont, p. 152–191. *In* D. S. Westerman (ed.), Guidebook for field trips in Vermont, Volume B2. New England Intercollagiate Geological Conference 1987, Norwich University, Northfield, Vermont.

DORSEY, R. J., P. C. AGNEW, C. M. CARTER, E. J. ROSENKRANTZ, AND R. S. STANLEY. 1983. Bedrock geology of the Milton quadrangle, northwestern Vermont. Vermont Geological Survey Special Bulletin, 3:1–14.

DOWLING, W. M. 1986. Depositional environment of the Oak Hill Group, southern Quebec: implications for the late Precambrian break-up of North America in the Quebec Reentrant. Unpub. M.Sc. thesis, University of Vermont, Burlington, 186 p.

DUNN, S. W. 1994. The Mohicans and their land: 1609–1730. Purple Mountain Press, Fleischmanns, NY.

DWIGHT, W. B. 1887. Recent explorations in the Wappinger valley limestone of Dutchess County, N. Y. American Journal of Science, 3rd Series, 34:27–32.

EBY, G. N. 1987. The Monteregian Hills and White Mountain alkaline igneous provinces, eastern North America, p. 433–447. *In* J. G. Fitton and B. G. J. Upton (eds.), Alkaline igneous rocks. Geological Society, Special Publication No. 30, Blackwell Scientific Publications, Oxford, U. K.

EMERSON, B. K. 1892. Outlines on the geology of the Green Mountain region in Massachusetts. U. S. Geological Survey, Geological Atlas, Hawley Sheet.

EMERSON, B. K. 1898. U. S. Geological Survey, Monograph 29.

EMMONS, E. 1842. Geology of New York. Part 2, comprising the survey of the Second Geological District, 437 p.

EMMONS, E. 1844. The Taconic System: based on observations in New York, Massachusetts, Maine, Vermont, and Rhode Island. Carroll and Cook, Printers, Albany, 68 p.

ENGELDER, T., AND P. GEISER. 1979. The relationship between pencil cleavage and and lateral shortening in lateral shortening within the Devonian section of the Appalachian Plateau. Geology, 7:460–464.

ENGELDER, T., AND P. GEISER. 1980. On the use of regional joing sets as trajectories of paleostress fields during the development of the Appalachian Plateau, New York. Journal of Geophysical Research, 85:6319–6241.

ENGELDER, T., P. GEISER, AND D. BAHAT. 1987. Alleghanian deformation within shales and siltstones of the Upper Devonian Appalachian Basin, Finger Lakes district, New York, p. 113–118. *In* D. C. Roy (ed.), Centennial Field Guide. Volume 5. Northeastern Section of the Geological Society of America, 481 p.

ENGLISH, A. M., E. LANDING, AND G. C. BAIRD. 2006. Snake Hill—reconstructing eastern Taconic foreland basin litho- and biofacies from a giant mélange block in eastern New York, USA. Palaeogeography, Palaeoclimatology, Palaeoclimatology, 242:201–213.

ERDTMANN, B.-D. 1982. A re-organization and proposed phylogenetic classification of planktic Tremadoc (Early Ordovician) dendroid graptolites. Norsk Geologisk Tiddskrift, 62:121–145.

ERICKSON, J. M. 1993a. Cambro–Ordovician stratigraphy, sedimentation and ichnobiology of the St. Lawrence Lowlands–Frontenac Arch to the Champlain valley of New York. New York State Geological Association, 65th Annual Meeting, Field Trip Guidebook, p. 68–95.

ERICKSON, J. M. 1993b. A preliminary evaluation of dubiofossils from the Potsdam Sandstone. New York State Geological Association, 65th Annual Meeting, Field Trip Guidebook, p.121–130.

ERICKSON, J. M., AND T. W. BJERSTEDT. 1993. Trace fossils and stratigraphy in the Potsdam and Theresa Formations of the St. Lawrence Lowland, New York. New York State Geological Association, 65th Annual Meeting, Field Trip Guidebook, p. 97–119.

ERICKSON, J. M., P. CONNETT, AND A. R. FETTERMAN. 1993. Distribution of trace fossils preserved in high energy deposits of the Potsdam Sandstone, Champlain, New York. New York State Geological Association, 65th Annual Meeting, Field Trip Guidebook, p. 133–143.

ETHINGTON, R.L., AND D. L. CLARK. 1981. Lower and Middle Ordovician conodonts from the Ibex area, western Millard County, Utah. Brigham Young University Geology Studies, 28, 155 p.

EVITT, W. R. 1953. Observations on the trilobite *Ceraurus*. Journal of Paleontology, 27:33–48.

FISHER, D. W. 1955. Time span of the Theresa and Potsdam Formations in the region peripheral to the Adirondack Mountains. Geological Society of America Bulletin, 66:1558, 1559.

FISHER, D. W. 1965. Mohawk valley strata and structure, Saratoga to Canajoharie. New York State Geological Association Guidebook, Union College, 58 p.

FISHER, D. W. 1961, Stratigraphy and structure in the southern Taconics (Rensselaer and Columbia Counties, New York), p. D10–D27. *In* R. L. LaFleur (ed.), Guidebook to field trips. New York State Geological

Association, 33rd Annual Meeting, Troy, NY.

FISHER, D. W. 1968. Geology of the Plattsburgh and Rouses Point quadrangles, New York and Vermont. New York State Museum, Map and Chart Series, 10, 37 p.

FISHER, D. W. 1977. Correlation of the Hadrynian, Cambrian, and Ordovician rocks in New York State. New York State Museum, Map and Chart Series, 25, 75 p.

FISHER, D. W. 1984. Bedrock geology of the Glens Falls–Whitehall region, New York. New York State Museum, Map and Chart Series, 35, 65 p.

FISHER, D. W., AND G. F. HANSEN. 1951. Revisions in the geology of Saratoga Springs, New York, and vicinity. American Journal of Science, 249:795–814.

FISHER, D.W., AND S. J. MAZZULO. 1976. Lower Ordovician (Gasconadian) Great Meadows Formation in eastern New York: Geological Society of America Bulletin, 87:1143–1148.

FISHER, D. W., Y. W. ISACHSEN, AND L. V. RICHARD. 1970. Geologic map of New York State, 1970, Adirondack sheet. New York State Museum, Map and Chart Series, No. 15.

FLOWER, R.H. 1964. The nautiloid order Ellesmeroceratidae (Cephalopoda). New Mexico Bureau of Mines and Mineral Resources, Memoir 12, 234 p.

FORBES, E. 1849. On *Oldhamia*, a new genus of Silurian fossils. Geological Society of Dublin, Journal, 4:20.

FORD, S. W. 1873. Remarks on the distribution of the fossils in the lower Potsdam rocks at Troy, N. Y., with descriptions of a few new species. American Journal of Science, 3d Series, 9:134–140.

FORD, S. W. 1877. On some embryonic forms of trilobites from the Primordial rocks at Troy, N. Y. American Journal of Science, 3d Series, 13:265–273.

FORD, S. W. 1878. Note on the development of *Olenellus asaphoides*. American Journal of Science, 3d Series, 15:129, 130.

FORD, S. W. 1881. On additional embryonic forms of trilobites from the Primordial rocks of Troy, N. Y., with observations on the genera *Olenellus, Paradoxides, and Hydrocephalus*. American Journal of Science, 3d Series, 15:129, 130.

FORD, S. W. 1884. Note on the discovery of Primordial fossils in the Town of Stuyvesant, Columbia County, New York. American Journal of Science, 128:35–37.

FORTEY, R. A., 1983. Cambrian–Ordovician trilobites from the boundary beds in western Newfoundland and their phylogenetic significance. Special Papers in Palaeontology 30:179–211.

FOWLER, P. 1950. Stratigraphy and structure of the Castleton area, Vermont. Vermont Geological Survey, Bulletin 2.

FRANZI, D. A., AND K. B. ADAMS. 1993. The Altona Flat Rock jack pine barrens: a legacy of fire and ice.Vermont Geology, 7:43–61.

FRANZI, D. A., AND K. B. ADAMS. 1999. Origin and fate of the sandstone pavement pine barrens in northeastern New York, p. 201–212. *In* S. F. Wright (ed.), Guidebook to field trips in Vermont and adjacent New Hampshire and New York. New England Intercollegiate Geological Conference, 91st Annual Meeting.

FRANZI, D. A., J. A. RAYBURN, C. H. YANSA, AND P. L. K. KNEUPFER. 2002. Late Wisconsinan lacustrine and marine history of the Champlain Lowland and its paleoclimatic implications, p. A5/1–A5/23. *In* J. McLelland and P. Karabinos (eds.), Joint meeting of the New England Intercollegiate Geological Conference (94th Annual Meeting) and New York Geological Society (74th Annual Meeting), Guidebook for Field Trips in New York and Vermont.

FRIEDMAN, G. M. 1979. Sedimentary environments and their products: shelf, slope, and rise of Proto-Atlantic (Iapetus) Ocean, Cambrian and Ordovician Periods, eastern New York State, p. 47–86. *In* G. F. Friedman (ed.), Guidebook for field trips. New York State Geological Association 51st Annual Meeting and New England Intercollegiate Geologic Conference 71st Annual Meeting, Troy, NY.

FRIEDMAN, G. M. 1980. Dolomite is an evaporate mineral: evidence from the rock record and from sea-marginal ponds of the Red Sea, p. 69–80. *In* D. H. Zenger, J. B. Dunham, and R. L. Ethington (eds.),

Concepts and models of dolomitization. SEPM Special Publication 28.

GARRISON, R. E., M. KASTNER, AND D. H. ZENGER (EDS.). 1984. Dolomites of the Monterey Formation and other organic-rich units. Society of Economic Paleontologists, Pacific Section, 41, 215 p.

GATES, A. E., D. W. VALENTINO, J. R. CHIARENZELLI, G. S. SOLAR, AND M. A. HAMILTON. 2004. Exhumed Himalayan-type syntaxis in the Grenville orogen, northeastern Laurentia. Journal of Geodynamics, 37:337–359.

GETTY, P. R., AND J. W. HAGADORN. 2006. Producing and preserving *Climactichnites*. Geological Society of America, Abstracts with Programs, 38, in press.

GEYER, G., AND E. LANDING (EDS.). 1995. MOROCCO '95—The Lower–Middle Cambrian standard of Gondwana. Beringria Special Issue 2, 269 p., 85 figs.

GEYER, G., AND E. LANDING. 2004. A unified Lower–Middle Cambrian chronostratigraphy for West Gondwana. Acta Geologica Polonica, 54:179–218.

GEYER, G., AND E. LANDING. 2006. Morocco 2006. Ediacaran–Cambrian depositional environments and stratigraphy of the western Atlas regions. Explanatory description and field excursion guide. Beringeria Special Issue 6, 120 p.

GILMAN CLARK, M., AND A. B. SHAW. 1968a. Paleontology of northwestern Vermont. XV. Trilobites of the Upper Cambrian Gorge Formation (lower bed 3). Journal of Paleontology, 42:382–396.

GILMAN CLARK, M., AND A. B. SHAW. 1968b. Paleontology of northwestern Vermont. XVI. Trilobites of the Upper Cambrian Gorge Formation (upper bed 3). Journal of Paleontology, 42:1014–1025.

GLOBENSKY, Y. 1982a. Géologie de la region de Lachute. Ministère de l'Énergie et des Ressources du Québec. Rapport Géologique, 199, 120 p.

GLOBENSKY, Y. 1982b. Géologie de la region de Vaudriel. Ministère de l'Énergie et des Ressources du Québec. MM85-02, 43 p.

GOLDRING, W. 1938. Algal barrier reefs in the lower Ozarkian of New York. New York State Museum Bulletin, 315:5–75.

GOLDRING, W. 1943. Geology of the Coxsackie quadrangle, New York. New York State Museum Bulletin, 322, 374 p.

GORDON, C. E. 1911. Geology of the Poughkeepsie quadrangle. New York State Museum Bulletin 148, 121 p.

GORSLINE, D. S., AND K. O. EMERY. 1959. Turbidity-current deposits in San Pedro and Santa Monica Basins off southern California. Geological Society of America Bulletin, 70:279–290.

HAGADORN, J. W., AND E. S. BELT. In press. Stranded in upstate New York: Cambrian medusae from the Potsdam Sandstone. Palaios, 59 ms pp.

HAGADORN, J. W., R. H. DOTT, JR., AND D. DAMROW. 2002. Stranded on a Late Cambrian shoreline: medusae from central Wisconsin. Geology, 30:147–150.

HAGADORN, J. W., R. H. DOTT, JR., AND D. DAMROW. 2003. Upper Cambrian medusae from Wisconsin. Geological Society of America Abstracts with Programs, 35:106.

HALL, J. 1847. Palaeontology of New York, Volume 1. Containing descriptions of the remains of the lower division of the New York System. C. Van Benhuysen, Albany, 338 p.

HALL, J. 1859. New American trilobites from Hudson River Group of Vermont. Canadian Journal, New Series, 4:491–493.

HALL, J. 1860a. On the formation of mountain ranges. Canadian Journal, New Series, 5:542–544.

HALL, J. 1860b. Note on the trilobites of the shales of the Hudson River Group in the Town of Georgia, Vt. New York State Cabinet Annual Report, 13:113–119.

HALL, J. 1863. Preliminary notice of the fauna of the Potsdam Sandstone. New York State Cabinet of Natural History, 16th Annual Report, p. 119–222.

HALL, J. 1886. Note on some obscure organisms in the roofing slate of Washington County, New York. Trustees of the New York State Museum of Natural History, 39th Annual Report, 160, pl. 11.

HALL, L. M. 1968. Times of origin and deformation of bedrock in the

Manhattan Prong, p. 117–127. *In* E. Zen, W. S. White, J. B. Hadley, and J. B. Thompson, Jr. (eds.), Studies of Appalachian Geology: Northern and Maritime. Interscience Publishers, John Wiley & Sons, New York.

HAWLEY, J. E., AND R. C. HART. 1934. Cylindrical structures in sandstones. Geological Society of America Bulletin, 45:1017–1034.

HAYMAN, N. W., AND W. S. F. KIDD. 2002. The Champlain thrust system in the Whitehall–Shoreham area: influence of pre- and post-thrust normal faults on the present thrust geometry and lithofacies distribution, p. A7-1–A7-24. *In* J. McLelland and P. Karabinos (eds.), Guidebook for field trips in New York and Vermont. New England Intercollegiate Geological Conference 94th Annual Meeting and New York State Geological Association 74th Annual Meeting, Lake George, New York, September 27–29, 2002.

HERNICK, L. V. 1999. Silas Watson Ford: a major but little-known contributor to the Cambrian paleontology of North America. Earth Sciences History, 18:246–263.

HILOWLE, M. A., J. A. DONALDSON, AND R. W. C. ARNOTT. 2000. Biofilm-mediated structures in quartz arenites of the Cambro-Ordovician Nepean Formation. Canadian Society of Exploration Geophysicists, Annual Meeting, Abstracts, http://www.cseg.ca/conferences/2000/2000abstracts/868.PDF, 1 p.

HINTZE, L. F. 1953. Lower Ordovician trilobites from western Utah and eastern Nevada. Utah Geological and Mineralogical Survey Bulletin, 48, 249 p.

HOWELL, B. F. 1937. Cambrian *Centropleura vermontensis* fauna of northwestern Vermont. Geological Society of America Bulletin, 48:1147–1210.

HOWELL, B. F. 1937–1938. The Cambrian Rugg Brook Formation of Franklin County. Report of the State Geologist on the Geology of Vermont, 1937–1938:97–101.

HOWELL, B. F. 1939. New Upper Cambrian formations in northwestern Vermont. Geological Society of America Bulletin, 50:1964 (abstract).

HOWELL, B. F., AND H. G. RICHARDS. 1937. The fauna of the "Champlain Sea" of Vermont. The Nautilus, 51:8–10.

HOXIE, C. T., AND J. W. HAGADORN. 2005. Late Cambrian arthropod trackways in subaerially exposed environments. Geological Society of America Abstracts with Programs, Northeastern Section, 37:12.

HUBERT, J. F., A. A. REED, W. L. DOWDALL, AND J. M. GILCHRIST. 1978. Guide to the Mesozoic redbeds of central Connecticut. State Geological and Natural History Survey of Connecticut, Guidebook No. 4, 129 p.

HUEY, P. R. 1992–1993. The Mahicans, the Dutch, and the Schodack islands in the 17th and 18th centuries, p. 96–118. *In* N. A. Rothschild and D. di Zerega Wall (eds.), From prehistory to the present: studies in northeastern archaeology in honor of Bert Salwen. Northeast Historical Archeology, 21–22.

HUEY, P. R. 1996. A short history of Cuyper Island, Towns of East Greenbush and Schodack, New York, and its relation to Dutch and Mahican culture. Journal of Middle Atlantic Archaeology, 12:131–147.

ISACHSEN, Y. W., W. M. KELLY, C. SINTON, R. A. COISH, AND M. T. HEIZLER. 1988. Dikes of the northeast Adirondack region—introduction to their distribution, orientation, mineralogy, chronology, magnetism, chemistry and mystery. New York State Geological Association, 60th Annual Meeting, Field Trip Guidebook, p. 215–244.

ISACHSEN, Y. I., E. LANDING, J.M. LAUBER, L.V. RICKARD, AND W.B. ROGERS (EDS.). 1992. Geology of New York: a simplified account. New York State Museum Educational Leaflet 28, 294 p.

JACOBI, L. L. Peripheral bulge—A causal mechanism for the Lower/Middle Ordovician unconformity along the westrn margin of the northern Appalachians. Earth and Planetary Science Letters, 56:245–251.

JACOBS, E. C. 1935. Green Mountains of northern Vermont. Geological Society of America Proceedings, 1934, p. 85. (abstract)

JENSEN, S., J. G. GEHLING, M. L. DROSER, AND S. W. F. GRANT. 2002. A scratch circle origin for the medusoid fossil *Kullingia*. Lethaia, 35:291–299.

KALJO, D., N. BOROVKO, H. HEINSALU, K. KHASANOVICH, K. MENS, L. POPOV, S. SERGEEVA, R. SOBOLEVSKAYA, AND V. VIIRA. 1986. The Cambrian–Ordovician boundary in the Baltic Lagoda Clint area (north Estonia and Leningrad region, USSR). Proceedings of the Academy of Sciences of the Estonian SSR, Geology, 35:97–108.

KAVANAGH, S. J. 1888–1889. On modern concretions from the St. Lawrence, with remarks by J. W. Dawson on cylinders found in the Potsdam Sandstone. Canadian Record of Science, 3:292–294.

KAY, M. 1943. Mohawkian Series on West Canada Creek, New York. American Journal of Science, 241:597–606.

KAY, M. 1953. Geology of the Utica quadrangle, New York. New York State Museum, Bulletin 347, 126 p.

KEITH, A. 1923. Cambrian succession in northwestern Vermont. American Journal of Science, Series 5, 5:97–139.

KEITH, A. 1924. Cambrian succession in northwestern Vermont. Report of the Vermont State Geologist, 1923–1924, 14:105–126.

KEITH, A. 1932. Stratigraphy and structure of northwestern Vermont. Journal of the Washington Academy of Science, 22:357–379, 393–406.

KEITH, B. D., AND G. M. FRIEDMAN. 1977. A slope–fan–basin–plain model, Taconic sequence, New York and Vermont. Journal of Sedimentary Petrology, 47:1200–1241.

KEITH, B. D., AND G. M. FRIEDMAN. 1978. A slope–fan–basin–plain model, Taconic sequence, New York and Vermont, 178–199. *In* D. M. Curtis (ed.), Enviromental problems in ancient sediments. Society of Economic Paleontologists and Mineralogists, Reprint Series, 6, 240 p.

KEMP, J. F., AND V. F. MARSTERS. 1893. The trap dikes of the Lake Champlain region. U. S. Geological Survey Bulletin, 107:11–62.

KEPPIE, J. D. 2004. Terranes of Mexico revisited: a 1.3 billion year odyssey. International Geology Review, 46:765–794.

KINDLE, C. H., AND P. TASCH. 1948. Lower Cambrian fauna of the Monkton Formation of Vermont. Canadian Field Naturalist, 62:133–139.

KIRCHGASSER, W., AND G. THEOKRITOFF. 1971. Precambrian and Lower Paleozoic stratigraphy, northwest Saint Lawrence and north Jefferson Counties, New York. New York State Geological Association, Annual Meeting, Field Trip Guidebook, p. B1–B24.

KOBAYASHI, T. 1935. The *Briscoia* fauna of the late Upper Cambrian in Alaska with descriptions of a few Upper Cambrian trilobites from Montana and Nevada. Japanese Journal of Geology, 12:39–57.

KOLATA, D. R., W. D. HUFF, AND S. M. BERGSTRÖM. 1996. Ordovician K-bentonites of eastern North America. Geological Society of America, Special Paper, 313, 84 p.

KRÖGER, B., AND E. LANDING. In press a. The earliest Ordovician cephalopods of eastern Laurentia—ellesmerocoids of the Tribes Hill Formation, eastern New York. Journal of Paleontology (2007).

KRÖGER, B., AND E. LANDING. In press b. Onset of the Ordovician cephalopod radiation—evidence from the Rochdale Formation (Lower Ordovician, Stairsian), eastern New York. Geological Magazine.

KRYNINE, P. D. 1948. Possible Algonkian in New York State (abstract). Geological Society of America Bulletin, 59:1333, 1334.

KUMARAPELI, P. S., A. GOODACRE, AND M. THOMAS. 1981. Gravity and magnetic anomalies of the Sutton Mountains region, Quebec and Vermont: expressions of rift volcanics related to the opening of Iapetus. Canadian Journal of Earth Sciences, 18:680–682.

KUMARAPELI, P. S., G. R. DUNNING, H. PINTSON, AND J. SHAVER. 1989. Geochemistry and U-Pb age of comenditic metafelsites of the Tibbit Hill Formation. Canadian Journal of Earth Sciences, 26:1374–1383.

KURTZ, V. E. 1975. Franconian (Upper Cambrian) trilobite faunas from the Elvins Group of southeast Missouri. Journal of Paleontology, 49:1009–1043.

LANDING, E. 1974. Early and Middle Cambrian conodonts from the Taconic allochthon, eastern New York. Journal of Paleontology, 48:1241–1248.

LANDING, E. 1976. Early Ordovician (Arengian) conodont and graptolite biostratigraphy of the Taconic allochthon, eastern New York. Journal of Paleontology, 50:614–646.

LANDING, E. 1979a. Conodonts and biostratigraphy of the Hoyt Limestone (Late Cambrian, Trempealeauan), eastern New York. Journal of Paleontology, 53:1023–1029.

LANDING, E. 1979b. Studies in Late Cambrian–Early Ordovician conodont biostratigraphy and paleoecology, northern Appalachian region. University of Michigan, Ann Arbor, 309 p.

LANDING, E. 1983. Highgate gorge: Upper Cambrian and Lower Ordovician continental slope deposition and biostratigraphy, northwestern Vermont. Journal of Paleontology, 57:1149–1187.

LANDING, E. 1984. Skeleton of lapworthellids and the suprageneric classification of tommotiids (Early and Middle Cambrian phosphatic problematica). Journal of Paleontology, 58:1380–1398.

LANDING, E. 1988a. Cambrian–Ordovician boundary in North America: Revised Tremadocian correlations, unconformities, and "glacioeustasy," p. 48–58. *In* E. Landing (ed.), The Canadian Paleontology and Biostratigraphy Seminar, Proceedings. New York State Museum Bulletin 462, 157 p.

LANDING, E., 1988b, Depositional tectonics and biostratigraphy of the western portion of the Taconic allochthon, eastern New York state, p. 96–110. *In* E. Landing (ed.), The Canadian Paleontology & Biostratigraphy Seminar, Proceedings of Meeting. New York State Museum Bulletin 462, 157 p.

LANDING, E. 1993. Cambrian–Ordovician boundary in the Taconic allochthon, eastern New York, and its interregional correlation. Journal of Paleontology, 67:1–19.

LANDING, E. 1994. Precambrian–Cambrian global stratotype ratified and a new perspective of Cambrian time. Geology, 22:179–182.

LANDING, E. 1998a. Avalon 1997—A pre-meeting viewpoint, p. 1–3. *In* E. Landing and S.R. Westrop (eds.), AVALON 1997—The Cambrian standard. Third International Field Conference of the Cambrian Chronostratigraphy Working Group and I.G.C.P. Project 366 (Ecological Aspects of the Cambrian Radiation). New York State Museum Bulletin 492, 92 p.

LANDING, E. 1998b. Cambrian subdivisions and correlations: introduction. Canadian Journal of Earth Sciences, 35:321, 322.

LANDING, E. 2002. Early Paleozoic sea levels and climates: New evidence from the east Laurentian shelf and slope, p. C6-1–C6-22. *In* J. McLelland and P. Karabinos (eds.), Guidebook for fieldtrips in New York and Vermont. New England Intercollegiate Geological Conference 94th Annual Meeting and New York State Geological Association 74th Annual Meeting, Lake George, New York.

LANDING, E. 2003a. Avalon—non-Gondwanan microcontinent by the late Precambrian: new evidence from the Precambrian–Cambrian boundary interval. Geological Society of America, Abstracts with Programs, 35(3):18.

LANDING, E. 2003b. Black, green, and red: Early Paleozoic slate colors, correlations, and passive margin–early orogenic history on the outer margins of the Taconian allochthons, eastern Laurentia. Geological Society of America, Abstracts with Programs, 35(3):86.

LANDING, E. 2003c. Sauk "sequence" and the Knox unconformities: practical base of the Upper Ordovician. Geological Society of America, Abstracts with Programs, 35(6):544, 545.

LANDING, E. 2003d. Self-taught American scientist—Charles Doolittle Walcott. New York Archives, 2(4):13–15.

LANDING, E. 2004. America's oldest scientific parks: John M. Clarke's "Scientific Reservations." Geological Society of America, Abstracts with Programs, 36(2):115.

LANDING, E. 2005a. Early Paleozoic Avalon–Gondwana unity: an obituary—response to "Palaeontological evidence bearing on global Ordovician–Silurian continental reconstructions" by R.A. Fortey and L.R.M. Cocks. Earth-Science Reviews, 69:169–175.

LANDING, E. 2005b. Geology and plate tectonics, p. 632–636, 2 figs. *In* P. Eisenstadt and L.-E. Moss (eds.), The Encyclopedia of New York

State. Syracuse University Press, Syracuse, New York.

LANDING, E., AND K.E. BARTOWSKI. 1996. Oldest shelly fossils from the Taconic allochthon and late Early Cambrian sea-levels in eastern Laurentia. Journal of Paleontology, 70:741–761.

LANDING, E., AND A. P. BENUS. 1985. The Levis Formation: passive margin slope processes and dynamic stratigraphy in the "western area," Excursion 3, 11 p. *In* J. Riva (ed.), Field Trips Guidebook, 1985 Canadian Paleontology and Biostratigraphy Seminar: Université Laval, Ste-Foy, Quebec.

LANDING, E., AND R. LUDVIGSEN. 1984. Classification and conodont-based age of the Ordovician trilobite *Ellsaspis* (middle Arenigian, Ville Guay, Quebec). Canadian Journal of Earth Sciences, 21:1483–1490.

LANDING, E., AND S. R. WESTROP (EDS.). 1998. Avalon 1997—The Cambrian standard. Third International field conference of the Cambrian Chronostratigraphy Working Group and I.G.C.P. Project 366 (Ecological Aspects of the Cambrian Radiation). New York State Museum Bulletin 491, 92 p.

LANDING, E., AND S. R. WESTROP. 2004. Environmental patterns in the origin and evolution and diversification loci of Early Cambrian skeletalized Metazoa: evidence from the Avalon microcontinent, p. 93–105. *In* J. H. Lipps and B. Wagoner (eds.), Neoproterozoic–Cambrian biological revolutions. Paleontological Society Papers, 10, 130 p.

LANDING, E., AND S. R. WESTROP. 2006. Early Ordovician faunas, stratigraphy, and sea-level history of the middle Beekmantown Group, northeastern New York. Journal of Paleontology, 80:958–980.

LANDING, E., R. LUDVIGSEN, AND P. H. VON BITTER. 1980. Upper Cambrian–Lower Ordovician conodont biostratigraphy and biofacies, District of Mackenzie. Royal Ontario Museum Life Sciences Contributions 126, 44 p.

LANDING, E., C. R. BARNES, C.R., AND R. K. STEVENS. 1986. Tempo of earliest Ordovician graptolite faunal succession: conodont-based correlations from the Tremadocian of Quebec. Canadian Journal of Earth Sciences, 23:1928–1949.

LANDING, E., G. M. NARBONNE, AND P. MYROW (EDS.). 1988. Trace fossils, small shelly fossils, and the Precambrian–Cambrian boundary. New York State Bulletin 463, 81 p.

LANDING, E., A. P. BENUS, AND P. W. WHITNEY. 1992. Early and early Middle Ordovician continental slope deposition: shale cycles and sandstones in the New York Promontory and Quebec Reentrant region. New York State Museum Bulletin 474, 40 p.

LANDING, E., S. R. WESTROP, AND L. A. KNOX. 1996, Conodonts, stratigraphy, and relative sea-level changes of the Tribes Hill Formation (Lower Ordovician, east-central New York). Journal of Paleontology, 70:656–680.

LANDING, E., S. A. BOWRING, K. DAVIDEK, S. R. WESTROP, G. GEYER, AND W. HELDMAIER. 1998. Duration of the Early Cambrian: U-Pb ages of volcanic ashes from Avalon and Gondwana, p. 329–338. *In* E. Landing (ed.), Cambrian subdivisions and correlations. Canadian Journal of Earth Sciences, 35.

LANDING, E., G. GEYER, AND K. E. BARTOWSKI. 2002, Latest Early Cambrian small shelly fossils, trilobites, and Hatch Hill dysaerobic interval on the Québec continental slope. Journal of Paleontology, 76:287–305.

LANDING, E., S. R. WESTROP, AND L. VAN ALLER HERNICK. 2003a. Uppermost Cambrian–Lower Ordovician faunas and Laurentian platform sequence stratigraphy, eastern New York and Vermont. Journal of Paleontology, v. 77:78–98.

LANDING, E., G. PE-PIPER, W. S. F. KIDD, AND K. AZMY. 2003b. Tectonic setting of outer trench slope volcanism: pillow basalt and limestone in the Taconian orogen of eastern New York. Canadian Journal of Earth Sciences, 40:1773–1787.

LANDING, E., G. GEYER, AND W. HELDMAIER. 2006. Distinguishing eustatic and epeirogenic controls on Lower–Middle Cambrian boundary successions in West Gondwana (Morocco and Iberia). Sedimentology, 54:899–918.

LANDING, E., J. D. KEPPIE, AND S. R. WESTROP. In press. Terminal

Cambrian and lowest Ordovician succession of Mexican West Gondwana—biotas and sequence stratigraphy of the Tiñu Formation. Geological Magazine.

LEGGETT, J. K. 1978. Eustasy and pelagic regimes in the Iapetus Ocean during the Ordovician and Silurian. Earth and Planetary Science Letters, 41:163–169.

LEWIS, T. L. 1963. A paleocurrent study of the Potsdam Sandstone of New York, Quebec, and Ontario. Unpublished Ph.D. dissertation, Ohio State University, Columbus, Ohio, 147 p.

LOCHMAN, C. 1956. Stratigraphy, paleontology, and paleogeography of the *Elliptocephala asaphoides* strata in Cambridge and Hoosick quadrangles, New York. Geological Society of America Bulletin, 67:1331–1396.

LOCHMAN-BALK, C. 1971. The Cambrian of the craton of the United States, p. 79–167. *In* C. H. Holland (ed.), Cambrian of the New World. Wiley-Interscience, New York, 456 p.

LOCHMAN-BALK, C. Upper Cambrian faunal patterns on the craton. Geological Society of America Bulletin, 81:3197–3224.

LUDVIGSEN, R., AND S. R. WESTROP. 1983. Franconian trilobites of New York. New York State Museum Memoir, 23, 83 p.

MACNAUGHTON, R. B., J. W. HAGADORN, AND R. H. DOTT, JR. 2003. Did the *Climactichnites* organism leave the water? Palaeoecological insights from the Upper Cambrian of central Wisconsin. Canadian Paleontology Conference, Proceedings, Geological Association of Canada, No. 1:26, 27.

MARSHAK, S. 1990. Structural geology of Silurian and Devonian strata in the mid-Hudson valley, New York: fold-thrust belt tectonics in miniature. New York State Museum Map and Chart Series, 41, 66 p.

MAYORAL, E., E. LIÑAN, J. A. GAMEZ VINTANED, F. MUNIZ, AND R. GOZALO. 2004. Stranded jellyfish in the lowermost Cambrian (Corduban) of Spain. Revista Espanola de Paleontologia, 19:191–198.

MAZZULO, S. J. 1974. Sedimentology and depositional environments of the Cutting and Fort Ann Formations (Lower Ordovician) in New York and adjacent southwestern Vermont. Unpub. Ph.D. dissertation, Rensselaer Polytechnic Institute, Troy, N. Y., 203 p.

MCLELLAND, J., M. HAMILTON, B. SELLECK, J. MCLELLAND, D. WALKER, AND S. ORRELL. 2001. Zircon U-Pb geochronology of the Ottawan orogeny, Adirondack Highlands, New York: regional and tectonic implications. Precambrian Research, 109:39–72.

MCRAE, L. E., G. D. JOHNSON, AND N. M. JOHNSON. 1986. Temporal reevaluation of late Hadrynian non-marine facies in the Adirondack border region, New York State, southeastern Ontario, and southwestern Quebec. Geological Society of America, Abstracts with Programs, 18(1):54.

MEHRTENS, C. J., AND G. GREGORY. 1984. An occurrence of *Salterella conulata* Clark in the Dunham Dolomite (Lower Cambrian) of northwestern Vermont, and its stratigraphic significance. Journal of Paleontology, 58:1143–1150.

MERRILL, F. J. H. 1902. New York City. U. S. Geological Survey, Folio No. 83.

MILLER, J. F. 1969. Conodont fauna of the Notch Peak Limestone (Cambro-Ordovician), House Range, Utah. Journal of Paleontology, 43:413–439.

MILLER, J. F. 1980. Taxonomic revisions of some Upper Cambrian and Lower Ordovician conodonts with comments on their evolution. University of Kansas Paleontological Contributions, Paper 99, 44 p.

MILLER, J. F., M. E. TAYLOR, J. H. STITT, R. L. ETHINGTON, L. F. HINTZE, AND J. F. TAYLOR. 1982. Potential Cambrian–Ordovician boundary stratotype sections in the western United States, p. 155–180. *In* M. G. Bassett and W. T. Dean (eds.), The Cambrian–Ordovician boundary: sections, fossil distributions, and correlations. National Museum of Wales, Geological Series No. 3, 227 p.

MITCHELL, C.E., CHEN X., S. M. BERGSTRÖM, ZHANG Y.-D., WANG Z.-H., B. D. WEBBY, AND S. C. FINNEY. 1997. Definition of a global boundary stratotype for the Darwillian Stage of the Ordovician System. Episodes, 20:158–166.

MOCK, T. D. 1989. Bedrock geology of the East Fletcher–Bakersfield area, northern Vermont. Vermont Geological Survey, Special Bulletin 10, 28 p.

MÜLLER, K. J. 1959. Kambrische Conodonten. Deutsche Geologische Gesellschaft Zeitschrift, 111:434–485.

MYROW, P. 1983. Sedimentology of the Cheshire Formation in west-central Vermont. Unpublished M.Sc. thesis, University of Vermont, Burlington, 177 p.

NARBONNE, G. M., P. MYROW, E. LANDING, AND M. M. ANDERSON. 1987. A candidate stratotype for the Precambrian–Cambrian boundary, Fortune Head, Burin Peninsula, southeastern Newfoundland. Canadian Journal of Earth Sciences, 24:1277–1293.

NICKELSEN, R. P., AND V. D. HOUGH. 1967. Jointing in the Appalachian Plateau of Pennsylvania. Geological Society of America Bulletin, 78:609–630.

NIELSEN, A. T. 2004. Ordovician sea level changes: a Baltoscandian perspective, p. 84–93. *In* B. D. Webby, F. Paris, M. L. Droser, and I. G. Percival (eds.), The Great Ordovician Biodiversification Event. Columbia University Press, 484 p.

NORTH AMERICAN COMMISSION ON STRATIGRAPHIC NOMENCLATURE. 1983. North American Stratigraphic Code. American Association of Petroleum Geologists Bulletin, 67:841–875.

OCCHIETTI, S., M. PARENT, W. W. SCHILTS, J. DIONNE, E. GOVARE, AND D. HARMAND. 2001. Late Wisconsinan glacial dynamics, deglaciation, and marine incursion in southern Quebec, p. 243–270. *In* T. K. Weddle and M. J. Retelle (eds.), Deglacial history and relative sea-level changes, northern New England and adjacent Canada. Geological Society of America, Special Paper 351.

OLSSON, R. K., T. G. GIBSON, H. J. HANSEN, AND J. P. OWENS. 1986. Geology of the northern Atlantic coastal plain; Long Island to Virginia, p. 87–107. *In* J. A. Grow, and R. E. Sheridan (eds.), The Atlantic coastal margin. The Geology of North America, Geological Society of North America, 1, 2.

OSBERG, P. H. 1952. The Green Mountain anticlinorium in the vicinity of Rochester and East Middlebury, Vt. Vermont Geological Survey, Bulletin 5.

OSBERG, P. H. 1959. Trip F—The stratigraphy and structure of the Cox Mountain area, Vermont, p. 45–51. *In* E. Zen (ed.), Stratigraphy and structure of west central Vermont and adjacent New York. Guidebook for the Fifty-First Annual Meeting of the New England Intercollegiate Geological Conference, October 17, 18, 1959, Rutland Vermont.

PAIR, D. L., AND C. G. RODRIGUES. 1993. Late Quaternary deglaciation of the southwestern St. Lawrence Lowland, New York and Ontario. Geologocal Society of America Bulletin, 105:1151–1164.

PAIR, D., P. F. KARROW, AND P. U. CLARK. 1988. History of the Champlain Sea in the central St. Lawrence Lowland, New York, and its relationship to water levels in the Lake Ontario basin, p. 107–123. *In* N. R. Gadd (ed.), The Late Quaternary development of the Champlain Sea basin. Geological Association of Canada, Special Paper 35.

PALMER, A.R. 1971. The Cambrian of the Appalachian and eastern New England regions, eastern United States, p. 169–217. *In* C. H. Holland (ed.), Cambrian of the New World. Wiley Interscience, New York.

PALMER, A. R. 1998. A proposed nomenclature for stages and series for the Cambrian of Laurentia, p. 323–338. *In* E. Landing (ed.), Cambrian subdivisions and correlations. Canadian Journal of Earth Sciences, 35.

PALMER, A.R., AND N. P. JAMES. 1979. The Hawke Bay event: A circum-Iapetus regression near the Lower–Middle Cambrian boundary, p. 15–18. *In* D. R. Wones (ed.), The Caledonides in the U.S.A., Proceedings. Virginia Polytechnic Institute and State University, Department of Geology, Memoir 1.

PERKINS, G. H. 1885. The Winooski or Wakefield Marble of Vermont. The American Naturalist, 24:128–136.

PFLÜGER, F. 1999. Matground structures and redox facies. Palaios, 14:25-39.

78   *Ed Landing, David A. Franzi, James W. Hagadorn, Stephen R. Westrop, Björn Kroger and James C. Dawson*

PITCHER, M. 1964. Evolution of Chazyan (Ordovician) reefs of eastern United States and Canada. Bulletin of Canadian Petroleum Geology, 12:632–691.

POSTEL, A. W., A. E. NELSON, AND D. R. WIESNET. 1959. Geologic map of the Nicholville quadrangle, New York. U. S. Geological Survey Quadrangle Map GQ-123.

POTTER, D.B. 1972, Stratigraphy and structure of the Hoosick Falls area, New York–Vermont, east-central Taconics. New York State Museum, Map and Chart Series, 19, 71 p.

POTTER, D.B. 1979. Thrust sheets of the central Taconic region, p. 167–185. *In* G. F. Friedman (ed.), Guidebook for field trips. New York State Geological Association 51st Annual Meeting and New England Intercollegiate Geologic Conference 71st Annual Meeting, Troy, NY.

PRINDLE, L. M., AND E. B. KNOPF. 1932. Geology of the Taconic quadrangle. American Journal of Science, 5th Series, 24:256–302.

PROUT, H. G. 1851. Description of new graptolite fauna in the Lower Silurian rocks near the Falls of the St. Croix River. American Journal of Science, Series 2, 11:187–191.

RATCLIFFE, N. M. 1987. High TiO$_2$ metadiabase dikes of the Hudson Highlands, New York and New Jersey: possible late Proterozoic rift rocks in the New York recess. American Journal of Science, 287:817–850.

RAYBURN, J. A., P. L. K. KNEUPFER, AND D. A. FRANZI. 2005. A series of Late Wisconsinan meltwater floods through the Champlain and Hudson valleys, New York, p. 2410–2419. *In* T. G. Fisher and A. J. Russell (eds), Re-assessing the role of meltwater processes during Quaternary glaciations. Quaternary Science Reviews, 24.

RAYBURN, J. A., D. A. FRANZI, AND P. L. K. KNEUPFER. 2006. Evidence from the Lake Champlain valley for a later onset of the Champlain Sea and implications for late glacial meltwater routing to the North Atlantic. Palaeogeography, Palaeoclimatology, Palaeoecology, 246:62–74.

RAYBURN, J. A., J. A. BRINER, AND D. A. FRANZI. 2007. Cosmogenic exposure dating of an ice-marginal flood scour and boulder bar near the New York/Quebec border. Geological Society of America, 2007 Abstracts with Programs, Northeast Regional Meeting Meeting, Durham, New Hampshire.

RAYMOND, P. E. 1913. Ordovician of Montreal and Ottawa. 12th International Geological Congress, Montreal, Quebec. Guidebook 3, p. 137–162.

RAYMOND, P. E. 1923–1924. New Upper Cambrian and Lower Ordovician trilobites from Vermont. Vermont State Geologist Report, 14:137–203.

RAYMOND, P. E. 1924a. The oldest coral reef. Report of the Vermont State Geologist, 14:72–77.

RAYMOND, P. E. 1924b. New Upper Cambrian and Lower Ordovician trilobites from Vermont. Proceedings of the Boston Society of Natural History, 37:386–466.

RAYMOND, P. E. 1937. Upper Cambrian and Lower Ordovician Trilobita and Ostracoda from Vermont. Geological Society of America Bulletin, 48:1079–1146.

RASETTI, F. 1944. Upper Cambrian trilobites from the Lévis conglomerate. Journal of Paleontology, 18:229–258.

RASETTI, F. 1966. New Lower Cambrian trilobite faunule from the Taconic sequence of New York. Smithsonian Miscellaneous Collections, 148(9), 52 p.

RASETTI, F. 1967. Lower and Middle Cambrian trilobite faunas from the Taconic sequence of New York. Smithsonian Miscellaneous Collections, 152(4), 111 p.

RESCHKE, C. 1990. Ecological Communities of New York State. New York State Heritage Program, Latham, New York, 96 p.

RESSER, C. E. 1937. Elkanah Billings' Lower Ordovician trilobites and associated species. Journal of Paleontology, 11:43–54.

RESSER, C. E. 1942. New Upper Cambrian trilobites. Smithsonian Miscellaneous Collections, 103, 136 p.

RESSER, C. E., AND B. F. HOWELL. 1938. Lower Cambrian *Olenellus* Zone of the Appalachians. Geological Society of America Bulletin,

49:195–248.

RODGERS, J., 1937, Stratigraphy and structure in the upper Champlain Valley. Geological Society of America Bulletin, 48:1573–1586.

RODGERS, J. 1968. The eastern edge of the North American continent during the Cambrian and Early Ordovician, p. 141–149. *In* E. Zen, W. S. White, J. B. Hadley, and J. B. Thompson, Jr. (eds.), Studies of Appalachian Geology: Northern and Maritime. Interscience Publishers, New York.

ROGERS, W. B., Y. W. ISACHSEN, T. D. MOCK, AND R. E. NYAHAY. 1990. New York State geological highway map. New York State Museum, Educational Leaflet 33.

ROSS, C. A., AND J. R. P. ROSS. 1995. North American Ordovician depositional sequences and correlations, p. 309–313. *In* J. D. Cooper, M. L. Droser, and S. C. Finney (eds.), Ordovician Odyssey: Short papers for the Seventh International Symposium on the Ordovician System. Society for Economic Paleontology and Mineralogy, Pacific Section, Fullerton, California, 498 p.

ROSS, R. J., JR. 1951. Stratigraphy of the Garden City Formation in northeastern Utah, and its trilobite faunas. Peabody Museum of Natural History, Bulletin, 6, 161 p.

ROSS, R. J., JR., L. F. HINTZE, R. L. ETHINGTON, J. F. MILLER, M. E. TAYLOR, AND J. E. REPETSKI. 1997. The Ibexian, lowermost series in the North American Ordovician, p. vi–50. *In* M. E. Taylor (ed.), Early Paleozoic biochronology of the Great Basin, western United States. U. S. Geological Survey, Professional Paper 1579.

ROUSE, C. 1986. Fire effects in the northeastern forests: jack pine. U. S. Department of Agriculture and Forest Service, General Technical Report NC-106.

ROWE, J. S., AND G. W. SCOTTER. 1973. Fire in the boreal forest. Quaternary Research, 3:444–464.

ROWELL, A. J., D. J. MCBRIDE, AND A. R. POWELL. 1973. Quantitative study of Trempealeauian (latest Cambrian) trilobite distributions in North America. Geological Society of America Bulletin, 84:3429–3442.

ROWLEY, D. B., AND W.S. F. KIDD. 1981. Stratigraphic relationships and detrital composition of the Middle Ordovician flysch of western New England: implications for the tectonic evolution of the Taconic orogeny. Journal of Geology, 89:199–218.

ROWLEY, D. B., W. S. F. KIDD, AND L. L. DELANO. 1979. Detailed stratigraphic and structural features of the Giddings Brook slice of the Taconic allochthon in the Granville area, p. 186–242. *In* G. F. Friedman (ed.), Guidebook for field trips. New York State Geological Association 51st Annual Meeting and New England Intercollegiate Geologic Conference 71st Annual Meeting, Troy, NY.

RUEDEMANN, R. 1901. Hudson River Beds near Albany and their taxonomic equivalents. New York State Museum Bulletin, 42:489–587.

RUEDEMANN, R. 1902. The graptolite (Levis) facies of the Beekmantown Formation in Rensselaer County, New York. New York State Museum Bulletin, 52:546–575.

RUEDEMANN, R. 1903. The Cambric *Dictyonema* fauna in the slate belt of eastern New York. New York State Museum Bulletin, 60:934–958.

RUEDEMANN, R. 1908. Graptolites of New York. Part II. Graptolites of the higher beds. New York State Museum, Memoir 11.

RUEDEMANN, R. 1912. The Lower Siluric shales of the Mohawk Valley. New York State Museum Bulletin, 162, 151 p.

RUEDEMANN, R. 1921. Report on Trenton fossils from the so-called Trenton and Utica beds of Grand Isle, Vermont. Vermont State Geologist Report, 12:90–

RUEDEMANN, R. 1929. Note on *Oldhamia* (*Murchisonites*) *occidens* (Walcott). New York State Museum Bulletin, 281:47–50).

RUEDEMANN, R. 1930. Geology of the Capital District (Albany, Cohoes, Troy, and Schenectady quadrangles). New York State Museum Bulletin, 285, 218 p.

RUEDEMANN, R. 1942. The geology of the Catskill and Kaaterskill quadrangles. Part 1. Cambrian and Ordovician geology of the Catskill quadrangle. With a chapter on glacial geology by John H. Cook. New York State Museum Bulletin, 331, 247 p.

RUEDEMANN, R. 1947. Graptolites of North America. Geological Society of America, Memoir 19, 652 p.

RUEDEMANN, R., AND T. Y. WILSON. 1936. Eastern New York cherts. Geological Society of America Bulletin, 47:1535–1586.

RUEDEMANN, R., J. H. COOK, AND D. H. NEWLAND. 1942. Geology of the Catskill and Kaaterskill quadrangles: Part 1. Cambrian and Ordovician geology of the Catskill quadrangle. New York State Museum Bulletin, 331, 251 p.

SAGEMAN, B.B., P. B. WIGNALL, AND E. G. KAUFFMAN. 1991. Biofacies models for oxygen-deficient facies in epicontinental seas: Tool for paleoenvironmental analysis, p. 30–59. *In* G. Einsele, W. Ricken, and A. Seilacher (eds.), Cycles and Environments in Stratigraphy. Springer-Verlag, New York.

SALAD HERSI, O., D. LAVOIE, A. H. MOHAMED, AND G. S. NOWLAN. 2002. Subaerial unconformity at the Potsdam–Beekmantown contact in the Quebec Reentrant: regional significance for the Laurentian continental margin history. Bulletin of Canadian Petroleum Geology, 50:419–440.

SALAD HERSI, O., D. LAVOIE, AND G. S. NOWLAN. 2003. Reappraisal of the Beekmantown Group sedimentology and stratigraphy, Montréal, southwestern Quebec: implications for understanding the depositional evolution of the Lower–Middle Ordovician Laurentian passive of eastern Canada. Canadian Journal of Earth Sciences, 40:149–176.

SARWAR, G., AND G. M. FRIEDMAN. 1995. Post-Devonian sediment cover over New York State. Lecture Notes in Earth Sciences, 58, 113 p.

SCHARNBERGER, C., S. BAXTER, S. KRAMER, D. A. FRANZI, S. REESE, A. MELTZER, AND W.-Y. KIM. 2006. Lamont-Doherty Cooperative Seismic Network. Seismological Society of America, 78th Annual Meeting, Eastern Section, Ottawa, Ontario, Canada, October 2006.

SCHUCHERT, C. 1933. Cambrian and Ordovician stratigraphy of northwestern Vermont. American Journal of Science, Fifth Series, 25:353–381.

SCHUCHERT, C. 1937. Cambrian and Ordovician of northwestern Vermont. Geological Society of America Bulletin, 48:1001–1078.

SCOTESE, C. R., AND W. S. MCKERROW. 1990. Revised world maps and introduction. Geological Society of London Memoir, 12:1–21.

SEILACHER, A. 1999. Biomat-related lifestyles in the Precambrian. Palaios, 14:86–93.

SEILACHER, A., AND F. PFLÜGER. 1994. From biomats to benthic agriculture: a biohistoric revolution, p. 97–105. *In* W. Krumbein, D. M. Paterson, and L. J. Stal, (eds.), Biostabilization of Sediments. Bibliotheks und Informationssystem der Universität Oldenburg.

SEILACHER, A., W. E. REIF, AND F. WESTPHAL, F. 1985. Sedimentological, ecological and temporal patterns of fossil Lagerstatten. Philosophical Transactions of the Royal Society of London, B311:5–23.

SHAW, A. B. 1951. Paleontology of northwestern Vermont. I. New Cambrian trilobites. Journal of Paleontology, 25:97–114.

SHAW, A. B. 1952. Paleontology of northwestern Vermont. II. Fauna of the Upper Cambrian Rockledge conglomerate near St. Albans. Journal of Paleontology, 26:458–483.

SHAW, A. B. 1953. Paleontology of northwestern Vermont. III. Miscellaneous Cambrian fossils. Journal of Paleontology, 27:137–146.

SHAW, A. B. 1954. Lower and lower Middle Cambrian faunal succession in northwestern Vermont. Geological Society of America Bulletin, 65:1033–1046.

SHAW, A. B. 1955a. Paleontology of northwestern Vermont. IV. A new trilobite genus. Journal of Paleontology, 29:187.

SHAW, A. B. 1955b. Paleontology of northwestern Vermont. V. The Lower Cambrian fauna. Journal of Paleontology, 29:775–805.

SHAW, A. B. 1957. Paleontology of northwestern Vermont. VI. The early Middle Cambrian fauna. Journal of Paleontology, 31:785–792.

SHAW, A. B. 1958. Stratigraphy and structure of the St. Albans area, northwestern Vermont. Geological Society of America Bulletin, 69:519–568.

SHAW, A. B. 1962a. Paleontology of northwestern Vermont. VIII. Fauna of the Hungerford Slate. Journal of Paleontology, 36:314–321.

SHAW, A. B. 1962b. Paleontology of northwestern Vermont. IX. Fauna of the Monkton Quartzite. Journal of Paleontology, 36:322–345.

SHAW, A. B. 1966a. Paleontology of northwestern Vermont. X. Fossils from the (Cambrian) Skeels Corners Formation. Journal of Paleontology, 40:269–295.

SHAW, A. B. 1966b. Paleontology of northwestern Vermont. XI. Fossils from the Middle Cambrian St. Albans Shale. Journal of Paleontology, 40:843–858.

SHAW, A. B. 1966c. Paleontology of northwestern Vermont. XII. Fossils from the Ordovician Highgate Formation. Journal of Paleontology, 40:1312–1330.

SHAW, A. B., AND M. GILMAN CLARK. 1968. Paleontology of northwestern Vermont. XIV. Type section of the Upper Cambrian Gorge Formation. Journal of Paleontology, 42:374–381.

SHAW, F. C. 1968. Middle Early Ordovician Chazy trilobites of New York. New York State Museum Memoir, 17, 163 p. [The trilobite-bearing strata of the Chazy Group are now referred to the lower Upper Ordovician (see Mitchell *et al.*, 1997)]

SKEHAN, J. W. 1961. The Green Mountain anticlinorium in the vicinity of Wilmington and Woodford, Vermont. Vermont Geological Survey, Bulletin 17, 159 p.

SKEHAN, J. W. 2001. Roadside Geology of Massachusetts. Mountain Press Publishing Company, Missoula, Montana, 379 p.

SKOVSTED, C. B. 2006. Small shelly fauna from the upper Lower Cambrian Bastion and Ella Island Formations, North-east Greenland. Journal of Paleontolohy, 80:1087–1112.

SLOSS, S. L. 1963. Sequences in the cratonic interior of North America. Geological Society of America Bulletin, 74:93–111.

STERGAS, R. L., AND K. B. ADAMS. 1989. Jack pine barrens in northeastern New York: postfire macronutrient concentrations, heat content, and understory biomass. Canadian Journal of Forest Research, 19:904–910.

STITT, J. H. 1971. Cambrian–Ordovician trilobites, western Arbuckle Mountains, Oklahoma. Oklahoma Geological Survey Bulletin, 110, 82 p.

STITT, J. H. 1977. Late Cambrian and earliest Ordovician trilobites, Wichita Mountains area, Oklahoma. Oklahoma Geological Survey Bulletin, 124, 79 p.

STONE, S. W., AND J. G. DENNIS. 1964. The geology of the Milton quadrangle, Vermont. Vermont Geological Survey Bulletin, 26, 79 p.

STREEPY, M. M., C. LITHGOW-BERTELLONI, B. A. VAN DER PLUIJM, E. J. ESSENE, AND J. F. MAGLOUGHLIN. 2004. Exhumation of a collisional orogen: a perspective from the North American Grenville Province, p. 391–410. *In* R. P. Tollo, L. Corriveau, J. McLelland, and M. J. Bartholomew (eds.), Proterozoic evolution of the Grenville orogen in North America. Geological Society of America Memoir 197.

SULLIVAN, N., J. BARNETT, AND D. K. MARTIN. 1970. A History of the Town of Chazy, Clinton County, New York. George Little Press, Inc., Burlington, Vermont, 360 p.

SWEET, W. C, R. L. ETHINGTON, AND C. R. BARNES. 1971. North American Middle and Upper Ordovician conodont faunas, p. 163–193. *In* W. C. Sweet and S. M. Bergström (eds.), Symposium on conodont biostratigraphy. Geological Society of America Memoir, 127.

SZANIAWSKI, H., AND S. BENGTSON. 1998. Late Cambrian euconodonts from Sweden. Palaeontologica Polonica, 58:7–29.

TASCH, P. 1949. A new fossil locality in the Lower Cambrian Monkton Formation of Vermont. Canadian Field-Naturalist, 63:210, 211.

TAYLOR, J. F., D. J. KENNEDY, J. F. MILLER, AND J. E. REPETSKI. 1991. Uppermost Cambrian slope deposits at Highgate gorge, Vermont: a minor miscorrelation with major consequences for conodont and trilobite-based chronocorrelation. Journal of Paleontology, 65:855–863.

TAYLOR, M. E. 1976. Indigenous and redeposited trilobites from Late Cambrian basinal environments of central Nevada. Journal of Paleontology, 50:668–700.

TAYLOR, M. E. 1977. Late Cambrian of western North America: trilobite biofacies, environmental significance, and biostratigraphic implications, p. 397–425. *In* E. G. Kauffman and J. E. Hazel (eds.), Concepts and Methods of Biostratigraphy. Dowden, Hutchinson, and Ross, Inc., Stroudsburg, Pennsylvania.

TAYLOR, M. E., AND R. B. HALLEY. 1974. Systematics, environment, and biogeography of some Late Cambrian and Early Ordovician trilobites from eastern New York state. U.S. Geological Survey, Professional paper 834, 38 p.

THEOKRITOFF, G. 1959. Stratigraphy and structure of the Taconic sequence in the Thorn Hill and Granville quadrangles, p. 53–58. *In* New England Intercollegiate Geologic Conference, 51st Annual Meeting, Rutland, Vermont.

THEOKRITOFF, G. 1964. Taconic stratigraphy in northern Washington County, New York. Geological Society of America Bulletin, 75:171–190.

THEOKRITOFF, G. 1968. Cambrian biogeography and biostratigraphy in New England, p. 9–22. *In* E. Zen, W. S. White, J. B. Hadley, and J. B. Thompson, Jr. (eds.), Studies of Appalachian Geology: Northern and Maritime. Interscience Publishers, John Wiley & Sons, New York.

THEOKRITOFF, G. 1985. Early Cambrian biogeography in the north Atlantic region. Lethaia, 18:283–293.

THOMAS, W. A. 1977. Evolution of the Appalachian–Ouachita salients and recesses from reentrants and promontories in the continental margin. American Journal of Science, 277:1233–1278.

ULRICH, E. O., AND H. P. CUSHING. 1910. Age and relationships of the Little Falls Dolostone (Calciferous) of the Mohawk Valley. New York State Museum Bulletin, 140:97–140.

VAN DIVER, B. B. 1985. Roadside Geology of New York. Mountain Press Publishing Company, Missoula, Montana, 397 p.

VAN DIVER, B. B. 1987. Roadside Geology of Vermont and New Hampshire. Mountain Press Publishing Company, Missoula, Montana, 230 p.

VAN INGEN, G. 1902. The Potsdam Sandstone of the Lake Champlain Basin, notes on field work in 1901 with map. New York State Museum Bulletin, 52:529–545.

VAN HOUTEN, F. B. 1969. Late Triassic Newark Group, north central New Jersey and adjacent Pennsylvania and New York, p. 314–347. *In* S. S. Subitsky (ed.), Geology of Selected Areas in New Jersey and Pennsylvania, and Guidebook. Rutgers University Press.

VAN WAGONER, J. C., H. W. POSAMENTIER, R. M. MITCHUM, P. R. VAIL, J. F. SARG, T. S. LOUITT, AND J. HARDENBOL. 1988. An overview of the fundamentals of sequence stratigraphy and key definitions, p. 39–45. *In* C. K. Wilgus, H. Posamentier, C. A. Ross, and C. G. St. C. Kendall (eds.), Sea-level changes: an integrated approach. Society of Economic Paleontologists and Mineralogists, Special Publication No. 42, 407 p.

WALCOTT, C. D. 1879. Description of new species of fossils from the Calciferous Formation. New York State Museum Annual Report, 32:129–131.

WALCOTT, C. D. 1886. Second contribution to the studies on the Cambrian faunas of North America. U. S. Geological Survey Bulletin, 30, 369 p.

WALCOTT, C. D. 1890. Descriptions of new forms of Upper Cambrian fossils. U. S. National Museum Proceedings, 13:267–279.

WALCOTT, C. D. 1891a. The fauna of the Lower Cambrian or *Olenellus* Zone. U. S. Geological Survey 10th Annual Report, Part 1, p. 509–762.

WALCOTT, C. D. 1891b. Correlation papers, Cambrian. U. S. Geological Survey Bulletin, 81, 477 p.

WALCOTT, C. D. 1912. New York Potsdam–Hoyt fauna. Smithsonian Museum Miscellaneous Collections, 57:251–304.

WALCOTT, C. D. 1916. Cambrian geology and paleontology. III. No. 5. Cambrian trilobites. Smithsonian Miscelllaneous Collections, 64(5):303–456.

WASHINGTON, P. A., AND S. A. CHISICK. 1994. Foundering of the Cambro-Ordovician shelf margin in the northern and central Appalachians: onset of Taconic orogenesis or eustatic drowning, p. 203–216. *In* J. M. Dennison and F. R. Ettensohn (eds.), Sedimentary cycle control vs eustasy. SEPM Concepts in Sedimentology and Paleontology, 4.

WEBBY, B. B., 1998, Steps toward a global standard for Ordovician stratigraphy. Newsletters in Stratigraphy, 36:1–33.

WELBY, C., 1961, Bedrock geology of the central Champlain Valley of Vermont: Vermont Geological Survey, Bulletin 14.

WESTROP, S. R., L. A. KNOX, AND E. LANDING. 1993. Lower Ordovician (Ibexian) trilobites from the Tribes Hill Formation, central Mohawk Valley, New York State. Canadian Journal of Earth Sciences, 30:1618–1633.

WESTROP, S. R., J. V. TREMBLEY, AND E. LANDING. 1995. Declining importance of trilobites in Ordovician nearshore communities: Dilution or displacement? Palaios, 10:75–79.

WHEELER, R. R., 1942, Cambrian–Ordovician boundary in the Adirondack-border region. American Journal of Science, 240:518–524.

WHITFIELD, R. P. 1878. Remarks on some lamellibranchiate shells of the Hudson River Group with descriptions of four new species. Cincinnati Society of Natural History, 1:137–141.

WHITTINGTON, H. B. 1957. Ontogeny of *Elliptocephala, Paradoxides, Sao, Blainia* and *Triarthrus* (Trilobita). Journal of Paleontology, 31:934–946.

WHITTLE, C. L. 1891. The occurrence of Algonkian rocks in Vermont and the evidence for their subdivision. Journal of Geology, 2:396–429.

WIESNET, D. R. 1961. Composition, grain size, roundness and sphericity of the Potsdam Sandstone (Cambrian) in northwestern New York. Journal of Sedimentary Petrology, 31:5–14.

WILLIAMS, H. 1978. Tectonic lithofacies map of the Appalachian orogen. Map 1, Memorial University of Newfoundland, St. John's, Map 1.

WILLIAMS, J. H., R. J. REYNOLDS, D. A. FRANZI, E. A. ROMANOWICZ, AND F. L. PAILLET. In review. Hydrogeology of the Potsdam Sandstone in northern New York. Canadian Journal of Water Resources.

WILMARTH, M. G. 1938. Lexicon of geologic names of the United States (including Alaska). U. S. Geological Survey, Bulletin 896, 2,396 p.

WILSON, J. L. 1951. Franconian trilobites of the central Appalachians. Journal of Paleontology, 25:617–654.

WINDLEY, B. 1986. Comparative tectonics of the western Grenville and the western Himalaya, p. 341–348. *In* J. M. Moore, A. Davidson, and A. J. Baer (eds.), The Grenville Province. Geological Association of Canada, Special Paper 31.

WOLF, R. R., AND R. W. DALRYMPLE. 1985. Sedimentology of the Cambro-Ordovician sandstones of eastern Ontario. Ontario Geological Survey Miscellaneous Paper, 127:112–118.

YOCHELSON, E. 1998. Charles Doolittle Walcott, Paleontologist. Kent State University Press, 2 vols.

YORK, A., J. W. HAGADORN, AND J. BERNSTEIN. 2005. Upper Cambrian sand stromatolites of central Wisconsin. Geological Society of America, Abstracts with Programs, 37:444.

YOUNG, G. A., AND J. W. HAGADORN, J. W. 2007. The fossil record of cnidarian medusae. Tenth International Symposium on Fossil Cnidaria and Porifera, Abstracts with Programs. St. Petersburg, Russia, 1 p.

ZEN, E. 1964. Taconic stratigraphic names: definitions and synonymies. U. S. Geological Survey, Bulletin 1174, 95 p.

ZEN, E. 1967. Time and space relationships of the Taconic allochthon and autochthon. Geological Society of America, Special paper 97, 107 p.

ZEN, E. 1972. The Taconide zone and the Taconic orogeny in the western part of the northern Appalachian orogen. Geological Society of America, Special Paper 135, 72 p.

ZENGER, D. H. 1980. Stratigraphy and petrology of the Little Falls Dolostone (Upper Cambrian), east-central New York. New York State Museum, Map and Chart 34, 138 p.

ABSTRACTS OF ORAL AND POSTER PRESENTATIONS

LOWER CAMBRIAN EODISCOID TRILOBITES FROM SCANDINAVIA AND THEIR IMPLICATIONS FOR INTERCONTINENTAL CORRELATION

AHLBERG, PER; NIKLAS AXHEIMER, Department of Geology, GeoBiosphere Science Centre, Lund University, Sölvegatan 12, SE-223 62 Lund, Sweden; and PETER CEDERSTRÖM, Axelvoldsvägen 27, SE-241 35 Eslöv, Sweden

Intercontinental correlation within the traditional Lower Cambrian is hampered by the strongly provincial character of trilobite faunas. However, several genera and species of eodiscoids seem to have a wider geographic distribution than polymerid trilobites, and provide a basis for long-distance correlations of the upper Lower Cambrian. Eodiscoids are generally rare in the Lower Cambrian of Scandinavia, and only two species have been described—*Calodiscus lobatus* (Hall) and *Runcinodiscus* cf. *index* Rushton. The former is common in the *Holmia kjerulfi* Assemblage Zone, and several thousand specimens have been recovered from the uppermost Gärdsjön Formation in Jämtland, central Sweden, and from the Gislöv Formation of Scania, southern Sweden. This material reveals entirely new details of the morphology and all of the ontogenetic stages. Recently, *C. lobatus* has been recorded from the Evjevik Member (*Ornamentaspis? linnarssoni* Assemblage Zone) at Skyberg in the Mjøsa district, southeast Norway (J. Ahlgren, Mariestad, personal commun., 2006). *Runcinodiscus* cf. *index* is known only from a single pygidium from the Tømten Member (*H. kjerulfi* Assemblage Zone) at Tømten in the Mjøsa district. A yet unpublished find of *Luvsanodiscus* cf. *gammatus* Korobov from the Gärdsjön Formation in Jämtland has been noted by one of us (PC).

Calodiscus lobatus is geographically widespread in the North Atlantic region, including North and North-East Greenland. It is recorded from deposits that represent a variety of environments, ranging from slope successions in the Taconic region of New York to shallow-water deposits in Scandinavia. Beds with *C. lobatus* can generally be correlated with strata yielding eodiscoid trilobites of the *Serrodiscus bellimarginatus-Triangulaspis annio-Hebediscus attleborensis* assemblage in Avalonia, West Gondwana, Taconic Laurentia, and Siberia. The species has, however, also been recorded from slightly younger strata in the Taconic region of New York State (beds with the *Pagetides* assemblage), England (Protolenus Limestone), and Morocco (*Cephalopyge notabilis* or upper *Hupeolenus* Zone). Thus, *C. lobatus* seems to be a fairly long-ranging species.

Recently, a lower Cambrian eodiscoid fauna was recovered from the upper Lower Cambrian in the Torneträsk area of northern Swedish Lapland. Associated polymerid trilobites include *Orodes? lapponica* (Ahlberg), *Strenuaeva inflata* Ahlberg & Bergström, and *Holmia* sp. The material is from a bioclastic limestone that forms the top of the Torneträsk Formation at Mount Luobákti (also known as Luopahta or Luopakte). This formation is upwardly truncated by the Hawke Bay unconformity. The precise age of the Luobákti trilobite fauna cannot be determined, but its generic composition and stratigraphical position at the top of the Lower Cambrian (provisional Series 2) suggest that it was recovered from the *Ornamentaspis? linnarssoni* Assemblage Zone. The fauna includes two eodiscoids previously unknown from Baltica [i.e., *Neocobboldia* aff. *dentata* (Lermontova) and *Chelediscus acifer* Rushton], of which the latter provides a new tie-line between Lower Cambrian successions in Baltica and Avalonia.

Chelediscus acifer is known from the middle Purley Shales ('Protolenus' Zone) of Warwickshire, England, where it is associated with, for example, *Serrodiscus ctenoa* Rushton, *Acidiscus theristes* Rushton, *Tannudiscus balanus* Rushton, and *Condylopyge amitina* Rushton. A similar *Condylopyge-Chelediscus-Tannudiscus* assemblage, including *C. acifer* and *T. balanus*, is known from the middle St. Mary's Member of the lower–middle Brigus Formation (*Hupeolenus* Zone) in southeast Newfoundland. The record of *C. acifer* from the Torneträsk area, northern Swedish Lapland, indicates that the *O.? linnarssoni* Assemblage Zone of Scandinavia can be correlated with the Protolenid-strenuellid Zone ('Protolenus' Zone) of eastern Avalonia (England) and the middle *Hupeolenus* Zone (*Tannudiscus balanus* Subzone) of western Avalonia (southeast Newfoundland). Thus, the *O.? linnarssoni* Assemblage Zone is younger than strata yielding eodiscoid trilobites of the *Serrodiscus bellimarginatus-Triangulaspis annio-Hebediscus attleborensis* assemblage in Avalonia, Morocco, Taconic Laurentia, and Siberia, and older than the *Acidiscus-Cephalopyge* Assemblage 'Zone' (*Cephalopyge notabilis* Zone) of Avalonia and Morocco.

CORRELATION AND TAPHONOMY OF THE INDIAN SPRINGS LAGERSTÄTTE, POLETA FORMATION (CAMBRIAN: STAGE 3), NEVADA

BABCOCK, LOREN E., ADAM M.ENGLISH, School of Earth Sciences, The Ohio State University, Columbus, Ohio 43210; and J. STEWART HOLLINGSWORTH, Institute for Cambrian Studies, 729 25 Road, Grand Junction, Colorado 81505

Fine siliciclastics of the Indian Springs Lagerstätte (Poleta Formation, middle member) of Esmeralda County, Nevada, yield a mix of biomineralized and non-biomineralized body fossils, as well as trace fossils, that documents an important interval in the reorganization of marine ecosystems during the

Cambrian. Trilobite biostratigraphy, sequence stratigraphy, and preliminary carbon isotopic data constrain the deposition to Cambrian Stage 3. The unit was deposited in a transgressive systems tract (TST) to highstand systems tract (HST) following flooding of a carbonate-dominated shelf rich in archaeocyathan bioherms. Carbon isotopic evidence suggests correlation with the Cambrian Arthropod Radiation isotope Excursion (CARE).

The Indian Springs Lagerstätte is dominated by body fossils of biomineralizing animals. Most numerous are helicoplacoid ossicles, trilobite sclerites, hyoliths, and inarticulate brachiopods. Chancelloriids and their separated sclerites are present in variable numbers. Non-biomineralizing demosponges, arthropods, and problematic organisms are relatively uncommon. Mantle setae of brachiopods, alimentary tracts of hyoliths, and nonbiomineralized trilobite tissues are moderately common to rare. Brachiopod setae are preserved by phosphatization, iron oxides, and clay mineral replication. Hyolith guts are usually sediment-filled. Arthropod cuticle is typically preserved by clay mineral replication. Articulated trilobites are unusual, and articulated helicoplacoids are only locally common.

Trace fossils in the Indian Springs Lagerstätte include coprolites, traces in sediment, and a healed bite mark on a trilobite. Coprolites, some containing helicoplacoid and broken trilobite sclerites, are common. Fragmented sclerites, many of which were possibly broken by durophagous predators, litter some bedding planes. Bedding plane-parallel traces are locally common, and vertical bioturbation is nearly absent.

The Indian Springs Lagerstätte was deposited on a shallow, storm-dominated shelf. Oxic water conditions are inferred, but anoxic conditions that lead to fossil diagenesis probably were developed below the sediment–water interface. Abundant evidence for predation, including sediment disturbance by predatory trilobites, suggests that biodegradation was a major factor in limiting opportunities for non-biomineralized tissues to become buried and preserved under exceptional conditions.

COMPARISON OF TWO SUPERIMPOSED LATE MIDDLE CAMBRIAN FAUNAS FROM CHRISTMAS HILLS, NORTHWESTERN TASMANIA

BENTLEY, C. J., PO Box 194, Burra, South Australia 5417, Australia; and J.B. JAGO, School of Natural and Built Environments, University of South Australia, Mawson Lakes, South Australia 5095, Australia

At Christmas Hills, in far northwest Tasmania, two late Middle Cambrian faunas of very similar age are juxtaposed with an abrupt faunal change between the lower and upper faunas (Jago and Buckley, 1971). The lower fauna includes the polymerid trilobites *Nepea narinosa, Tasmacephalus platypus,* two *Dorypyge* species, the earliest known member of the Asaphidae (new genus and species), a new genus and species of the Anomocaridae, a member of the Pagodiinae, and a damesellid. Agnostoid trilobites include *Tasagnostus debori, Valenagnostus imitans, Clavagnostus milli, Ammagnostus laiwuensis, Paraclavagnostus neglectus,* and a specimen of what may be the oldest known representative of *Glyptagnostus* (Jago and Daily, 1974; Jago, 1976; Bentley and Jago, 2004; Jago and Bentley, in review). In addition, a bradoriid, an inarticulate brachiopod, and nine hyolithid specimens are known. Laurie *et al.* (1995) suggested a *Lejopyge laevigata* I Zone age (on the northern

Australian biochronological scale) for the lower fauna. Jago and Bentley (in review) suggest a *Lejopyge laevigata* I or II Zone age.

The upper fauna is more cosmopolitan, but only the agnostoids have been described (Jago, 1976). It includes the cosmopolitan polymerid trilobites *Centropleura, Fuchouia, Pianaspis,* and others. Agnostoid trilobites include *Lejopyge laevigata, Ptychagnostus aculeatus, Goniagnostus spiniger, Diplagnostus planicauda, Hypagnostus brevifrons,* and *Megagnostus? glandiformis.* Quilty (1971) described the dendroids. In addition, sponge spicules and about 60 inarticulate brachiopods were seen in the upper fauna. Jago and Anderson (2004) described a bivalved arthropod. Jago and Bentley (in review) suggest correlation with either the *Lejopyge laevigata* I or II Zone in northern Australia; it is equivalent to the *Lejopyge laevigata* Zone in Hunan.

All of the specimens are internal or external molds in siltstone. The lower fauna occurs within a buff colored, laminated siltstone; the upper fauna occurs in a darker, more clearly laminated siltstone. Jago (1973) regarded the lower fauna as more proximal than the upper fauna. All available specimens of both faunas have been counted; in order to avoid duplication only internal molds were counted. We used the same methodology as Pratt (1992), in which the number of individuals of a particular species is regarded as the number of complete specimens plus whichever is greater of the number of available cephala or pygidia. By this method, 1044 individuals were counted from the lower fauna. About 3.1% of the individuals, with the same percentage for agnostoids and polymerids, occur as complete specimens. Agnostoids comprise 67.6% of the trilobite fauna, the polymerids 32.4%. The fauna is dominated by *Tasagnostus debori,* which comprises about 54% of the total trilobite fauna and about 80% of the agnostoids. The next most abundant agnostoid, *Valenagnostus imitans,* comprises 6.8% of the total fauna and 10.1% of the agnostoid fauna. *Nepea narinosa* comprises about 63% of the polymerids and 20.5% of the total fauna. The next most abundant polymerid, *Tasmacephalus platypus,* comprises about 21% of the polymerids and 6.9% of the total fauna. Although the percentage of the dominant species, *Tasagnostus debori,* is over 50%, it falls within the range of species distribution of early Late Cambrian faunas described by Pratt (1992) from Canada.

232 individuals were counted from the upper fauna, in which there is a much more even distribution of species, with agnostoids and polymerids comprising 68.1% and 31.9% of the trilobite fauna, respectively. About 7.8% of the individuals, with very similar percentages for both agnostoids and polymerids, occur as complete specimens. The agnostoids *Goniagnostus spiniger, Lejopyge laevigata,* and *Diplagnostus planicauda* comprise 24.1%, 19.4%, and 13.4% of the total trilobite fauna, and 35.4%, 28.5%, and 19.6% of the agnostoid fauna, respectively. The most abundant polymerid is a *Fuchouia* species that comprises 29.7% of the polymerids and 9.5% of the total trilobite fauna. Three other polymerids, including *Centropleura* and *Pianaspis* species, each make up between 4 and 6% of the total trilobite fauna.

It is difficult to know what these variations indicate. The data provided by Pratt, (1992, appendix) show considerable variation in terms of species percentages within different faunas. A high agnostoid component is a general indicator of deep-water deposition (e.g., Jago, 1973; Pratt, 1992). The fact that the lower fauna is dominated by one species may suggest that the fauna is under greater environmental stress than the upper fauna, but it is not clear why this should be the case. The greater abundance of agnostoids in both faunas may simply indicate that there were more agnostoids in the living assemblage, or it could indicate that the agnostoids molted at a faster rate than the polymerids.

REVIEW OF THE TIMING AND CONSTRAINTS ON THE NEOPROTEROZOIC–CAMBRIAN RECORD OF METAZOAN EVOLUTION

BOWRING, SAMUEL A., Department of Earth, Atmospheric, and Planetary Science, Massachusetts Institute of Technology, Cambridge MA 02139

The integration of high-precision U-Pb geochronology, paleontology, and chemostratigraphy has revolutionized our understanding of the Neoproterozoic origin and the Cambrian diversification of metazoans. It is now possible by using U-Pb geochronology to date rocks of this age to $\pm < 1$ Ma, and this allows for detailed correlation of glacial deposits, chemostratigraphic signals, and biostratigraphic developments. In the Neoproterozoic, the number, age, and duration of glacial events is debated, although most agree that the best documented is the ca. 635 Ma "Marinoan" event followed by the ca 582 Ma Gaskiers. Sponge biomarkers and acritarchs are ca. 635 Ma in southern China. The first megascopic Ediacaran fossils appear at ca. 578 Ma in eastern Newfoundland, followed by a rapid reorganization of the carbon cycle, oxygenation of the oceans, and the first appearance of complex trace fossils and *Kimberella* at ca. 555–560 Ma. At 542 Ma, a global carbon isotope excursion coincides with the abrupt last-appearance of most, if not all, Ediacaran organisms, as well as the calcified metazoans *Cloudina* and *Namacalathus*. Large amplitude, high frequency oscillations in seawater $\partial^{13}C$ follow the end-Ediacaran extinction, and disappear with the first appearance of abundant calcified Metazoa at the end of the Nemakit-Daldynian over a time span of approximately 10 Ma. Future work must concentrate on the timing, duration, and relationship between large fluctuations in the carbon cycle and the rise and diversification of metazoans.

CAMBRIAN TRILOBITES ENDEMIC TO THE SINO-KOREAN BLOCK IN THE DEEP-WATER FACIES OF THE TAEBAEKSAN BASIN, KOREA, AND THEIR STRATIGRAPHIC AND PALEOGEOGRAPHIC SIGNIFICANCE

CHOI, DUCK K., School of Earth and Environmental Sciences, Seoul National University, Seoul 151-747, Republic of Korea

In the Early Paleozoic, the Taebaeksan Basin was a shallow marine, mixed siliciclastic-carbonate system with two juxtaposed, but contrasting, types of lithofacies and biofacies. The shallow marine facies (Taebaek Group) yields diverse trilobite taxa endemic to the Sino-Korean block, whereas the deep-water, oceanic facies (Yeongwol Group) is characterized by a predominance of cosmopolitan and pelagic trilobites. The Cambrian shows three faunal provinces in east Asia: 1. the Hwangho faunal province, characterized by endemic taxa that inhabited shal-

low-marine environments; 2. the Chuantien faunal province, dominated by Early to Middle Cambrian redlichiid trilobites, with later forms poorly represented; and 3. the Jiangnan faunal province, with a large number of cosmopolitan and pelagic forms that indicate a deep-water, oceanic setting. The Cambrian trilobite faunas of the Taebaek Group are assigned to the Hwangho fauna, whereas those of the Yeongwol Group are referable to the Jiangnan fauna.

Earlier paleogeographic studies have invariably shown that eastern Asia was divided into the Sino-Korean and Yangtze blocks, which were separate and behaved independently during the Early Paleozoic. Differences in trilobite faunas between the Taebaek and Yeongwol Groups suggest that the Taebaek Group belonged to the Sino-Korean block, while the Yeongwol Group was part of the Yangtze block in the Early Paleozoic. If this is correct, the Taebaek and Yeongwol Groups must have formed in separate sedimentary basins. It has also been suggested that these contrasts in Cambrian faunas can be attributed to differences in depositional environments in a contiguous normal marine setting (i.e., the Taebaek Group was deposited in the inner shelf, and the Yeongwol Group represents a more offshore, deeper water environment. This study supports the latter interpretation on the basis of the occurrence of trilobites endemic to the Sino-Korean block in the Machari Formation (deep water facies) of the Yeongwol Group. The information is also very significant in refining the correlation of the Cambrian of the Sino-Korean block with other parts of the world.

Trilobites endemic to the Sino-Korean block occur in the *Eochuangia hana* Zone of the Machari Formation, and include *Changshania, Metachangshania,* and *Dikelocephalites,* among others. Of particular note is *Changshania,* a representative Furongian trilobite restricted to the Sino-Korean block that has been employed as a zonal taxon for the middle Furongian (*Changshania-Irvingella* Zone) in North China. *Metachangshania* and *Dikelocephalites* are also limited to the *Changshania-Irvingella* Zone in North China. These data enable a confident correlation of the *Eochuangia hana* Zone of Korea with the *Changshania-Irvingella* Zone of North China, and provide a reference for the correlation of the Furongian between the two facies. The dominance of laminated dark gray to black shale and cosmopolitan trilobites in the Machari Formation has been interpreted to indicate deposition in a dyoxic, deep-water environment. The occurrence of *Changshania* along with some endemic polymerid trilobites, though uncommon, in the deeper-water facies suggests that the Machari Formation was deposited in the offshore region that fringed the Sino-Korean block during the Early Paleozoic. The offshore region was likely shallow enough to allow intermittent introduction of local faunas endemic to the Sino-Korean block.

BIVALVED ARTHROPODS (BRADORIIDA) FROM THE LOWER–MIDDLE CAMBRIAN TRANSITION OF SCANIA, SOUTHERN SWEDEN

DIES ÁLVAREZ, MARÍA EUGENIA, Department of Geology, GeoBiosphere Science Centre, Lund University, Sölvegatan 12, SE-223 62 Lund, Sweden; RODOLFO GOZALO, Departamento de Geología, Universitat de València, Dr. Moliner 50, E-46110 Burjassot, Spain;

PER AHLBERG, Department of Geology, GeoBiosphere Science Centre, Lund University, Sölvegatan 12, SE-223 62 Lund, Sweden; and PETER CEDERSTRÖM, Axelvoldsvägen 27, SE-241 35 Eslöv, Sweden

The order Bradoriida *s.s.*, excluding the Phosphatocopina, comprises small (generally less than 1 cm long), bivalved arthropods of uncertain affinity with a Lower Cambrian–Lower Ordovician range. Bradoriids are generally sparsely represented in the Cambrian of Scandinavia, and most taxa are known only from glacial erratics. Thus, little is known of their stratigraphic ranges and geographic distribution. One notable exception is *Anabarochilina primordialis* (Linnarsson), a common and well-documented species in the Middle Cambrian *Lejopyge laevigata* Zone of Scandinavia and England and in correlative strata of Siberia.

We report on three species of bradoriids from the Lower–Middle Cambrian transitional interval in Scania (Skåne), southern Sweden, and briefly discuss their biostratigraphic potential. The Lower–Middle Cambrian transition displays significant biotic turnovers and environmental changes associated with regressive and transgressive events. In Scania, this interval is represented by the Gislöv Formation (top of the traditional Lower Cambrian) and the lowermost Alum Shale Formation (base of the traditional Middle Cambrian). The Gislöv consists of calcareous siltstones and bioclastic limestones, upwardly truncated by a diachronous erosive unconformity, the Hawke Bay unconformity. The Gislöv Formation is richly fossiliferous, and yields a diverse fauna with trilobites, brachiopods, helcionellid molluscs, hyoliths, and a few bradoriids. The lowermost Alum Shale Formation [i.e. the succession below the Forsemölla Limestone bed (previously referred to as "Fragment Limestone") of the *Ptychagnostus gibbus* Zone] predominantly consists of dark gray to almost black shales and mudstones. This part of the succession lacks trilobites and other calcareous-shelled fossils, but has yielded linguliformean brachiopods and bradoriids. It is tentatively assigned to the *Acadoparadoxides oelandicus* Superzone.

Bradoriids represent significant but generally neglected components in many Cambrian faunas. Most species are apparently short-ranging, and hence appear to have considerable potential for biostratigraphy and correlations. Three species are known from the Lower–Middle Cambrian transitional interval of Scania: *Beyrichona tinea* Matthew, *Hipponicharion eos* Matthew, and *Liangshanella* aff. *nitida* (Wiman). The first two species provide additional biostratigraphic data on the age and correlation of this interval.

Beyrichona tinea was originally described from the middle Hanford Brook Formation (*Protolenus elegans* Zone) in New Brunswick, eastern Canada. The record of this species in the upper Gislöv Formation (*Ornamentaspis? linnarssoni* Zone) at Brantevik in southeastern Scania suggests a broad correlation between the "*Protolenus* Zone" (*Hupeolenus* Zone) of western Avalon and the *O? linnarssoni* Zone of Scandinavia. *Hipponicharion eos* is also based on material from the Hanford Brook Formation in New Brunswick. It has subsequently been recorded from the *A. oelandicus* Superzone of Poland, and hence appears to be a long-ranging species. In Scania, it has been recorded from the lowermost Alum Shale Formation in the Almbacken drill core (2.15 and 1.87 m below the Forsemölla Limestone bed).

Liangshanella nitida is based on material from an erratic sandstone boulder ("Rostiger Sandstone") on Åland in the southern part of the Gulf of Bothnia. In Scania, a closely comparable species has been recorded from the lowermost Alum Shale Formation in the Almbacken drill core (0.80 m below the Forsemölla Limestone bed). *Liangshanella nitida* is, however, of limited biostratigraphic value because the precise stratigraphic origin of the type material is unknown.

THE GENUS *PROTOLENUS* MATTHEW IN SPAIN

DIES ÁLVAREZ, MARIA EUGENIA, Department of Geology, Lund University, SE- 22362 Lund, Sweden; ELADIO LIÑÁN, Departamento de Ciencias de la Tierra, Universidad de Zaragoza, E-50009 Zaragoza, Spain; and RODOLFO GOZALO, Departamento de Geología, Universitat de València, E-46100 Burjassot, Spain

Genus *Protolenus* Matthew was defined from the Lower Cambrian of southern New Brunswick (Canada). The diagnosis of this genus has been emended over the years by many authors. Some of them have pointed to the necessity for a significant revision. This revision is not easy because many similar genera are included within the Proteleninae.

New information obtained during the last years in the Iberian Chains and earlier data about this genus show two patterns related to the anterior border of the cranidium that may be diagnostically useful. In the first morphologic pattern, the anterior border is (at least abaxially) rounded (sag.) and narrower (sag.) than the preglabelar field. This morphology is shown, for instance, in *P. elegans*, *P. interscriptus*, and *P. jilocanus*. The second morphology shows a flat anterior border of the cranidium (with or without furrows) which is generally as wide or wider as the preglabellar field. This morphology is shown, for example, in *P. dimarginatus*, *P. pisidianus*, and *P. termierelloides*. According to this division, the type species of *P.* (*Hupeolenus*) could be included in both groups because its specimens show both a flat and rounded anterior border and a wide to narrow preglabellar field. For this reason, we prefer not to divide *Protolenus* into subgenera.

We agree with the necessity for a significant revision of the genus, and assign the following species to it: *Protolenus elegans* Matthew; *P.? articephalus* (Matthew); *P. czarnocki* Orlowski and Bednarczyk; *P. interscriptus* Geyer; *P. pisidianus* Dean; *P. termierelloides* Geyer; *P. dimarginatus* Geyer, 1990; *P. jilocanus* (Liñán and Gozalo); *P. expectans* Orlowski; *P. mckillopi* Fletcher, and, likely, *P. polonicus* Orlowski, although this latter species shows an anterior border slightly wider (axially).

The species of *Protolenus* identified in the Iberian Chains are: *P. dimarginatus* Geyer, *P. interscriptus* Geyer, *P. termierelloides* Geyer, *P. jilocanus* (Liñán and Gozalo) and *P. pisidianus* Dean. All the specimens were found in the upper Valdemiedes Formation and show tectonic distortion. *Protolenus dimarginatus* specimens are preserved as the original carapace in gray limestones and as external moulds. Some librigenae are preserved as internal moulds in green shales. The material from the Iberian Chains shows the characteristic furrow that divides the anterior border on the cranidium into two equal bands. It occurs in the *Protolenus dimarginatus* Zone and in the lower *Protolenus jilocanus* Zone. *Protolenus insterscriptus* specimens are preserved as internal and external molds in green shale. It differs from *P. jilo-*

canus in the presence of a parafrontal band and a flat preglabelar field. It occurs in the *Protolenus jilocanus* Zone. *Protolenus termierelloides* specimens are preserved as the original carapace in grey limestones and internal and external molds in green shales. All specimens show the features of the holotype. It occurs in the *Protolenus dimarginatus* and *Protolenus jilocanus* zones. *Protolenus jilocanus* specimens are preserved as the original carapace in grey limestone, and as internal and external molds in green shale. It shows many similarities with the type species of the genus, but its preglabelar field is narrower relative to the anterior border and less convex than those in *P. elegans*. *P. jilocanus* occurs in the eponymous zone. *Protolenus pisidianus* specimens are preserved as the original carapace in gray limestone, and internal and external molds in grey and yellow shale. Some of the Spanish specimens show a shorter anterior branch of the facial suture than those from Turkey. This species is similar to *P. jilocanus*, but its preglabellar field is not convex and the anterior border is more flat in the axial region. It occurs in the *P. jilocanus* zone. In Turkey, this species has been found above the Valdemiedes Event interval with *Acadoparadoxides mureroensis*. The identification of this *Protolenus* species in Spain allows a better correlation with Morocco and Turkey. [This work is a contribution to Project CGL2006-12975 (Secretaría de Estado de Universidades e Investigación. MEC). Dies Alvarez is a postdoctoral research fellow at Lund University (ref. 2005-1019. Secretaría de Estado de Universidades e Investigación. MEC).]

MIDDLE CAMBRIAN PREDATOR-PREY SYSTEMS—A CASE STUDY FROM SWEDEN

ERIKSSON, MATS E., FREDRIK TERFELT, and PER AHLBERG, Department of Geology, GeoBiosphere Science Centre, Lund University, Sölvegatan 12, SE-223 62 Lund, Sweden

Albeit being difficult to reconstruct, ancient food webs offer invaluable insights into long-lost ecosystems. Coprolites provide compelling evidence for diet, and can also be used to infer the size-relationships of predators to prey and allow ancient food chains to be reconstructed. Here we report exceptionally preserved, latest Middle Cambrian coprolites that demonstrate predator-prey relationships. These 500 Myr-old fecal pellets strongly suggest that protoconodonts (ancestral chaetognaths) were active predators, and fed on tiny bivalved arthropods (phosphatocopines).

The coprolites were recovered from the abandoned Alum Shale quarries at Andrarum in Scania, south Sweden. The top 0.5 m of the uppermost Middle Cambrian (provisional Series 3) *Agnostus pisiformis* Zone yielded 30 coprolites from shale and bituminous limestone (stinkstone). The coprolites comprise millimeter-sized, elongate to sub-circular aggregates of densely packed and stacked valves of phosphatocopines that belong to at least three genera: *Veldotron*, *Cyclotron*, and *Trapezilites*. The aggregates commonly have a mottled, brownish-beige to dark brown tint, as compared to the dark-grey surrounding matrix—a likely consequence of higher organic content. In order to test if the aggregates may comprise coincidental associations or taphocoenoses accumulated by such hydrodynamic factors as currents, we measured the orientation of the in-aggregate phosphatocopines and the orientation of trilobite exuviae (cephala and pygidia of *A. (Homagnostus) obesus*) and scattered

phosphatocopines from the coprolite-yielding strata, as well as from fossiliferous beds immediately above. Statistical analysis (χ2-test; P = 0.05) demonstrated that all of the slabs and coprolites have fossils with a random distribution (i.e., they were deposited in a low-energy environment more-or-less devoid of bottom currents). This agrees with other information on the depositional setting of these strata. Moreover, the net rate of accumulation of compacted sedimentary rock was very low, on the order of 1–10 mm/1000 years.

Elemental mapping on a coprolite preserved in stinkstone revealed strongly elevated levels of phosphorous distinctly limited to the aggregate, as compared to the surrounding host rock which is primarily composed of calcium carbonate. Such an elevated level of phosphorous in the aggregate groundmass is consistent with a fecal origin.

The coprolites are preserved in an anomalous, phosphatocopine-rich biofacies devoid of trilobites. Protoconodontid elements (e.g., of *Phakelodus*) are associated with the coprolites. Protoconodonts are closely related to extant chaetognaths, or arrow worms, that are known to feed on such small arthropods as copepods. Therefore it seems plausible that the protoconodonts of the latest Middle Cambrian fed on phosphatocopines, and hence are responsible for producing the coprolites. The coprolite size is, moreover, assumed to reflect the terminal diameter of the alimentary tract, which in turn is a proxy for the length of the predator. The Andrarum coprolites are, in general, 1–5.5 mm in diameter, whereas the actual width of the unflattened, expelled feces was probably half of that. Applying a calculation based on an arthropod (anomalocaridid) as an example, the predator would be approximately 2.5–13.5 cm long, which also fits well with the size range of extant chaetognaths and the estimated size of protoconodonts. It obviously cannot, however, be excluded that the predator may have been a soft-bodied metazoan that for taphonomic reasons was not preserved.

Predator-prey systems were well developed already by the Early Cambrian, and triggered evolutionary innovations that increased trophic complexity. Phosphatocopines probably lived near the bottom, and along with bradoriids and other tiny arthropods seem to have played an important role as "recyclers" in the Cambrian seas. The Andrarum coprolites provide evidence that phosphatocopines were the targets of predators, and that they formed an important part of the lower-level Cambrian food chains, as hyper-, epi-, or meiobenthic prey.

THE BASE OF THE SAUK SEQUENCE: IS IT WORLDWIDE?

HOLLINGSWORTH, J. STEWART, Institute for Cambrian Studies, 729 25 Road, Grand Junction, Colorado 81505

To achieve the goal of recognizing and correlating stages within the lower half of the Cambrian, the conventional approach of selecting biostratigraphic markers based on the FAD of cosmopolitan species is not applicable since there is little correlation between paleocontinents due to extreme endism in these early faunas. A multiplicity of techniques will be required to confidently establish correlations from a chosen GSSP in one region with other parts of the Cambrian world. One method that should be helpful is the application of sequence stratigraphy, especially in the recognition of worldwide eustatic events. One such event may be the base of the Sauk sequence in Laurentia.

The concept of the Sauk supersequence originally involved the transgressive basal Cambrian sandstone unit that transgressed Laurentia and submerged a weathered Precambrian surface. The position of this sequence boundary in relatively complete sections has not been firmly established, but work by J. Cooper and associates proposes that this major eustatic event, the Sauk transgression, began in western Laurentia with a brief lowering of sea levels followed by sustained sea level rise. The lowering of sea levels is indicated by the ravinement surface at the top of the lower member of the Wood Canyon Formation in southern California, followed by deposition of fluviatile quartz pebble conglomerate of the middle member of the Wood Canyon Formation (MMWCF). Some doubt remains whether this eustatic event is correctly interpreted as the base of the Sauk supersequence, but I propose to discuss the potential worldwide correlation of this event, beginning with western Laurentia.

North of the Death Valley region, the White-Inyo facies is an entirely marine sequence with the fluviatile lowstand systems tract at the base of the MMWCF. A prominent flooding surface at the top of the shallow-water carbonates and siliciclastics of the Deep Spring Formation [which contains the Ediacaran–Cambrian boundary in its upper half] is overlain by fine-grained, dark-colored siliciclastics of the Campito Formation. Much of this formation was deposited in dysoxic waters, and even simple trace fossils are absent in the lower parts of the unit. The upper third of the 1150 m-thick Campito Formation contains an Atdabanian-equivalent fauna. The flooding event recorded at the base of this unit is interpreted as the beginning of the Sauk transgression. The similarity of this event to the base of the black shale development in the Lower Cambrian of south China suggests that this may be a worldwide eustatic event.

In the Northwest Territories of Canada, coarse siliciclastics in the lower Backbone Ranges Formation rest on an unconformity surface with shallow water carbonates and siliciclastics of basal part of the formation. The underlying Ingta Formation contains *Trichophycus pedum*. In eastern Laurentia, the lower part of the Cambrian is included in the Chilhowee Group in Tennessee. The basal unit of this group, the Cochran Formation, which consists of conglomeratic, feldspathic sandstone with red shaley intervals, rests unconformably on Neoproterozoic rocks and represents the base of the Sauk sequence.

In Siberia, an unconformity is reported at or near the base of the Tommotian with the reddish limestone of the Pestrotsvet Formation above dolostone and limestone with small shelly fossils. In some areas, these latter limestones occur with siliciclastics that rest unconformably on crystalline basement. In Baltica, the earliest Cambrian includes siliciclastics with *Platysolenites antiquisissmus*, separated from overlying siliciclastics by a ravinement surface representing the Sauk eustatic event. Eastern Newfoundland (part of western Avalonia) exhibits the GSSP for the base of the Cambrian in generally deep-water siliciclastics. Either the unconformity at the base of the Mystery Lake Member of the Chapel Island Formation, below the *Watsonella crosbyi* Zone or at the base of the Bonavista Group, base of the *Sunnaginia imbricata* Zone, are likely candidates for the Sauk event. In the English Midlands (eastern Avalonia), the Cambrian begins with conglomeratic arenites that rest unconformably on Precambrian rocks. The succeeding Lower Comley

Sandstone has brachiopods, bradoriids, hyoliths and a single trilobite which suggest that the base of the Cambrian here rests on the Sauk unconformity. In Morocco, the basal of the Cambrian is within the lower Adoudou Formation, a mixed siliciclastic and volcanic unit. The Sauk event possibly correlates with the base Tifnout Member with its shallow water limestone and dolomite. In most of Spain, the basal unit of the Cambrian is one of several siliciclastic formations with a varied ichnofauna that rests unconformably on Neoproterozoic rocks; this unconformity is the equivalent of the Sauk I unconformity. In south-central Spain, the Azorejo Formation appears to be unconformable on mudstones and phosphatic black shales with small shelly and trace fossils, and which locally represent pre-Sauk Cambrian rocks. In the Arrowie Basin of South Australia, the Uratanna Formation consists of channel sandstones deposited in a lowstand systems tract followed by siltstone and shale with phosphatic nodules in the transgrssive systems tract. Sabelliditids occur in this interval. This could be a pre-Sauk sequence but is more likely to be an initial part of the Sauk transgression.

South China has a unique and widespread facies developed on a flooding surface at the base of the Niutitang, Shujantou, and other formations. Phosphatic and highly carbonaceous shale with local exhalative metallic sulfide deposits considered to be Tommotian-equivalent in age rests unconformably on phosphate-bearing carbonates with abundant small shelly fossils. These anoxic sediments are interpreted to be the result of the Sauk eustatic event flooding in tectonically closed basins with hydrothermal vents that supplied the metals.

This discussion is far from exhaustive. Some areas have only younger lower Cambrian rocks, while others deserve additional study.These preliminary observations suggest that a major sequence boundary including ravinement and rapid eustatic rise occurred in the Early Cambrian about the beginning of the Tommotian Age in Siberia which should be useful for intercontinental correlation.

DIVERSIFICATION OF LATE EARLY TO EARLY MIDDLE CAMBRIAN PTYCHOPARIIDS FROM SHANDONG, NORTH CHINA

KANG, IMSEONG, School of Earth and Environmental Sciences, Seoul National University, Seoul 151-747, Korea;
HYUN-SUK LEE, Korea Institute of Geoscience & Mineral Resources (KIGAM), Daejeon 305-350 Korea;
ZUOZHEN HAN, College of Geo-Information Science and Technology, Shandong University of Science and Technology, Shandong, People's Republic of China; and
DUCK K. CHOI, School of Earth and Environmental Sciences, Seoul National University, Seoul 151-747, Korea

Ptychopariids appeared in the Early Cambrian. Because their relatively simple, generalized forms exhibit considerable morphological variations, ptychoparoid taxonomy is difficult. Ptychoparoid families are seldom adequately diagnosed, and their diagnoses often repeat lists of shared characters. Early–Middle Cambrian ptychopariids of the Sino-Korean block also have very simple, generalized, and consequently non-distinctive morphologies, but have been assigned to a number of genera and families. The relationship among the families is unclear, and some of the families are poorly understood.

To investigate the morphological characteristics of early ptychopariids of the Sino-Korean block, we selected the Jiulongshan section near Laiwu City, Shandong Province, China, where a nearly complete Cambrian succession that yields well-preserved trilobites is well exposed. The Jiulongshan Cambrian section comprises, in ascending order, the Zhushadong, Mantou, Zhangxia, Gushan, and Chaomidian Formations. Late Early to early Middle Cambrian trilobites come from the Mantou Formation. The Zhushadong Formation (ca. 30 m thick) is composed of wavy/lenticular laminated dolomudstone, homogeneous lime mudstone, limestone-shale couplets, cross-bedded packstone, and domal stromatolites. The Mantou Formation can be divided into three parts based on lithologic associations. The lower Mantou Formation (ca. 90 m thick) is characterized by alternations of limestone-shale couplets and purple siltstone, and is capped by massive oolitic beds. The middle Mantou Formation (ca. 110 m thick) comprises homogeneous purple mudstone; wavy/lenticular, laminated purple mudstone with mudcracks; hummocky–swaley to cross-stratified, dark purple, calcareous, fine-grained sandstone, and swaley to cross-bedded fine-grained sandstone. The upper Mantou Formation (ca. 40 m thick) is composed of trough cross-stratified, oolitic grainstone or calcareous sandstone; laminated marlstone; cross-stratified bioclastic grainstone; and bioturbated calcareous sandstone. The uppermost Mantou Formation is a 4 m-thick greenish gray shale bed that is overlain by the Zhangxia Formation, itself composed dominantly of oolitic and bioclastic grainstone of shallow-marine origin.

Eight trilobite horizons were located in the Mantou Formation in this study. As trilobites are mainly preserved in limestones, the fossiliferous horizons are more frequently observed in the upper part of the formation. They include two horizons in the lower part, one horizon in the middle, and five horizons in the upper part. This preliminary result shows that the eight fossiliferous horizons are roughly representative, in ascending order, to the established zones in North China: *Redlichia chinensis, Yaojiayuella, Shantungaspis, Hsuchuangia-Ruichengella, Ruichengaspis, Sunaspis, Poriagraulos,* and *Bailiella* Zones.

Several thousand specimens have been collected from the section, and are provisionally assigned to the following genera: *Probowmania, Probowmaniella, Shantungaspis, Psilostracus, Yaojiayuella, Ziboaspis, Eosoptychoparia,* and *Yuehsienszella* of the family Ptychopariidae; *Parachittidilla, Metagraulos, Poriagraulos,* and *Plesiagraulos* of the Agraulidae; *Eotaitzuia, Megagraulos, Latilorenzella, Ruichengaspis,* and *Inouyella* of the Wuaniidae; *Lorenzella, Lonchinouyia, Inouyops,* and *Porilorenzella* of the Lorenzellidae; and *Inouyia* of the Inouyiidae. The systematic study of these trilobites is expected to reveal the relationships and diversification of late Early to early Middle Cambrian ptychopariids of the Sino-Korean block.

TRILOBITE FAUNAL SUCCESSIONS ACROSS THE CAMBRIAN–ORDOVICIAN BOUNDARY IN THE TAEBAEK GROUP, KOREA

LEE, SEUNG-BAE, JANG WON SOHN, and DUCK K. CHOI, School of Earth and Environmental Sciences, Seoul National University, Seoul 151-747, Korea

In Korea, the Cambrian–Ordovician boundary lies within the Joseon Supergroup—a thick siliciclastic-carbonate sequence exposed in the Taebaeksan Basin. The Joseon Supergroup ranges in age from late Early Cambrian to Middle Ordovician, and is divided into the Taebaek, Yeongwol, Yongtan, Pyeongchang, and Mungyeong Groups. The Cambrian–Ordovician boundary is defined in the Taebaek and Yeongwol Groups. The Cambrian–Ordovician boundary in the Yeongwol Group has been placed at the base of the *Yosimuraspis* Zone within the Mungok Formation where an index fossil for the lowermost Ordovician, *Jujuyaspis sinensis*, occurs. The Cambrian–Ordovician boundary in the Taebaek Group has been traditionally drawn at the contact between the Hwajeol and Dongjeom Formations, but has not been critically examined over the last several decades.

Recent intensive investigations on the Taebaek Group have located fossiliferous horizons within the Hwajeol and Dongjeom Formations that allow recognition of five trilobite faunas: the *Ptychaspis, Quadraticephalus, Mictosaukia, Pseudokoldinioidia,* and *Richardsonella* faunas in ascending order. The *Ptychaspis* and *Quadraticephalus* faunas occur in the lower and middle parts of the Hwajeol Formation, respectively. The *Mictosaukia* fauna spans the upper Hwajeol Formation and the lowermost Dongjeom Formation, and the *Pseudokoldinioidia* and *Richardsonella* faunas occur successively in the lower Dongjeom Formation. The *Ptychaspis* fauna consists mainly of *Ptychaspis, Tsinania,* and *Haniwa,* along with some agnostoids. The *Quadraticephalus* fauna comprises *Quadraticephalus elongatus, Sinosaukia angulata, Tsinania canens, Haniwa* sp., and *Hamashania pulchera.* The *Mictosaukia* fauna includes *Mictosaukia* sp., *Changia* sp. cf. *longiformis, Koldinioidia* sp., *Pagodia* sp., and *Fatocephalus* sp. The *Pseudokoldinioidia* fauna is characterized by *Pseudokoldinioidia perpetis* and *Onychopyge borealis.* The *Richardsonella* fauna is composed of *Richardsonella* spp., *Platypeltoides* sp., and *Yosimuraspis* sp. The discovery of a lowermost Ordovician taxon endemic to the Sino-Korea, *Yosimuraspis,* in the *Richardsonella* fauna in the lower Dongjeom Formation is very useful in pin-pointing the newly-ratified Cambrian–Ordovician boundary within the Taebaek Group. In addition, the upper Furongian to lower Tremadocian trilobite successions of the Taebaek Group can be identified zone-by-zone with those of North China, and demonstrate a close faunal linkage between the two regions.

SMALL SHELLY FOSSIL BIOSTRATIGRAPHY IN SOUTH CHINA: IMPLICATIONS FOR SUBDIVISION AND CORRELATION OF CAMBRIAN SERIES 1

LI, GUOXIANG, State Key Laboratory of Palaeobiology and Stratigraphy, Nanjing Institute of Geology and Palaeontology, Nanjing 210008, China; MICHAEL STEINER, Geological Department, Technical University Berlin, ACK 14, Ackerstrasse 71-76, 13355 Berlin, Germany; MAOYAN ZHU, State Key Laboratory of Palaeobiology and Stratigraphy, Nanjing Institute of Geology and Palaeontology, Nanjing 210008, China

The worldwide abrupt appearance of diversified small shelly fossils (SSFs) during the Precambrian–Cambrian transitional interval not only represents a major piece of evidence for the

Cambrian Explosion, but also provides an important biostrati-graphic tool for subdivision and correlation of the Lower Cambrian. With well developed Lower Cambrian successions and abundant small shelly fossils, South China has been one of the most important regions for studying biostratigraphic zona-tion and correlation of the pre-trilobitic Cambrian. During the past three decades, extensive information has been acquired on the occurrence of Early Cambrian SSFs in South China.

The Lower Cambrian of South China has traditionally been subdivided into 4 stages. In ascending order these are the Meishucunian, Qiongzhusian (Chiungzhussian), Canglang-puan (Tsanglungpuan), and Longwangmiaoan (Lungwang-miaoan). Peng, in 1999, divided the Lower Cambrian into two series, each of which consists two stages. The subdivision of the 'Lower Cambrian" into two series [i.e., the 1st and 2nd Series of the Cambrian System (Ogg, 2005)] has been widely accepted since the Lower Cambrian is dated at 542–510 Ma. It represents more than half of the Cambrian (542–488 Ma). If the boundary between Cambrian Series 1 and Series 2 is defined at the FAD of trilobites, the sub-trilobitic Meishucunian of South China can be approximately equated Cambrian Series 1, and the other three stages may be approximately equated with Cambrian Series 2.

There are no archaeocyathans in the sub-trilobitic Cambrian of South China, and, consequently, small shelly fossils have been the major tool for zonation and correlation of the Meishucunian Stage. Based on the SSF record, four zones have been recognized for the Meishucunian Stage. In ascending order, they are: *Anabarites trisulcatus-Protohertzina anabarica*, *Paragloborilus subglobosus-Purella squamulosa*, *Watsonella crosbyi* (formerly *Heraultipegma yunnanensis* Zone), and *Sinosachites fla-belliformis-Tannuolina zhangwentangi* Assemblage Zones. The *P. subglobosus-P. squamulosa* Assemblage Zone was earlier termed the *Paragloborilus subglobosus-Siphogonuchites triangularis* Assemblage Zone, but was recently renamed by Steiner as *S. tri-angularis* has a long range from the *A. trisulcatus-P. anabarica* Zone into the *W. crosbyi* Zone. The four zones mentioned above are mainly recognized in the shallow water realm (e.g., eastern Yunnan and western Sichuan). In the deeper water realm (e.g., Guizhou and Hunan), the first zone is represented by the *Protohertzina anabarica-Kaiyangites novilis* Assemblage Zone, while the other three biozones can not be recognized. SSFs also provide some implications for the correlation of the Qiongzhusian Stage—two zones (i.e., the *Ninella tarimen-sis–Cambroclavus fangxianensis* Assemblage Zone and the *Rhombocorniculum cancellatum* Range Zone) can be recognized in northern Sichuan, southern Shaanxi, and northern Hubei, while the *Pelagiella subangulata* Range Zone can be recognized in east-ern Yunnan.

Although there remain considerable uncertainties about the international correlations of the Lower Cambrian due to the strong provincialism of the SSFs and trilobites and to facies dependence of archaeocyathans, some SSF taxa, such as *Anabarites trisulcatus, Protohertzina unguliformis, P. anabarica, Watsonella crosbyi, Pelagiella subangulata, Rhombocorniculum can-cellatum, Allonnia, Lapworthella, Microdictyon,* etc., may exhibit a worldwide occurrence and enable biostratigraphic correlations of the Lower Cambrian between different regions. Among them, the FADs of *A. trisulcatus, P. unguliformis,* and *P. anabarica* have been taken as important index fossils for defining the Ediacaran–Cambrian boundary in carbonate-dominated facies

(e.g., South China and Siberia). The FAD of *W. crosbyi* can poten-tially be an important marker for defining the Stage 1–2 bound-ary of Cambrian Series 1. The FADs of *Allonnia* and *Lapworthella* are in the upper part of Series 1. *Pelagiella subangulata, R. cancel-latum,* and *Microdictyon* are important index fossils for lower Cambrian Series 2.

The Lower Cambrian of South China has commonly been correlated with that of Siberia despite the correlation being con-troversial. Based on bio- and chemostratigraphic evidence, Based on bio- and chemo-stratigraphic evidence, the Meishucunian can be roughly correlated with the Nemakit-Daldynian + Tommotian + lowest Atdabanian, and the Qiongzhusian with the Atdabanian + lower Botomian.

LOWER FURONGIAN SILICIFIED TRILOBITE FAUNAL ASSEMBLAGES FROM THE SESONG FORMATION, TAEBAEK GROUP, KOREA

PARKH, TAE-YOON, JANG WON SOHN, SANG MIN LEE, and DUCK K. CHOI, School of Earth and Environmental Sciences, Seoul National University, Seoul 151-747, Korea

The Sesong Formation of the Taebaek Group occurs in the Taebaeksan Basin of Korea, and is composed largely of dark gray sandstone and siltstone with local limestone conglomer-ates. The formation has late Middle Cambrian to early Furongian trilobite assemblages. Five zones have been proposed in the Sesong Formation: the *Stephanocare, Drepanura, Prochuangia, Chuangia,* and *Kaolishania* Zones, in ascending order.

The Sesong Formation is well exposed along the Jikdong val-ley, and relatively well-preserved, silicified trilobites were recovered from fifteen horizons in the middle part of the forma-tion. The faunal assemblages are referable to the *Drepanura, Prochuangia,* and *Chuangia* Zones. The *Drepanura* Zone yields *Drepanura* sp., *Liostracina* sp., *Teinistion* sp., *Huzhuia tropis, Liostracina* sp. cf. *L. simesi,* and *Parachangshania monkei.* The *Prochuangia* Zone has a relatively high species diversity, and yields *Baikadamaspis* sp., *Fenghuangella* sp., *Parachangshania* sp., *Placosema convexus, Prochuangia* sp., *Maladioides coreanicus, Proceratopyge?* sp., *Yokusenia?* sp., ceratopygid sp. A., and genus and species indeterminate. The *Chuangia* Zone is poorly repre-sented by the occurrence of *Chuangia* sp. and ceratopygid sp. B. Of these, the following genera are documented for the first time in Korea: *Teinistion, Parachangshania, Baikadamaspis, Placosema, Fenghuangella,* and *Huzhuia.*

Baikadamaspis has been reported from the lowermost Furongian of Kazakhstan, the uppermost Middle Cambrian to lowermost Furongian of South China, and, questionably, from Queensland, Australia. *Placosema* occurs in the *Glyptagnostus stolidotus* and *G. reticulatus* Zones in South China. In Antarctica, *Placosema* is found just above the *G. reticulatus*–bearing horizon. *Liostracina* cf. *simesi* has been associated with *Glyptagnostus stoli-dotus* in Victoria Land, Antarctica. In Jikdong valley, a significant faunal change was observed at the lowest appearance of *Baikadamaspis* and *Placosema,* and this may mark the Series 3–Furongian Series boundary in Korea.

Although *Prochuangia* has long been employed as a zonal taxon in Korea and North China, it is generally poorly repre-sented. In addition, the first appearance datum (FAD) of the genus does not coincide with the significant faunal turnover documented in the Jikdong section. Thus, the lower boundary of the *Prochuangia* Zone in Korea is re-defined herein on the basis of the FAD of *Baikadamaspis*, *Placosema*, and *Fenghuangella*, among others. It has to be confirmed that the base of the Furongian in Korea should be drawn at the boundary between the *Drepanura* and *Prochuangia* Zones in the Sesong Formation. *Prochuangia* occurs mainly in the *Glyptagnostus reticulatus* Zone and equivalent horizons elsewhere, with an exceptional occurrence from much younger (Iverian) strata of Queensland, Australia.

EARLY CAMBRIAN BALANG FAUNA FROM EASTERN GUIZHOU, CHINA

PENG JIN, Department of Earth Sciences, Nanjing University, Nanjing, China, 210093;
YUANLONG ZHAO, College of Resource and Environment Engineering, Guizhou University, Guiyang, Guizhou, China, 550003; and
HONGZHEN FENG, Department of Earth Sciences, Nanjing University, Nanjing, China, 210093

The Balang Formation in eastern Guizhou is composed gray, gray-greenish silty shale or muscovite-rich shale and mudrock. It was deposited in a slope facies belt between the Yangtze Platform to the west and the Jiangnan Basin to the east. The upper part of the Balang Formation yields an important fossil deposit with exceptional preservation. The Early Cambrian Balang Fauna contains fossils that represent six invertebrate phyla— arthropods (e.g., trilobites, bradoriids, and large bivalved arthropods), coelenterates, brachiopods, priapulids, mollusks, and stalked eocrinoid echinoderms—along with algae and a rich ichnofauna. Among them, a new eocrinoid and trilobites [*Redlichia* (*Pteroredlichia*)] are the most common and characteristic taxa. Preservation of unusually large numbers of well-preserved, articulated eocrinoids indicates the fauna was smothered by obrution events. Based on trilobite biostratigraphy, the age of the fauna is upper Lower Cambrian (Dunyunian Stage), which is equivalent to the upper Chanlangpuian in Yunnan Province and Botomian in Siberia.

The Balang Fauna not only consists of a diverse fossil assemblage with biomineralized hard parts, but also contains shows soft-part preservation. For example, soft-bodied fossils (e.g., priapulids and non-trilobite arthropods) and a hyolith specimen with intact helens and operculum also occur in the fauna. Although the current scale of excavation of the Balang Fauna is not comparable with other more famous deposits, its faunal elements are transitional between the Early Cambrian Chengjiang Biota and the middle Kaili Biota in South China. The age-equivalent Guanshan Biota was deposited in shallow water settings, whereas Balang Biota was deposited in deeper water, shelf margin to slope facies. Nevertheless, the Balang Biota is the most important shelf margin fauna in the Lower Cambrian of South China and contains direct ancestors that lead to the Middle Cambrian Kaili Biota.

ASSESSMENT OF THE POTENTIAL GSSP SECTIONS FOR CAMBRIAN SERIES 3 USING THE FAD OF *ORYCTOCEPHALUS INDICUS*

SUNDBERG, FREDERICK A., Show Low High School, 500 W. Old Linden Rd., Show Low, Arizona, United States, 85901;
LINDA B. MCCOLLUM, Department of Geology, 130 Science Building, Eastern Washington University, Cheney, Washington, United States, 99004-2499

The FAD of *Oryctocephalus indicus* is one of the most viable lower boundary candidates for Cambrian Series 3. This FAD is far from perfect, with problems in taxonomy, biostratigraphy, paleogeography, sedimentology, accessibility, and politics. However, the FAD is one of the few horizons relatively close to the classical Lower–Middle Cambrian boundary in Asia and North America.

Although much discussion has focused on this potential boundary, few attempts have been made to do side-by-side comparisons of the potential location of the GSSP boundary and accessory sections. There are three potential boundary sections: in the Kaili Formation, Balang, China; Emigrant Formation, Split Mountain, Nevada; and Kuonamka Formation on Molodo River, Russia. The Kuonamka Formation is included in this discussion due to the possible occurrence of *Oryctocephalus indicus*, as suggested by some authors, although its occurrence has not been verified. Each section is evaluated by the status of their taxonomy, biostratigraphy, sedimentology, and accessibility.

The taxonomy and biostratigraphic advantages of this FAD are that all sections can be correlated to shallow-water sections and faunas, have a few taxa found on other continents, and contain articulated specimens. The Kaili Formation has a well-defined boundary with abundant taxa above and below the boundary, and it correlates with the traditional Lower–Middle Cambrian boundary of Asia. The taxa have been extensively studied and illustrated. The disadvantages of the Kaili section are that specimens are relatively sparse, the taxa have been over split, and initial studies had local villagers collect specimens, which led to uncertain stratigraphic ranges. The Emigrant Formation has a well-defined boundary with abundant taxa below the boundary; the taxa have been extensively studied and illustrated, and specimens are relatively common. All specimens were precisely collected from intervals with a maximum of 0.5 m thickness. Disadvantages of the Emigrant candidate are that the boundary does not correlate with the traditional Lower–Middle Cambrian boundary of North America, there is limited taxonomic diversity above the boundary, and the strata are barren above the occurrence of *Oryctocephalus indicus*. The Kuonamka Formation has a boundary interval with abundant taxa below and above the potential boundary and contains *Paradoxides pinus*. The taxa have been studied and illustrated, and specimens are relatively common. Disadvantages of the Kuonamka candidate are that *O. indicus* has not been verified from the section; the taxa need restudy (in progress), and the boundary has not been firmly established.

The sedimentological advantages of this FAD are that all sections are deeper water, are composed of relatively uniform mudstones in a conformable sequence, and are well correlated to other sections within their respective paleocontinents. The Kaili Formation boundary interval is well exposed due to quarrying; the section is relatively thick, and a preliminary carbon isotope profile has been done. The disadvantage is that much of the Kaili Formation is poorly exposed. The Emigrant Formation boundary interval is well exposed as quarried and natural outcrops, and a carbon isotope profile has been done. The major disadvantage is the section is condensed with a distinct color change at the boundary. The Kuonamka Formation boundary interval is well exposed along river bank, mainly cliff, exposures. The major disadvantages are that the section is condensed, and a carbon isotope profile has not been done.

The access to the potential sections is variable. The Kaili Formation boundary interval can be reached by a flight to Guiyang from Beijing, then by paved road or train from the airport to the nearby town, and a paved road to the boundary section. Access is possible year round. The disadvantages are that collecting is by permit only, and much of the section is covered with crops. The Emigrant Formation boundary interval can be reached by a flight to Las Vegas from many international airports, then by paved road to Tonopah. There are car rentals in Las Vegas, and lodging is available in Tonopah. The area is open territory with no travel restrictions, and access is possible year round. Permits are not required for collecting, although extensive quarrying requires a Bureau of Land Management permit. The major disadvantage is the rough and sandy dirt road to the boundary section. The Kuonamka Formation boundary interval is difficult to reach. Yakutsk can be reached by a flight from Moscow, but the section is 350 km downstream from Zhigansk, which involves a helicopter flight (1000 km, 5 hours one way) from Yakutiya or a boat trip from Yakuysk to Zhigansk and then a helicopter flight to the section. There are no roads to the boundary section. Access is possible only for several months in the summer. A permit is required for collecting.

In summary, the best location of the GSSP for the base of Cambrian Series 3, if *Oryctocephalus indicus* is used, is in the Kaili Formation, Balang, China. This is reinforced by the Chinese government's pride in their science (indeed, paleontology has been designated "a career of excellence" in China), and the disregard and progressive de-funding of "academic" science by the United States and Russian governments.

REFINED BIOSTRATIGRAPHY AND EVENT STRATIGRAPHY IN SUNWAPTAN OUTER-PLATFORM AND SLOPE FACIES, CENTRAL APPALACHIANS

TAYLOR, JOHN F., Geoscience Department, Indiana University of Pennsylvania, Indiana, Pennsylvania 15705;
DAVIK K. BREZINSKI, Maryland Geological Survey, 2300 St. Paul Street, Baltimore, Maryland 21218; and
JOHN E. REPETSKI, U.S. Geological Survey, 926A National Center, Reston, Virginia 20192

Time control provided by an improved trilobite-based zonation within the thick (600–900m), peritidal, bank margin deposits of the Conococheague Formation confirms the lateral persistence over tens of kilometrers of four 3rd-order transgressive cycle peaks. Each highstand provided sufficient accommodation space to allow for deposition of a thick complex of microbial (thrombolitic) reefs and trilobite-bearing grainstone. Intervals with abundant dolomitic, planar microbial laminite accumulated during the intervening lowstands. Although present, microbial reefs are significantly smaller and less abundant.

The thick highstand reef/grainstone packages within the Conococheague have been numbered from bottom to top. The lowest such package (Thrombolite I) formed during the late Stepotean (*Elvinia* Zone) onlap at the base of the Sauk III Subsequence. Slightly higher in the formation, microbial reefs disappear at the Pterocephaliid–Ptychaspid Biomere boundary and are completely absent from the *Taenicephalus* Zone in the Conococheague, as they are from coeval inner-shelf deposits of the Gatesburg Formation (Ore Hill Member) to the west. Recovery of *Ptychaspis granulosa* very near the base of the next transgressive reef package (Thrombolite II) dates that submergence as a middle early Sunwaptan event, equivalent in age to the middle *Ptychaspis-Prosaukia* Zone in the Upper Mississippi Valley and the base of the *Ellipsocephaloides* Zone in Alberta. As in the central Appalachians, microbial reefs disappear at the base of the *Taenicephalus* Zone in Alberta, and remain scarce up to the base of the *Ellipsocephaloides* Zone where they once again occur in profusion. The conditions that promoted microbial reef growth to produce Thrombolite II on the southern Laurentian margin apparently triggered a similar development of thrombolitic reefs on the northern shelf of the paleocontinent.

Trilobites and conodonts just below and within Thrombolite III suggest that the reef complex created by the third transgression spans the boundary of the lower and upper Sunwaptan Substages (i.e., base of the *Illaenurus* Zone in west Laurentia. The basal reefs in this interval yield *Plethopeltis saratogensis*, while the upper part of the package has *Plethopeltis stitti*, a common component of the basal *Saukia* Zone in Oklahoma. In coeval shelf-break and off-platform deposits (Grove and Frederick Formations, respectively) to the east in the Frederick Valley of Maryland, new biostratigraphic data reveal profound changes in formation thickness both across and along depositional strike. Strike-parallel thickening of some units provides strong evidence for an embayed platform margin in that area. Among the most significant changes in style of deposition in the Frederick Valley succession is that at the base of the Adamstown Member of the Frederick Formation. The underlying Rocky Springs Station Member comprises > 1,000 m of proximal slope carbonate with abundant limestone conglomerate and coarse sandy grainstone. The Adamstown consists entirely of interlaminated, very thin-bedded lime mudstone and black shale. Thus, the sharp contact between these members marks a termination of carbonate sand and gravel input from shelf-margin to lower-slope environments. A trilobite fauna from the top few meters of the Rocky Springs Station Member has *Keithiella depressa* with *Onchonotus* and *Stenopilus*. Correlations between the Frederick Formation and the Conococheague (by way of the Shallow Bay Formation in western Newfoundland and Hoyt Member in New York) suggest the transgression that produced Thrombolite III also terminated down-slope transport of carbonate debris. This appears to correlate with an onlap of more fine-grained, distal slope facies onto the proximal debris apron at the base of the Downe's Point Member of the Shallow Bay Formation.

A relatively rich collection from Thrombolite IV with *Euptychaspis*, *Conococheaguea*, and *Prosaukia* establishes that this highest transgressive cycle peak in the Conococheague is middle late Sunwaptan, and equivalent to strata elsewhere of the *Saukiella junia* Subzone of the *Saukia* Zone.

TRACE ELEMENT GEOCHEMISTRY OF THE EDIACARAN–CAMBRIAN TRANSITION INTERVAL IN EASTERN GUIZHOU, SOUTH CHINA

XINGLIAN YANG, College of Resource and Environment, Guizhou University, Guiyang, Guizhou, China, 550003;
MAOYAN ZHU, State Key Laboratory of Palaeobiology and Stratigraphy, Nanjing Institute of Geology and Palaeontology, Chinese Academy of Sciences, Nanjing, Jiangsu, China, 210008;
ZHAO YUANLONG, College of Resource and Environment, Guizhou University, Guiyang, Guizhou, China, 550003;
ZHANG JUNMING, State Key Laboratory of Palaeobiology and Stratigraphy, Nanjing Institute of Geology and Palaeontology, Chinese Academy of Sciences, Nanjing, Jiangsu, China, 210008;
GUO QINGJUN, State Key Laboratory of Environmental Geochemistry, Institute of Geochemistry, Chinese Academy of Sciences, Guiyang, China, 550002; and
BINGXIA LI, College of Resource and Environment, Guizhou University, Guiyang, China, 550003

Samples of black-colored rocks from the Ediacaran–Cambrian transition in eastern Guizhou, South China, were analyzed for trace elements. There is a conspicuous accumulation of Ba, Pb, Ni, Cu, Zn, Li, V, and U transitional elements and chalcophile elements in the polymetallic ore layer in the Nangao section. Except for Sr, Li, and Cr, concentrations of all of the other elements are extremely high when compared with those of average shales. Cu, Pb, Rb, Ti, Ni, V, Th, Li, Cr, Zr, and Sc are present at equivalent levels in the Sandu section. The siliciclastics of the Laobao Formation in the Nangao section accumulated in a slightly oxic environment, as indicated by δU and $V/Ni+V$ values that lie below the critical paleoredox level. However, the δU and $V/Ni+V$ values indicate an anoxic environment for the black shale of the Niutitang Formation. δU values in the Zhalagou section at Sandu range from 1.75 to 2, with an average value of 1.92, and suggest more strongly reducing conditions and a deeper water environment for this section than for the Nangao section at Danzhai. $V/Ni+V$ values of siliciclastics in the Laobao Formation and the basal Zhalagou Formation range from 0.8–0.99 (average 0.95), which is higher than the critical value of 0.83, and suggest anoxic conditions. However, two brief oxic stages are recorded in the Laobao Formation. The $V/Ni+V$ values of the upper Zhalagou Formation range from 0.59–0.94 (average 0.71), and indicate oxic conditions during this interval. All U/Th values of siliciclastics of the Laobao Formation in the Nangao section at Danzhai are lower than 1, and preserve the geochemistry of these aqueous sediments. However, U/Th values of the carbonaceous shales are greater than 1, and demonstrate hydrothermal activity. The U/Th values of the Laobao Formation siliciclastics and the black shale of the lower Zhalagou Formation in the Zhalagou section at Sandu are greater than 1, and vary from 6.55 to 343.85, with an average of 49.41. These values indicate more frequent hydrothermal inputs in the area. Compared to average upper continental crust values, V and Ni show 9–10 times enrichment, and U shows about 100 times enrichment in the Ni-Mo metal layer. Thus, this horizon can also be used to define the Meishucunian–Qiongzhusian boundary.

LOWER CAMBRIAN ARCHAEOCYATHAN ZONATION OF THE YANGTZE PLATFORM AND BIOSTRATIGRAPHIC IMPLICATIONS

YANG, AIHUA, Earth Science Department of Nanjing University, Nanjing 210093, China;
MAOYAN ZHU, KEXING YUAN, Nanjing Institute of Geology and Palaeontology, Chinese Science Academy, Nanjing 210008, China; and
FRANCOISE DEBRENNE, CNRS UA, 12, Institut de Paléontologie, 8 rue de Buffon, 75005 Paris, France

Five archaeocyathan assemblage or range zones have been established on the Yangtze Platform. In ascending order, they are: I. *Archaeopharetra-Taylorcyathus* Assemblage Zone, II. *Graphoscyphia shanxiensis* Range Zone, III. *Spirillicyathus duplex* Range Zone; IV. *Sibirecyathus-Involucrocyathus* Assemlage Zone, and V. *Archaeocyathus yichangensis* Range Zone.

The ages and correlations of such Lower Cambrian lithologic units as the Xiannudong, Mingxinsi, Jindingshan, and Tianheban Formations on the Yangtze Platform have been discussed in detail. On the Yangtze Platform, archaeocyathan Zones I and II can be correlated with the middle and upper *Eoredlichia* Zone of the Qiongzhusian Stage, Zone III with the *Yunnanaspis-Yiliangella* Zone of the lower Canglangpuan Stage, Zone IV with the *Drepanuroides* Zone of the middle Canglangpuan, and Zone V with the *Megapalaeolenus* Zone of the upper Canglangpuan. The Xiannüdong Formation correlates with the middle–upper Atdabanian of the Siberian Platform, while the *Spirillicyathus duplex* Range Zone of the lower Canglangpuan Stage correlates with the Australian *Spirillicyathus tenulis* and *Jugalicyathus tardus* Assemblage Zones, and approximately with the upper Atdabanian in Siberia. *Archaeocyathus* is a widespread taxon, and its occurrence in the upper Canglangpuan on the Yangtze Platform best suggests a correlation with the Siberian middle Toyonian.

PHYLOGENY OF *ORYCTOCEPHALUS* WALCOTT, 1886 (TRILOBITA), AND ITS STRATIGRAPHIC SIGNIFICANCE

YUAN, JIN-LIANG, Nanjing Institute of Geology and Palaeontology, Chinese Academy of Sciences, Nanjing, China, 210008;
YUAN-LONG ZHAO, College of Resource and Environment of Guizhou University, Guiyang, China, 550003;
JIN PENG, Department of Earth Sciences, Nanjing University, Nanjing, China, 210093;
JIH-PAI LIN, School of Earth Sciences, The Ohio State University, Columbus, Ohio, USA, 43210; and
IGOR V. KOROVNIKOV, Institute Oil and Gas Geology, Siberian Branch of Russian Academy of Sciences, Academician Kopjug avenue 3, Novosibirsk, Russia, 630090

Oryctocephalus Walcott, 1886, from traditional Middle Cambrian strata is one of the most important oryctocephalids, and it has been reported in nearshore–offshore deposits in several important Cambrian faunal provinces [Laurentia (including Greenland), South China, Siberia, and Australia]. Based on the shape of the glabella, pattern of the glabellar furrows, width of the fixigenal field between palpebral lobes, numbers of thoracic segments, outline of thoracic segments, numbers of pygidial marginal spines, and relative pygidial size, *Oryctocephalus* can be subdivided into two subgenera: *Oryctocephalus* (*Oryctocephalus*) Walcott, 1886, and *O.* (*Eoryctocephalus*) Zhao and Yuan in Yuan *et al.*, 2002 . *Oryctocephalus* (*O.*) includes *O.* (*O.*) *primus* Walcott, 1886; *O.* (*O.*) *reynoldsi* Reed, 1899; *O.* (*O.*) *indicus* (Reed, 1910); *O.* (*O.*) *salteri* (Reed, 1910); *O.* (*O.*) *orientalis* Saito, 1934; *O.* (*O.*) *burgessensis* Resser, 1938; *O.* (*O.*) *walcotti* Resser, 1938; *O.* (*O.*) *maladensis* Resser, 1939; *O.* (*O.*) *reynoldsiformis* Lermontova, 1940; *O.* (*O.*) *reticulatus* (Lermontova, 1940); *O.* (*O.*) *matthewi* Rasetti, 1951; and *O.* (*O.*) *americanus* Sundberg and McCollum, 2003. *Oryctocephalus* (*Eoryctocephalus*) includes *O.* (*E.*) *sinensis* Zhao and Yuan in Yuan *et al.*, 2002; *O.* (*E.*) *yui* Zhao and Yuan in Yuan *et al.*, 2002; *O.* (*E.*) *lancastrioides* (Shergold, 1969); and *O.* (*E.*) *nyensis* Palmer in Palmer and Halley, 1979.

Among *Oryctocephalus* species, three evolutionary lineages can be observed. The first lineage is the *O.* (*E.*) *sinensis*–*O.* (*E.*) *yui*–*O.* (*E.*) *lancastrioides*–*O.* (*E.*) *nyensis* series. Based on stratigraphic appearances, older species, such as *O.* (*E.*) *sinensis* and *O.* (*E.*) *yui*, have sixteen thoracic segments; the intermediate species *O.* (*E.*) *lancastrioides* has fifteen segments; and the youngest species *O.* (*E.*) *nyensis* has fourteen segments. Reduction in thoracic segment number is regarded as a paedomorphic trend. Associated changes in this series include a progressive forward expansion of the glabella, a decrease in the width of fixigenae between the palpebral lobes, and an increase in the number of paired, marginal spines in the pygidium (one pair in *O.* (*E.*) *sinensis*, two pairs in *O.* (*E.*) *yui*, and three pairs in *O.* (*E.*) *lancastrioides* and *O.* (*E.*) *nyensis*).

The second evolutionary lineage is the *O.* (*O.*) *americanus*–*O.* (*O.*) *reticulatus* series. A notable increase in cranidium length from 2.7 mm in *O.* (*O.*) *americanus* to 8.0 mm in *O.* (*O.*) *reticulatus* is interpreted as a peramorphic condition. Additional changes, including a forward expansion of the glabella and an increase in pygidial marginal spines from two pairs in *O.* (*O.*) *americanus* to three pairs in *O.* (*O.*) *reticulatus*, are also observed. Both species have the same transglabellar furrow (S1) and twelve thoracic segments.

The third evolutionary lineage is the *O.* (*O.*) *indicus*–*O.* (*O.*) *orientalis*–*O.* (*O.*) *primus*–*O.* (*O.*) *reynoldsi*–*O.* (*O.*) *burgessensis* series. Paedomorphic reduction in the number of thoracic segments occurs from earlier to younger species—*O.* (*O.*) *indicus* with twelve segments, *O.* (*O.*) *orientalis*–*O.* (*O.*) *primus* with eight(?) to nine segments, to *O.* (*O.*) *burgessensis* with seven segments. Associated changes include a forward expansion of the glabella, decrease in the width of fixigenae between palpebral lobes; increase of pygidium size, and increase in the numbers of paired pygidial marginal spines— from *O.* (*O.*) *indicus* with two to three pairs to *O.* (*O.*) *orientalis*–*O.* (*O.*) *primus* with four to five pairs, to *O.* (*O.*) *burgessensis* with six pairs.

MIDDLE CAMBRIAN BIOSTRATIGRAPHY OF SINO-KOREA PLATFORM

YUAN, JIN-LIANG; YUE LI, Nanjing Institute of Geology and Palaeontology, Chinese Academy of Sciences, Nanjing, China, 210008; YUAN-LONG ZHAO, College of Resource and Environment of Guizhou University, Guiyang, China, 550003; and JIH-PAI LIN, School of Earth Sciences, The Ohio State University, Columbus, Ohio, USA, 43210

There is a long standing debate about the Cambrian biostratigraphy of North China. We propose herein a revision of the Middle Cambrian trilobite zonation of the North China–Korea platform to improve its utility for correlation utility. Specific correlation of trilobite zones between North China and Laurentia are outlined below. The upper *Drepanura premesnili* Zone can be correlated with the *Glyptagnostus stolidotus* Zone in Laurentia. The lower *Drepanura premesnili* Zone and *Blackwelderia paronai* Zone are age-equivalent to the *Linguagnostus reconditus* Zone and the upper *Proagnostus bulbus* Zone. The *Damesella paronai* Zone is approximately equivalent with the Laurentian interval that includes both the lower *Proagnostus bulbus* Zone and the upper and middle *Lejopyge laevigata* Zone. The *Liopeishania lubrica* Zone can be correlated with an interval that includes both the lower *Lejopyge laevigata* Zone and *Goniagnostus nathorsti* Zone. The *Taitzuia insueta* Zone can be correlated with the upper *Ptychagnostus punctuosus* Zone. The *Amphoton deois* Zone can be correlated with the lower *Ptychagnostus punctuosus* Zone and the upper *Ptychagnostus atavus* Zone. The *Crepicephalina convexa*–*Megagraulos coreanicus*–*Inouyella peiensis* Zones are age-equivalent to the lower and middle *P. atavus* Zone. The *Bailiella lantenoisi*–*Tonkinella flabelliformis* Zones are equivalent to the *P. gibbus* Zone. The *Inouyops titiana*–*Metagraulos nitidus* Zones can be correlated with the *Oryctocephalus reynoldsi*–*O. burgessensis* Zones in North America. The *Sunaspis laevis*–*Sinopagetia jinnanensis*–*Ruichengaspis mirabilis* Zones can be correlated to *Oryctocephalus orientalis* Zone. The *Hsuchuangia hsuchuangensis*–*Shantungaspis aclis*–*Yaojiayuella ocellata* Zones are correlated with the *Oryctocephalus indicus* Zone.

SINO-KOREA PLATFORM

Old Ser.	New Ser.	Stage	Trilobite zonation
U. Cam.		Kushanian	*Drepanura premesnili*
			Blackwelderia paronai
M. Cam.	Series 3	Changhian	*Damesella paronai*
			Liopeishania lubrica
			Taitzuia insueta
			Amphoton deois
			Crepicephalina convexa
			Megagraulos coreanicus
			Inouyella peiensis
		Hsuchuangian	*Bailiella lantenoisi*
			Tonkinella flabelliformis
			Inouyops titiana
			Metagraulos nitidus
			Sunaspis laevis
			Sinopagetia jinnanensis
			Ruichengaspis mirabilis
			Hsuchuangia hsuchuangensis
		Maochuangian	*Shantungaspis aclis*
			Yaojiayuella ocellata
L. Cam.	Series 2	Unnamed	*Bonnia-Redlichia*

OVATORYCTOCARA GRANULATA (TRILOBITA) FROM THE LOWER KAILI FORMATION AT BALANG, JIAHE COUNTY, GUIZHOU, SOUTH CHINA, AND DEFINITION OF THE BASE OF CAMBRIAN SERIES 3

ZHAO, YUANLONG, College of Resource and Environment of Guizhou University, Guiyang, China, 550003; JINLIANG YUAN, Nanjing Institute of Geology and Palaeontology, Chinese Academy of Sciences, Nanjing, China, 210008; and JIN PENG, Department of Earth Sciences, Nanjing University, Nanjing, China, 210093

Ovatoryctocara granulata Tchernysheva, 1962, which was previously reported from Siberia, Greenland and Newfoundland, has recently been described in southeast Guizhou. The First Appearance Datum (FAD) of *O. granulata* has been suggested as a potential key marker for the base of the Cambrian Series 3 (see Fletcher, 2003, *Ovatoryctocara granulata*: The key to a global Cambrian stage boundary and the correlation of the olenellid, redlichiid and paradoxidid realms, Special Papers in Palaeontology, v. 70, pp. 73–102). At present, the criteria for recognizing the base of this unnamed series are under debate, but the Kaili Formation contains many important cosmopolitan taxa. These include *Oryctocephalus indicus* (Reed, 1910) and *Ovatoryctocara granulata* Tchernysheva, 1962, both of which are potential candidates for defining the base of Cambrian Series 3. In the Wuliu-Zengjiayan section at Balang, Guizhou Province, China, the FAD of *O. indicus* occurs 52.8 m above the base of the Kaili Formation, and the FAD of *O. granulata* occurs 22 m above the base of the Kaili Formation. *Ovatoryctocara granulata* ranges to about 30.8 m, and occurs in with *Bathynotus*, *Oryctocephalops*, *Protoryctocephalus*, *Olenoides*, and *Redlichia*. *O. granulata* also occurs in the grey, thin-bedded, argillaceous limestone unit of the lower Aoxi Formation at Yaxi, Shizu, Tongren County, in eastern Guizhou. In the Aoxi Formation, *O. granulata* occurs with *Barklyella*, "*Ptychoparella*," and *Zacanthopsis*? This horizon can be approximately correlated with the upper Henson Gletscher Formation in North Greenland, and is immediately above the FAD of *Arthricocephalus chauveaui* Bergeron, 1899, at some localities. Thus, the Wuliu-Zengjiayan section of the Kaili Formation provides an excellent candidate GSSP for the base of Cambrian Series 3.

THE LOWER–MIDDLE CAMBRIAN BOUNDARY IN THE HOLY CROSS MTS (POLAND) COMPARED WITH THE WEST GONDWANA STANDARD

ZYLINSKA, ANNA, Faculty of Geology, University of Warsaw, al. Zwirki i Wigury 93, PL-02-089 Warsaw, Poland; ZBIGNIEW SZCZEPANIK; SYLWESTER SALWA, Holy Cross Branch of the Polish Geological Institute, ul. Zgoda 21, PL-25-953 Kielce, Poland; and MONIKA MASIAK, Institute of Geological Sciences, Polish Academy of Sciences, ul. Twarda 51/55, PL-00-818 Warszawa, Poland.

The Early Paleozoic paleogeographic affinity of the Holy Cross Mts. (HCM), part of the Trans-European Suture Zone, one of the main geotectonic domains of Europe, has long been a matter of debate. Its resolution has been unclear because the HCM comprises two tectonostratigraphic units (Kielce and Lysogóry) with unknown crystalline basement. Various studies undertaken to recognize the provenance of these units (e.g., geochemistry, isotope ages of detrital material, paleomagnetic and paleontologic analyses) have not yielded unequivocal results.

The interval selected for this study is the Lower–Middle Cambrian boundary interval. This interval is interesting due its high facies variability, as well as the fact that any future Cambrian Series 2–3 boundary interval will be characterized by a fairly high endemicity of its trilobite faunas. These features lead to problems in the selection of stratigraphic levels that can serve as global correlation horizons. In the case of the HCM, the succession in this interval can be compared to the West Gondwana standard (Geyer & Landing, 2004), with which it shares a comparable succession of trilobite assemblages. Accordingly, the Banian Stage, defined by an antatlasiine-strenuelline-saukiandine-dominated trilobite assemblage, passes into the Agdzian Stage defined by the dominance of protolenine-ellipsocephaline faunas. Thus, the West Gondwana Lower–Middle Cambrian boundary, or the Banian–Agdzian boundary, is marked by a facies-independent faunal turnover that evidently provides better resolution for correlation than the diachronous appearance of paradoxidids, as applied in the earlier literature.

The HCM succession includes a stratigraphic interval that encompasses the uppermost Lower Cambrian (*Protolenus-Strenuaeva* Zone) and the lowermost Middle Cambrian (*Paradoxides insularis* Zone) and belongs to four lithostratigraphic units (i.e., the Kamieniec, Ocieseki, Slowiec and Usarzów formations). The distribution of trilobites within these formations is random, and boundaries between the lithostratigraphic units are typically not exposed. In some cases, the clayey and silty deposits contain microfloral assemblages that supplement the trilobite data.

In the Kamieniec Formation (eastern HCM), a shaly unit with intercalations of fine sandstones comprises the *Protolenus-Strenuaeva* Zone, and is characterized by antatlasiines, protoleniines, as well as rare corynexochids and eodiscids. The sedimentary environment is referred to the outer shelf, with low-energy deep-water conditions. The trilobite assemblage indicates an interval corresponding to the *Hupeolenus–Cephalopyge notabilis* Zones of Morocco. The antatlasiines, which have never been found together with protoleniines, probably indicate older strata, corresponding possibly to the upper Banian *Sectigena* Zone of Morocco. Thus, the Banian–Agdzian boundary probably lies within the Kamieniec Formation. In the Zareby IG-1 Borehole (central HCM), trilobite-bearing strata with protoleniines, corynexochids, and eodiscids are overlain by a series with acritarch assemblages dominated by *Volkovia dentifera*, an acritarch species indicative of the *Volkovia-Liepaina* Assemblage Zone and correlated with the "*Ornamentaspis*" *linnarssoni* Zone of Scandinavia. Interestingly, *V. dentifera* is very abundant in the Zareby IG-1 Borehole, and, contrary to Baltica, does not occur with representatives of *Skiagia* and/or *Heliosphaeridium*, what might suggest a younger age of this acritarch assemblage in comparison to the trilobites below.

The shallow-water, fine-grained, bioturbated sandstones of the Ocieseki Formation is dominated by endemic ellipsocephaliids (*Kingaspidoides sanctacrucensis*, *Issafeniella orlowinensis*, and *Ornamentaspis* spp.), of which the latter co-occurs in the Usarzów Formation with a fauna indicative of the *Paradoxides insularis* and *Paradoxides pinus* zones. In Morocco, species of

Ornamentaspis appear in the *Cephalopyge notabilis* Zone and flourish in the *Ornamentaspis frequens* Zone. Thus the upper Ocieseki Formation possibly corresponds to the *Cephalopyge notabilis* Zone. No acritarch assemblages have been recognized so far from this formation.

Interesting trilobite data come from the Slowiec Formation in Brzechów (central HCM). The assemblage comprises ellipsocephaliids, the palaeolenid *Palaeolenus medius*, paradoxidids *Paradoxides* (*Acadoparadoxides*) *oelandicus* and *P.* (*A.*) cf. *mureroensis*, as well as a representative of the *Onaraspis* clade (*Myopsolenites kielcensis*). Most elements of this assemblage point to a correlation with the *Cephalopyge notabilis* Zone of Morocco. Significant, however, is the abundance of *Issafeniella*, which in Morocco appears in slightly older strata (*Antatlasia guttapluviae* and *Sectigena* Zones). Moreover, the co-occurrence of *P.* (*A.*) *oelandicus* with *P.* (*A.*) cf. *mureroensis* might suggest an earlier appearance of the first species than in Scandinavia, which would mean that the Brzechów sandstones do not have a correlative in the Cambrian succession of the epicontinental sea in Baltica. Baltic successions generally have a gap at the Lower–Middle Cambrian boundary that is approximately equivalent to the circum-Iapetus regressive stage of the "Hawke Bay Event." As a result, the FAD of *P.* (*A.*) *oelandicus* probably pre-dates its appearance in Baltica. So far, the deposits at Brzechów have not yielded any palynomorphs. Acritarch assemblages of similar age have been recognized in the Lenarczyce PIG-1 Borehole (eastern HCM), with *Adara alea*, *Liepaina plana*, and *Skiagia insigne*, considered indicative of the Volkovia-Leipaina Assemblage Zone.

As shown by the biostratigraphic analysis, although continuous sections are not exposed, it is highly probable that the HCM succession does not bear significant gaps across the Lower–Middle Cambrian transition. This differs with the West Gondwana standard, which records a regressive phase roughly coeval with the Hawke Bay event. However, the Slowiec and Usarzów Formations above the Ocieseki and Kamieniec Formations seem to show this regression because they were both deposited in shallower marine environments. The influence of a local tectonic phase at the Lower–Middle Cambrian boundary, which caused shallowing and local emergence is also plausible, and the succession might reflect the overprint of local tectonics on wider-scale events. [Financial support from the Ministry of Science and Higher Education (Grant no. 2 P04D 060 29) is gratefully acknowledged.]